D1066289

# ORGANIC PEROXIDES

*Their Chemistry, Decomposition, and Role in Polymerization*

# ORGANIC PEROXIDES

***Their Chemistry, Decomposition, and Role in Polymerization***

**ARTHUR V. TOBOLSKY** and **ROBERT B. MESROBIAN**

*Frick Chemical Laboratory*
*Princeton University*

*Polymer Research Institute*
*Polytechnic Institute of Brooklyn*

**INTERSCIENCE PUBLISHERS, INC., NEW YORK**

**INTERSCIENCE PUBLISHERS LTD., LONDON 1954**

Library of Congress Catalog Card Number 54-7234



Interscience Publishers, Inc., 250 Fifth Avenue, New York 1, N. Y.

*For Great Britain and Northern Ireland:*
Interscience Publishers Ltd., 88/90 Chancery Lane, London W. C. 2

PRINTED IN THE UNITED STATES OF AMERICA BY MACK PRINTING CO., EASTON, PA.

# PREFACE

This book was inspired mainly by the desire to elucidate the interesting role of organic peroxides in catalyzing chain reactions such as vinyl polymerization and oxidation with molecular oxygen. In order to understand this problem in its proper perspective we have organized the material into three sections. The first deals with the classification, structure, and synthesis of organic peroxides. It is not intended as a definitive and comprehensive treatment of the organic chemistry of peroxides, but rather as an elementary guide to this difficult subject. The second section treats the physical chemical aspects of the cleavages of the peroxide molecules, so far as these are presently understood. In the third section, we have discussed the role of peroxides in the initiation of homogeneous vinyl polymerizations in a detailed and quantitative manner. The second and third sections are of course intimately related.

We dedicate this book to those who aspire to contribute to the better quantitative understanding of organic reactions.

Arthur V. Tobolsky
Robert B. Mesrobian

November, 1953

ACKNOWLEDGMENT

**The authors wish to express appreciation to the Office of Naval Research and to the Committee on Tables of Constants of the National Research Council for supporting research activities in problems related to the subject matter of this book.**

## CONTENTS

**B. Decomposition of Peroxides** (*continued*)

# A. PREPARATION, PROPERTIES, AND STRUCTURAL CLASSIFICATION OF ORGANIC PEROXIDES

## I. Introduction

The organic peroxides may be regarded as derivatives of hydrogen peroxide, HOOH, obtained by replacing one or both of the hydrogen atoms by organic radicals. These substances all have the O—O link in common, and practically all the unique features of their chemistry are associated with this linkage.

A very wide variety of organic peroxides have been prepared and while their chemistry has not been completely elucidated, a sufficient amount of information has been gained to allow for a systematic discussion of their preparation, properties, and structural classification. Very important reviews in this field have been written by Rieche[1] and in recent years by Hawkins,[2] Criegee,[3] and Milas.[4] Several reviews[5–7] have also appeared in the past four years on specialized topics in peroxide chemistry. Criegee's review article[3b] is particularly noteworthy since it presents useful and detailed procedures for the synthesis of many organic peroxides. It also includes a table of the stabilities of these compounds which is presented in Appendix 2.

In the following sections, II–VII, the various classes of organic peroxides are considered in terms of their preparation and their struc-

[1] A. Rieche, *Alkyl Peroxyde und Ozonide*, Steinkopff, Dresden, 1931. A. Rieche, *Die Bedeutung, der organischen Peroxyde für die chemische Wissenschaft und Technik*, Enke, Stuttgart, 1931.

[2] E. G. E. Hawkins, *Quart. Reviews*, *4*, 251 (1950).

[3] (a) R. Criegee, *Fortschr. Chem. Forsch.*, *1*, 508 (1950). (b) R. Criegee, "Herstellung und Umwanglung von Peroxyden," in Houben-Weyl, *Methoden der organischen Chemie*, 4th ed., Thieme, Stuttgart, Vol. VIII, 1952.

[4] N. A. Milas, in *Encyclopedia of Chemical Technology*, edited by R. E. Kirk and D. Othmer, Interscience, New York–London, Volume X, 1953, p. 58.

[5] D. Swern, *Chem. Reviews*, *45*, 1 (1949).

[6] J. E. Leffler, *ibid.*, *45*, 385 (1949).

[7] (a) C. E. Frank, *ibid.*, *46*, 155 (1950). (b) D. Swern, J. T. Scanlon, and H. B. Knight, *J. Am. Oil Chemists' Soc.*, *25*, 193 (1948). (c) W. Eggersglüss, *Organische Peroxyde*, Verlag Chemie, Weinheim, 1951.

tural features. Analytical methods employed for estimation of peroxides are given in section VIII. A generic classification of organic peroxides in terms of their chemical constitution is presented in Appendix 1. This also lists the physical constants of a selected number of peroxides with references to the original literature or to review articles which list the original references. A table of some commercially available organic peroxides is given in Appendix 3.

## II. Peroxides of Structure ROOH (Hydroperoxides)

The monosubstituted derivatives of hydrogen peroxide ROOH (where R is alkyl or aralkyl) are known as hydroperoxides and are prepared by three general methods: (*a*) alkylation of hydrogen peroxide with alkyl halides, sulfates, or alcohols in the presence of strong acids; (*b*) Controlled oxidation of the hydrocarbon RH with molecular oxygen to give ROOH; (*c*) addition of oxygen to Grignard reagents.

The oxidation of hydrocarbons is known[8] to occur via a radical chain mechanism. The propagation steps of this reaction are:

$$R\cdot + O_2 \longrightarrow RO_2\cdot$$
$$RO_2\cdot + RH \longrightarrow ROOH + R\cdot$$

The initiating free radicals may be formed in various ways, *i.e.*, photochemically, or by the decomposition of radical producing catalysts such as benzoyl peroxide. The hydroperoxide that is formed also acts as a source for free radicals and hence the term autoxidation.

### 1. Saturated Aliphatic Hydroperoxides

Primary, secondary, and tertiary hydroperoxides of the aliphatic hydrocarbons have been prepared by all three methods. A few examples are given below:

| *Formula* | *Name* |
|---|---|
| $CH_3OOH$ | Methyl hydroperoxide |
| $CH_3CH_2OOH$ | Ethyl hydroperoxide |
| $(CH_3)_3COOH$ | *t*-Butyl hydroperoxide |
| (decalin ring structure with H and OOH) | *trans*-Decalin hydroperoxide (*trans*-Decahydro-4*a*-naphthyl hydroperoxide) |

[8] J. L. Bolland, *Quart. Reviews*, *3*, 1 (1949).

$CH_3$
COOH 1-Methylcyclopentyl hydroperoxide

OOH
$HC{\equiv}C{-}C{-}CH_3$ 3-Methyl-3-hydroperoxy-1-butyne
(1,1-Dimethyl-2-propynyl hydroperoxide)
$CH_3$

In several cases such as decalin hydroperoxide, the compound has been prepared by both methods (*a*) and (*b*) and has been shown to be identical when prepared by either method.[9]

In some cases the hydroperoxides prepared by either method (*a*) or method (*b*) can be purified by fractional distillation. In other cases, such as the hydroperoxides of methylcyclopentane, methylcyclohexane, and ethylcyclohexane, the purification has been accomplished by concentration of the metal salts of the hydroperoxides.[8,9–11]

*Preparation of t-Butyl Hydroperoxide by Methods* (*a*), (*b*), *and* (*c*). The preparation of *t*-butyl hydroperoxide by method (*a*) was reported by Milas and co-workers.[12] A solution of hydrogen peroxide was reacted with *t*-butyl alcohol in the presence of glacial metaphosphoric acid or anhydrous magnesium sulfate. The *t*-butyl hydroperoxide was removed by vacuum distillation.

$$(CH_3)_3COH + HOOH \xrightarrow[\text{metaphosphoric acid}]{\text{glacial}} (CH_3)_3COOH + H_2O$$

An alternate process is to treat *t*-butyl hydrogen sulfate in the cold with a concentrated solution of hydrogen peroxide.[12] More specifically, when equimolar quantities of *t*-butyl alcohol or isobutylene react in the cold with 70 per cent sulfuric acid, and hydrogen

[9] R. Criegee and H. Dietrich, *Ann.*, *560*, 135 (1948).

[10] K. I. Ivanov and V. K. Savinova, *Doklady Akad. Nauk S. S. S. R.*, *59*, 493 (1948).

[11] R. H. Hall and D. C. Quin, Brit. Pat. 610,293 (Oct. 13, 1948). E. G. E. Hawkins, D. C. Quin, and F. E. Salt, Brit. Pat. 641,250 (Aug. 9, 1950). R. H. Hall and D. C. Quin, U. S. Pat. 2,547,938 (April 10, 1951). G. P. Armstrong, R. H. Hall and D. C. Quin, *Nature*, *164*, 834 (1949); *J. Chem. Soc.* 666 (1950).

[12] N. A. Milas and S. A. Harris, *J. Am. Chem. Soc.*, *60*, 2434 (1938). N. A. Milas and D. M. Surgenor, *ibid.*, *68*, 205 (1946).

peroxide (30 per cent) is slowly added, a mixture of 50–70 per cent of *t*-butyl hydroperoxide and 50–30 per cent of di-*t*-butyl peroxide is obtained. The mixture can be separated by: (*1*) fractional distillation under reduced pressure; (*2*) extraction of the hydroperoxide from the reaction products by using an alkaline solution as an extraction agent:

$$(CH_3)_3C(HSO_4) + HOOH \longrightarrow (CH_3)_3COOH + H_2SO_4$$
$$2(CH_3)_3C(HSO_4) + HOOH \longrightarrow (CH_3)_3COOC(CH_3)_3 + 2H_2SO_4$$

To prepare *t*-butyl hydroperoxide by method (*b*), Vaughan and Rust describe the following procedure.[13] A vapor mixture of isobutane, oxygen, and hydrogen bromide (which acts as a sensitizer) in the molar ratio 8:8:1 is passed through a glass tube at 158°C. for a contact time of three minutes. The product yield is 75 per cent *t*-butyl hydroperoxide with water as a by-product.

To prepare *t*-butyl hydroperoxide by method (*c*), Walling and Buckler slowly added *t*-butyl MgCl to oxygen saturated ether at −71°C.[14] The product initially obtained is *t*-butyl OOMgCl, which is then hydrolyzed to the hydroperoxide. The yield of this reaction was as high as 91%. Other alkyl and aryl Grignard reagents were also converted to hydroperoxides by this method.

## 2. Hydroperoxides of Olefins

The olefin hydroperoxides are among the earliest studied organic peroxides, although the exact structures of these materials have been definitely established only recently. In 1900 Engler[15a] observed that pentene, 2-methyl-2-butene and hexene formed peroxides (*viz.* hydroperoxides) on standing in air and since that time a large number of other olefin hydroperoxides have been similarly prepared, *i.e.*, by reaction with air or molecular oxygen.

### (a) *2-Cyclohexen-1-yl Hydroperoxide*

The isolation and proof of structure of the organic peroxide formed

[13] W. E. Vaughan and F. F. Rust, U. S. Pat. 2,403,722 (July, 1946). See also E. R. Bell, J. H. Raley, F. F. Rust, F. H. Seubold, and W. E. Vaughan, *Ind. Eng. Chem., 41*, 2597 (1949) and *Faraday Soc. Discussion on Hydrocarbons, 10*, 242 (1951).

[14] C. Walling and S. A. Buckler, *J. Am. Chem. Soc., 75*, 4372 (1953).

[15] (a) C. Engler, *Ber., 33*, 1094 (1900). (b) H. N. Stephens, *J. Am. Chem. Soc., 50*, 568 (1928).

when cyclohexene is exposed to air in the presence of sunlight provides an interesting example of the work in this field. In 1928 Stephens[15b] observed that cyclohexene reacts with oxygen in the presence of light to form a liquid peroxide whose constitution he established as $C_6H_{10}O_2$. He supposed that this product was the double bond adduct I.

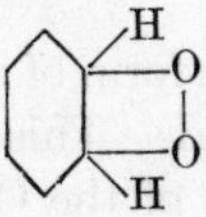

H O O H —OOH

(I) 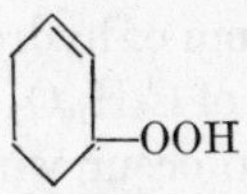 (II)

Hock and Schrader[16] reexamined Stephens' peroxide and, despite certain irregularities of its behavior, agreed with Stephens' formulation of the cyclic structure I. However, Criegee, and later Criegee, Pilz, and Flygare,[17] and also Hock and Gänicke[18] concluded that structure I was incorrect and that Stephens' peroxide was actually a hydroperoxide of structure II. This was amply confirmed by the extensive researches of Farmer and co-workers.[19] Farmer gave detailed instructions for preparing cyclohexene hydroperoxide, which he formed by shaking cyclohexene in a quartz flask attached to an oxygen reservoir in the presence of ultraviolet light (the temperature being about 35–40°C.). The best yields were obtained after relatively short times of illumination which, in this case, never exceeded twenty-four hours. The resultant oxidized cyclohexene could be separated into four fractions by distillation: (*1*) unreacted cyclohexene; (*2*) a fraction of b.p. *circa* 30°/0.2 mm. Hg; (*3*) the hydroperoxide boiling at 47–48°/0.2 mm. Hg; (*4*) a high boiling polymer peroxide substance. Fraction (*2*) was shown to consist mainly of 2-cyclohexen-1-ol and a smaller amount of epoxycyclohexane.

The fact that the hydroperoxide is formed by replacing a hydrogen atom on the methylenic group adjacent to the double bond (the $\alpha$-methylene group) is of great importance as a key to understanding the oxidation products of more complex olefins.

[16] H. Hock and O. Schrader, *Naturwiss.*, *24*, 159 (1936); *Angew. Chem.*, *39*, 565 (1936).

[17] R. Criegee, H. Pilz, and H. Flygare, *Ber.*, *B72*, 1799 (1939). R. Criegee, *Ann.*, *522*, 75 (1936).

[18] H. Hock and K. Gänicke, *Ber.*, *B71*, 1430 (1938); *ibid.*, *B72*, 2516 (1939).

[19] E. H. Farmer and A. Sundralingham, *J. Chem. Soc.*, *1942*, 121.

The evidence which supports the hydroperoxide structure II presented by Criegee and supported and supplemented by Hock and by Farmer includes the following:

(*a*) The substance $C_6H_{10}O_2$ adds molecular bromine mole per mole in a solution of carbon tetrachloride or acetic acid. This is strong evidence that the original double bond of the cyclohexene has remained intact.

(*b*) An atom of hydrogen is liberated in the form of methane from each molecule of $C_6H_{10}O_2$ by the reagent $CH_3MgI$. This is what might be expected to occur with the hydrogen atom of the OOH group in structure II.

(*c*) Reduction by strong alkalies or by sodium sulfite gives 2-cyclohexen-1-ol (eq. 1).

$$\text{(1)} \quad \text{(cyclohexenyl)}\text{—OOH} \xrightarrow{Na_2SO_3} \text{(cyclohexenyl)}\text{—OH}$$

(*d*) Oxidation products of the peroxide $C_6H_{10}O_2$ obtained by reaction with strong oxidizing agents such as permanganate consist of mixtures of acids of which $\alpha$-hydroxyadipic acid is most predominant (eq. 2).

$$\text{(2)} \quad \text{(cyclohexenyl)}\text{—OOH} \xrightarrow[KMnO_4]{\text{oxidation}} \begin{matrix} CHOHCOOH \\ (CH_2)_2 \\ CH_2COOH \end{matrix}$$

(*e*) The peroxide of 1-methylcyclohexene may be reduced to 2-methyl-2-cyclohexene-1-ol and the latter further reduced by catalytic hydrogenation to hexahydro-*o*-cresol (eq. 3).

$$\text{(3)} \quad HOO\text{—(2-methylcyclohexenyl, } CH_3\text{)} \xrightarrow[\text{[cat]}]{\text{[H]}} HO\text{—(2-methylcyclohexenyl, } CH_3\text{)} \xrightarrow[\text{[cat]}]{\text{[H]}} HO\text{—(2-methylcyclohexyl, } CH_3\text{)}$$

(*f*) Hydrogenation of the peroxide of cyclohexene with Adams' catalyst results in an almost quantitative yield of crystallizable cyclohexanol (eq. 4).

$$\text{(4)} \quad HOO\text{—(cyclohexenyl)} \xrightarrow[\text{[cat]}]{\text{[H]}} HO\text{—(cyclohexyl)}$$

(*g*) Salts of the peroxide can be formed with alkali.

Although the hydroperoxide nature of the peroxidic products

resulting from reaction of olefins with air or oxygen is very widely accepted at present, Paquot[20] has suggested that an additional type of peroxide is formed in this reaction:

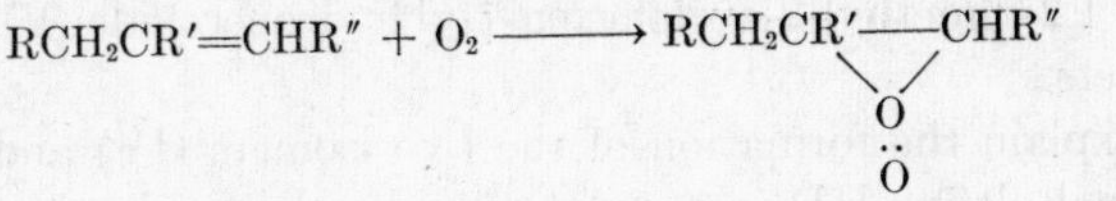

$$RCH_2CR'{=}CHR'' + O_2 \longrightarrow RCH_2CR'{-}CHR''\ (\text{bridged by } O{-}O)$$

This cyclic peroxide has never been isolated but was postulated as an intermediate in the formation of epoxides, glycols, and ethers which are found after extensive oxidation. On the other hand, hydroperoxides have been isolated in the initial phases of oxidation of olefins with molecular oxygen. Furthermore, most of the products obtained after extensive oxidation can be explained as due to breakdown products of the initially formed hydroperoxides. It must, therefore, be concluded that Paquot's intermediate cyclic peroxide has not yet been confirmed.

*(b) Hydroperoxides of Other Monoolefins*

In addition to cyclohexene, the structures of the hydroperoxides of the following olefins may be considered to be completely established: cyclopentene[17] (I), 1-methylcyclohexene[17,19,21] (II), 1,2-dimethylcyclohexene[19,21] (two forms, IV and V), and 3-*p*-menthene[22] (VI).

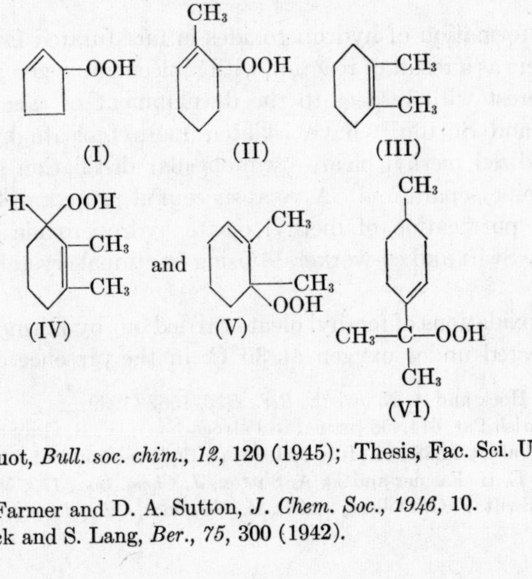

(I) (II) (III)

(IV) and (V) (VI)

[20] C. Paquot, *Bull. soc. chim.*, *12*, 120 (1945); Thesis, Fac. Sci. Univ. Paris, 1943.

[21] E. H. Farmer and D. A. Sutton, *J. Chem. Soc.*, *1946*, 10.

[22] H. Hock and S. Lang, *Ber.*, *75*, 300 (1942).

It has been definitely established[21] that a partial isomerization occurs during the oxidation of 1,2-dimethylcyclohexene (III) in view of the fact that both 2,3-dimethyl-2-cyclohexen-1-yl hydroperoxide (IV) and 1,2-dimethyl-2-cyclohexen-1-yl hydroperoxide (V) are found as products.

To explain the formation of the two isomers (IV) and (V) from the original olefin (III), one must consider the mechanism of hydroperoxide formation by reaction of hydrocarbons with molecular oxygen. One of the fundamental steps is the formation of a hydrocarbon free radical. In the case of radicals of the type —ĊH—CH=CH— which are formed during the oxidation of olefins, there exists a strong tendency for the following resonance to occur:

$$-\overset{1}{\dot{C}H}-\overset{2}{CH}=\overset{3}{CH}- \longleftrightarrow -\overset{1}{CH}=\overset{2}{CH}-\overset{3}{\dot{C}H}-$$

The hydroperoxide eventually formed may therefore be a mixture of a 1-hydroperoxide with the double bond between the 2 and 3 carbon atoms, and a 3-hydroperoxide with the double bond between the 1 and 2 carbon atoms.

Many other olefins have been observed to yield hydroperoxides upon oxidation with molecular oxygen,[23,24] but the structures of the hydroperoxides have not been definitely established. However, in many of these cases it is probable that the structures are the expected ones.

The formation of hydroperoxides in unsaturated fatty acids and their esters as a result of reaction with molecular oxygen is of considerable interest with respect to the development of rancidity in fats. Farmer and Sutton[25a] have isolated methyl oleate hydroperoxide from oxidized methyl oleate by molecular distillation and by chromatographic separation. A very successful procedure for the isolation and purification of methyl oleate hydroperoxide has been reported by Swift and co-workers[25b] using fractional crystallization from acetone.

The oxidations of methyl oleate carried out by Farmer and Sutton were effected under oxygen at 30°C. in the presence of ultraviolet

[23] H. Hock and A. Neuwirth, *Ber.*, *B72*, 1562 (1939).

[24] British Pat. 614,456 (issued to Petrocarbon); V. R. Gray and H. Steiner, U. S. Patent 2,538,844 (July 3, 1951) (to Petrocarbon Ltd.)

[25] (a) E. H. Farmer and D. A. Sutton, *J. Chem. Soc.*, *119*, 543 (1949). (b) C. E. Swift, F. G. Dollear, and R. R. O'Connor, *Oil and Soap*, *23*, 365 (1946).

light. The purified peroxidic product contains the same amount of unsaturation as was present in the original methyl oleate. (The unsaturation was measured both by iodine number and by hydrogenation.) Furthermore, the reduction of the compound by several methods (aluminum amalgam, hydriodic acid, catalytic) yields methyl hydroxy oleate and then methyl stearate. The action of alcoholic alkali solution is to form hydroxyoleic acid. These results prove that the peroxidic reaction product of oxygen and oleic acid is a hydroperoxide. Permanganate oxidation of methyl oleate hydroperoxide gives a mixture of products derived from octoic, pelargonic, suberic, and azelaic acids. This seems to indicate that the hydroperoxide of methyl oleate has several isomeric forms as postulated by Farmer and Sutton.[25–27] Ross and coworkers[26] have recently shown that hydroperoxidation of methyl oleate occurs at carbon atoms $C_8$, $C_9$, $C_{10}$, and $C_{11}$. The structures of methyl oleate and the four hydroperoxides of methyl oleate are:

$$\mathrm{CH_3(CH_2)_6\underset{8}{C}H_2\underset{9}{C}H{=}\underset{10}{C}H\underset{11}{C}H_2(CH_2)_6COOCH_3} \quad \text{methyl oleate}$$

$$\mathrm{CH_3(CH_2)_6\underset{8}{C}H(OOH)\underset{9}{C}H{=}\underset{10}{C}H\underset{11}{C}H_2(CH_2)_6COOCH_3}$$

$$\mathrm{CH_3(CH_2)_6\underset{8}{C}H_2\underset{9}{C}H(OOH)\underset{10}{C}H{=}\underset{11}{C}H(CH_2)_6COOCH_3}$$

$$\mathrm{CH_3(CH_2)_6\underset{8}{C}H{=}\underset{9}{C}H\underset{10}{C}H(OOH)\underset{11}{C}H_2(CH_2)_6COOCH_3}$$

$$\mathrm{CH_3(CH_2)_6\underset{8}{C}H_2\underset{9}{C}H{=}\underset{10}{C}H\underset{11}{C}H(OOH)(CH_2)_6COOCH_3}$$

The position of the hydroperoxide group was determined by converting the mixture of hydroperoxides to the corresponding methyl ketostearates, which were isolated and identified.[26]

An interesting class of olefins which do not oxidize mainly to hydroperoxides in the presence of molecular oxygen are the polymerizable vinyl or vinylidene monomers such as styrene, methyl methacrylate, and vinyl acetate. These substances form polymeric peroxides which will be discussed in section III-3.

Conjugated olefins such as 2,4-dimethyl-2,4-pentadiene do not form hydroperoxides upon reaction with molecular oxygen but in-

[26] J. Ross, A. I. Gebhart, and J. F. Gerecht, *J. Am. Chem. Soc.*, *71*, 282 (1949).

[27] D. Swern, H. B. Knight, J. T. Scanlon, and W. C. Ault, *J. Am. Chem. Soc.*, *67*, 1132 (1945).

stead form ring or chain peroxides. These will be discussed in section III-4.

### (c) *Hydroperoxides of Polyolefins Containing 1,4 Unsaturation*

The autoxidation of polyolefins containing double bonds in 1,4 positions results in the formation of the expected hydroperoxides as well as hydroperoxides of isomeric structure having conjugated double bonds. Frequently this is followed by formation of high molecular weight polymeric peroxides.

Bolland and Koch[28] have shown that the hydroperoxidic product obtained from the reaction of ethyl linoleate and oxygen contains several isomers, and that 70 per cent of the product contains the conjugated diene grouping. This last conclusion was obtained by analysis of the ultraviolet absorption spectrum of the oxidized material.

The formation of hydroperoxide isomers in the case of ethyl linoleate (assuming that the initial radical is formed on the 8 carbon atom exclusively):

$$CH_3(CH_2)_4\underset{6}{C}H{=}\underset{7}{C}H\underset{8}{C}H_2\underset{9}{C}H{=}\underset{10}{C}H{-}(CH_2)_7COOC_2H_5$$

is easily explained in terms of the possibility of resonance of the radical intermediate:

$$\underset{(I)}{-\underset{6}{CH}{=}\underset{7}{CH}{-}\underset{8}{\dot{C}H}{-}\underset{9}{CH}{=}\underset{10}{CH}-} \longleftrightarrow \underset{(II)}{-\underset{6}{CH}{=}\underset{7}{CH}{-}\underset{8}{CH}{=}\underset{9}{CH}{-}\underset{10}{\dot{C}H}-} \longleftrightarrow$$

$$\underset{(III)}{-\underset{6}{\dot{C}H}{-}\underset{7}{CH}{=}\underset{8}{CH}{-}\underset{9}{CH}{=}\underset{10}{CH}-}$$

From each of these resonating forms a corresponding hydroperoxide molecule may be derived.[29] *Cis-trans* isomers of the hydroperoxides are also found.[30]

The isomeric possibilities for the hydroperoxidic reaction product of a 1,4,7 triolefin such as ethyl linolenate and molecular oxygen are even greater.[31,32]

$$CH_3\underset{2}{C}H_2\underset{3}{C}H{=}\underset{4}{C}H\underset{5}{C}H_2\underset{6}{C}H{=}\underset{7}{C}H\underset{8}{C}H_2\underset{9}{C}H{=}\underset{10}{C}H(CH_2)_7COOC_2H_5 \text{ (ethyl linolenate)}$$

[28] J. L. Bolland and H. P. Koch, *J. Chem. Soc., 1945*, 445.
[29] E. R. H. Jones, *Trans. Faraday Soc., 42*, 250 (1946).
[30] H. H. Sephton and D. A. Sutton, *J. Soc. Chem. Ind., 1953*, 667.

By writing the various resonance possibilities for the two initially formed hydrocarbon free radicals (at positions 5 and 8) it is clear that six isomeric monohydroperoxides are to be expected.

The oxidation of the esters (glycerides) of linoleic and linolenic acid is of great practical importance in connection with the "drying" of linseed oil. Hydroperoxide formation seems likely to be an initial step in the drying process. The important physical changes associated with drying are probably due to intermolecular cross linkage (polymerization) initiated by the decomposition of the hydroperoxides. It is not known at present to what extent the cross linkage is direct carbon-carbon cross linkage, or to what extent carbon atoms are linked through intermediate oxygen atoms to form the cross links.[33,34]

### (d) *Hydroperoxides of Polyolefins Containing 1,5 Unsaturation*

The unsaturated 1,5 diolefin grouping is of particular importance because it occurs as a structural unit in natural rubber, many synthetic rubbers, and in many natural products such as fish oils:

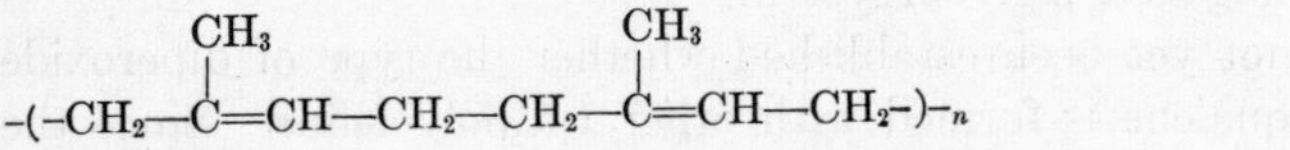

$$-(-CH_2-C(CH_3)=CH-CH_2-CH_2-C(CH_3)=CH-CH_2-)-_n \quad \text{Natural rubber}$$

$$-(-CH_2-CH=CH-CH_2-CH_2-CH=CH-CH_2-CH_2-CH(CH=CH_2)-)_n \quad \text{Polybutadiene}$$

$$H-CH_2-C(CH_3)=CH-CH_2-CH_2-C(CH_3)=CH-CH_2-H \quad \text{Dihydromyrcene}$$

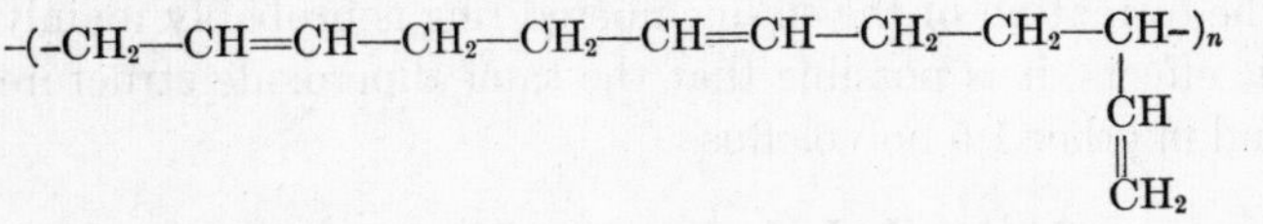

$$H-(CH_2-C(CH_3)=CH-CH_2)_3-H \quad \text{Dihydrofarnesene}$$

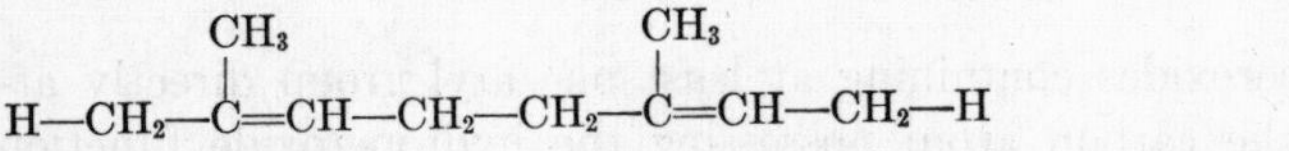

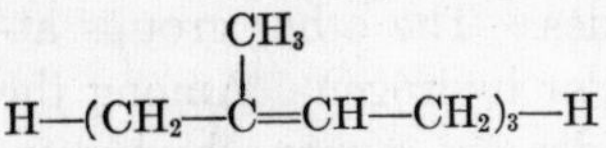

$$H-(CH_2-C(CH_3)=CH-CH_2)_3-(CH_2-CH=C(CH_3)-CH_2)_3-H \quad \text{Squalene}$$

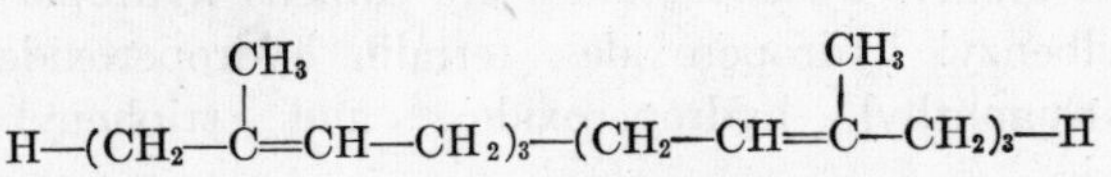

[31] E. H. Farmer, H. P. Koch, and D. A. Sutton, *J. Chem. Soc.*, *1943*, 51, 541.
[32] E. H. Farmer, *Trans. Faraday Soc.*, *42*, 228 (1946).
[33] A. J. Stirton, J. Turer, and R. W. Riemenschneider, *Oil and Soap*, *22*, 81 (1945).
[34] F. D. Gunstone and T. P. Hilditch, *J. Chem. Soc.*, *1946*, 836, 1022.

Farmer and Sutton[35] have stated that, in the photoactivated reaction of dihydromyrcene, dihydrofarnesene, and squalene with oxygen, most of the initially absorbed oxygen could be accounted for as hydroperoxide, and that the original unsaturation remains essentially unchanged.[35] There appears to be no formation of conjugated double bond structures.

Bolland and Hughes,[36] on the other hand, have found that the *thermal* oxidation product of squalene consists of a diperoxide in which four oxygen atoms are combined into one squalene molecule. Two of the oxygen atoms are hydroperoxidic and the other two form an intramolecular peroxide ring:

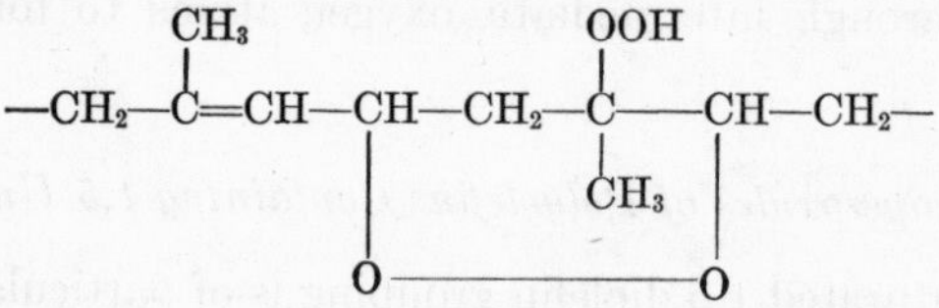

$$-CH_2-\overset{\overset{CH_3}{|}}{C}=CH-\underset{\underset{O}{|}}{CH}-CH_2-\underset{\underset{CH_3}{|}}{\overset{\overset{OOH}{|}}{C}}-\underset{\underset{O}{|}}{CH}-CH_2- \quad (O\text{—}O \text{ ring bond})$$

Among the structure proofs used by Bolland and Hughes was the fact that reduction of the oxidation product of squalene leads to a triol containing an $\alpha, \beta$ glycol system.

It has not yet been established whether the type of diperoxide found for squalene is formed with other 1,5 polyolefins. Since the reason for the formation of the six-membered ring is probably mainly due to steric effects, it is possible that the same diperoxide structure may be found in other 1,5 polyolefins.

### 3. *Aralkyl Hydroperoxides*

Hydroperoxides containing at least one aryl group directly attached to the carbon atom possessing the hydroperoxide function may be classified as aralkyl hydroperoxides. The other groups attached to this carbon may be alkyl, aryl, or hydrogen. Among the most widely studied aralkyl hydroperoxides are cumene hydroperoxide ($\alpha,\alpha$-dimethylbenzyl hydroperoxide), tetralin hydroperoxide (1,2,3,4-tetrahydro-1-naphthyl hydroperoxide), and triphenylmethyl hydroperoxide.

The aralkyl hydroperoxides are normally prepared by the method of controlled oxidation of the hydrocarbon with molecular oxygen

[35] E. H. Farmer and D. A. Sutton, *J. Chem. Soc., 1942*, 139.
[36] J. L. Bolland and H. Hughes, *J. Chem. Soc., 1949*, 492.

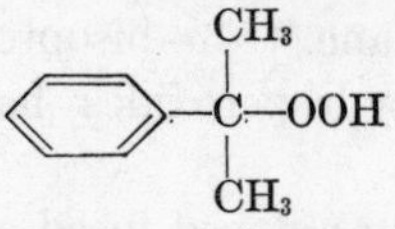

Cumene hydroperoxide

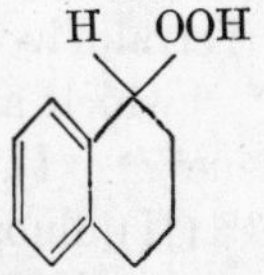

Triphenylmethyl hydroperoxide

Tetralin hydroperoxide

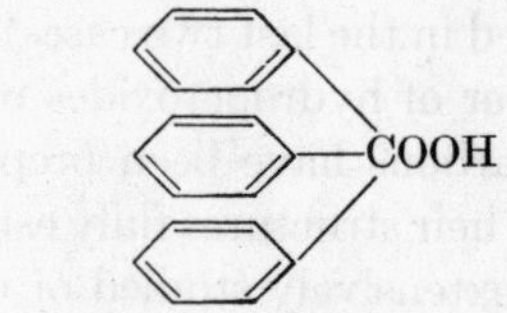

(method *b*). However, triphenylmethyl hydroperoxide has also been made[37] by the reaction of triphenylmethyl chloride with hydrogen peroxide. Also benzyl hydroperoxide, which has not been made by methods (*a*) and (*b*), has been prepared[14] from $C_6H_5CH_2MgCl$ by method (*c*). Also, one case has been reported where the hydrocarbon is quite resistant to air oxidation, but the corresponding hydroperoxide can be prepared as in equation (1).[38] In this reaction the role of the stannic chloride is to promote ionization of the chloride without catalyzing the decomposition of hydrogen peroxide.

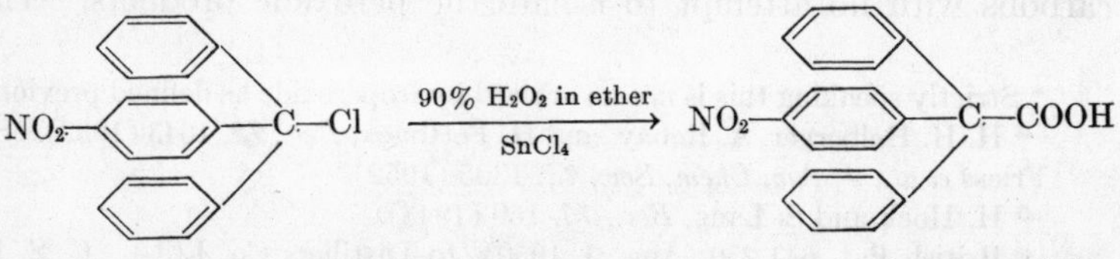

(1) $NO_2-C_6H_4-C(C_6H_5)_2-Cl \xrightarrow[SnCl_4]{90\%\ H_2O_2\ \text{in ether}} NO_2-C_6H_4-C(C_6H_5)_2-COOH$

Among the aralkyl hydrocarbons whose hydroperoxides have been prepared in a reasonable state of purity are the following: isopropylbenzene (cumene),[39–42] *sec*-butylbenzene,[43,44] *p*-xylene,[45]

[37] H. Wieland and J. Maier, *Ber.*, *64*, 1205 (1913).

[38] P. D. Bartlett and J. D. Cotman, *J. Am. Chem. Soc.*, *72*, 3095 (1950).

[39] H. Hock and S. Lang, *Ber.*, *77–79*, 257 (1944–46).

[40] K. I. Ivanov, V. K. Savinova, and E. G. Mikhailova, *J. Gen. Chem.* (*U. S. S. R.*), *8*, 51 (1938).

[41] British Pats. 610,293 (Oct., 1948) and 629,637 (Sept., 1949) (to Distillers Co. Ltd.).

[42] G. P. Armstrong, R. H. Hall, and D. C. Quin, *Nature*, *164*, 834 (1949); also *J. Chem. Soc.*, *1950*, 666.

[43] K. I. Ivanov, V. K. Savinova, and V. P. Zhakhovskaya, *Doklady Akad. Nauk. S. S. S. R.*, *59*, 703, 905 (1948); *Chem. Abstracts*, *42*, 6739, 6768 (1948).

[44] E. G. E. Hawkins, *J. Chem. Soc.*, *1949*, 2076.

[45] H. Hock and S. Lang, *Ber.*, *76*, 169 (1943).

cymene,[46] ethylbenzene,[47] diphenylmethane,[39] *o*-diisopropylbenzene,[2,48] and *p*-diisopropylbenzene[2,48] (dihydroperoxides have also been prepared in the last two cases).

A number of hydroperoxides of partially reduced fused aromatic ring hydrocarbons have been prepared by oxidation with molecular oxygen and their structures fully established. Tetralin hydroperoxide is the most extensively studied of this series,[49–56] which also includes the hydroperoxides of 1,4-dihydronaphthalene[57,58] (I), 1-methyltetralin,[59] 1-methyl-1,2-dihydronaphthalene*,[59,60] (II), fluorene[59] (III), indan[61] (hydrindene) (IV), and octahydroanthracene (V).[62]

Attempts[58,59] to prepare hydroperoxides of indene and 1,2-dihydronaphthalene by autoxidation were unsuccessful, although peroxide products were obtained which have been proved to be cyclic peroxides. The preparation and properties of these structures will be discussed in section III-4 dealing with transannular peroxides.

A great many aralkyl hydroperoxides of low purity have been prepared by straightforward hydrocarbon oxidation of aralkyl hydrocarbons with no attempt to isolate the peroxidic products. These

* Strictly speaking this is not an aralkyl hydroperoxide as defined previously.

[46] H. H. Helberger, A. Rebay, and H. Fettback, *Ber.*, *72*, 1643 (1939). S. L. Friess *et al.*, *J. Am. Chem. Soc.*, *74*, 1305 (1952).

[47] H. Hock and S. Lang, *Ber.*, *76*, 169 (1943).

[48] British Pat. 641,250 (Aug. 9, 1950) (to Distillers Co. Ltd.). U. S. Pat. 2,438,125 (Mar. 23, 1948) (to Hercules Powder Co.).

[49] A. Robertson and W. A. Waters, *J. Chem. Soc.*, *1948*, 1574, 1578.

[50] P. George, E. K. Rideal, and A. Robertson, *Nature*, *149*, 601 (1942).

[51] M. Hartman and M. Seiberth, *Helv. Chim. Acta*, *15*, 1390 (1932); *U. S. Pat.* 1,924,786 and British Pat. 396,351.

[52] H. Hock and W. Susemihl, *Ber.*, *66*, 61 (1933).

[53] W. Nussle, G. W. Perkins, and G. Toennies, *Am. J. Pharm.*, *107*, 29 (1935).

[54] S. S. Medvedev, *Acta Physicochim.* (*U. S. S. R.*), *9*, 395, 405 (1938).

[55] S. S. Medvedev and A. Podyapolskaya, *J. Phys. Chem. U. S. S. R.*, *12*, 719 (1939).

[56] K. I. Ivanov, V. K. Savinova, and E. G. Mikhailova, *Compt. rend. acad. sci.* (*U. S. S. R.*), *25*, 34 (1939).

[57] H. Hock and F. Depke, *Ber.*, *84*, 122 (1951).

[58] H. Hock and F. Depke, *Ber.*, *84*, 349 (1951).

[59] H. Hock, S. Lang, and G. Knauel, *Ber.*, *83*, 227 (1950); *83*, 238 (1950).

[60] H. Hock and S. Lang, *Ber.*, *75*, 302 (1942).

[61] H. Hock and S. Lang, *Ber.*, *75*, 1051 (1942).

[62] H. Hock and S. Lang, *Ber.*, *76*, 1130 (1943).

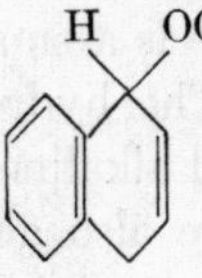

H OOH CH$_3$ H OOH

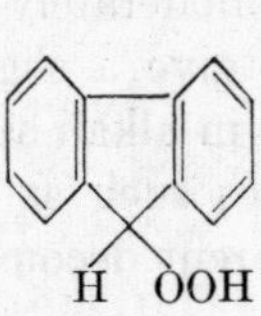

(I) 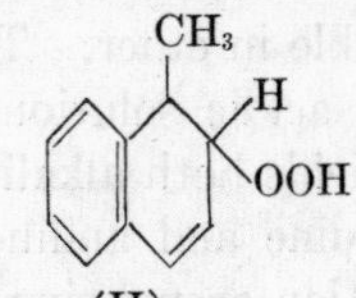 (II) H OOH (III)

H OOH H OOH

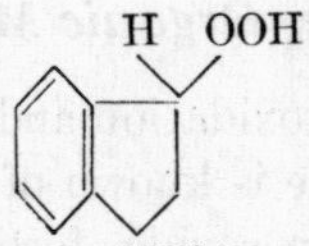

(IV) 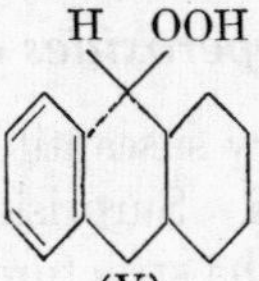 (V)

hydroperoxidic substances have been used, for example, as catalysts for redox emulsion polymerization.[63]

Oxidation of aralkyl hydrocarbons with molecular oxygen has also been carried out in alkaline emulsions.[11] It is found that considerably higher yields of hydroperoxide can be obtained by this technique than by autoxidation of the liquid hydrocarbon.

*Preparation of Tetralin Hydroperoxide.* In Hock and Susemihl's earliest procedure for the preparation of tetralin hydroperoxide,[52] a moderately brisk and well dispersed stream of air was led through tetralin for 50–60 hours at 75°C. The vapors evolved were trapped and returned by a reflux condenser. The solution becomes colored yellow after a short time due to secondary oxidation products. If the reaction is carried out beyond the suggested length of time the yield diminishes due to breakdown of the hydroperoxide. Approximately 80 per cent of the unreacted tetralin can be distilled from the solution at 50–60°C. under 1–2 mm. Hg pressure in an all-glass apparatus. The residue crystallizes after standing for a relatively long time; the crystallization may be accelerated by cooling to 0°C. or below. The crude hydroperoxide may then be suction filtered giving a yield of 15–17 weight per cent. For purification the product is twice crystallized from a large quantity of petroleum ether to give long, colored, star-shaped doubly refractive and odorless needles which melt at 56°C.

The solid hydroperoxide is soluble in all usual organic solvents

[63] J. E. Wicklatz, T. J. Kennedy, and W. B. Reynolds, *J. Polymer Sci.*, *4*, 45 (1951).

and is only moderately soluble in ether. There is a small solubility in water to give a slightly acidic solution. The hydroperoxide is very soluble in alkali and yields both alkali and alkaline earth salts. Organic bases such as pyridine and aniline are also good solvents and no apparent decomposition occurs since the peroxide is recoverable.

### *4. Hydroperoxides of Other Organic Molecules*

Ethers are very susceptible to autoxidation and the formation of peroxidic products. Surprisingly little is known of the autoxidation mechanism or of the structure of the peroxides formed. It has been reported that the initial oxidation product of diisopropyl ether is a hydroperoxide:[64,65]

$$CH(Me)_2OCH(Me)_2 + O_2 \longrightarrow HOOC(Me)_2OCH(Me)_2$$

The monohydroperoxide is formed in small yields, however, and is apparently rapidly converted to the dihydroperoxide, $HOOC(Me)_2$-$OC(Me)_2OOH$, since the latter is the main isolatable peroxide product.

Tetrahydrofuran and its alkyl substituted derivatives readily undergo autoxidation at 25–40°C. to yield stable peroxides that are hydroperoxides.[66]

$$\text{(tetrahydrofuran ring, O)} \xrightarrow{O_2} \text{(tetrahydrofuran ring, O)}\text{—OOH}$$

Hydroperoxides of ethers have also been prepared by method (*a*). It is reported in the patent literature that treatment of ethyl vinyl ether with hydrogen peroxide in sulfuric acid yields the peroxidic compound (I). Examples of other unsaturated ethers which yield hydroperoxides are also given:[4,67]

$$C_2H_5OCH{=}CH_2 + HOOH \xrightarrow{H_2SO_4} \underset{\text{(I)}}{C_2H_5OCH(OOH)CH_3}$$

[64] A. Rieche and K. Koch, *Ber.*, *75*, 1016 (1942).

[65] K. I. Ivanov, V. K. Savinova, and G. Mikhailova, *J. Gen. Chem.* (*U. S. S. R.*), *16*, 65, 1003, 1015 (1946); *Chem. Abstracts*, *41*, 2692 (1947).

[66] (a) A. Robertson, *Nature*, *162*, 153 (1948); also British Pats. 532,158 and 614,392. (b) H. Rein and R. Criegee, *Angew. Chem.*, *62*, 120 (1950).

[67] N. A. Milas, U. S. Pat. 2,223,807 (Dec. 3, 1940).

It has been reported[68] that 1,2,3,4-tetrahydrocarbazole and its homologues yield peroxides upon autoxidation. These are hydroperoxides similar to structure (II).

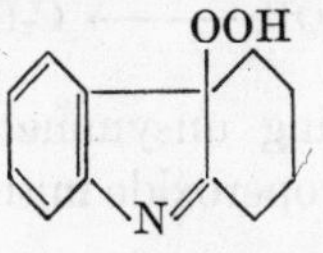

OOH

N

(II)

The reaction product of phenylhydrazine and ketones or aldehydes is often used for the identification of these latter substances:

$$\underset{\text{phenylhydrazine}}{C_6H_5NHNH_2} + \underset{\text{ketone}}{RR'CO} \longrightarrow \underset{\text{phenylhydrazone}}{C_6H_5NH{-}N{=}CRR'}$$

The phenylhydrazones are readily subject to oxidation to form peroxides known as Busch peroxides.[69a] It is believed that these peroxides have the structure given below:[69b,c]

$$C_6H_5NH{-}N{=}CRR' + O_2 \longrightarrow C_6H_5N{=}N{-}\overset{\overset{\displaystyle OOH}{|}}{C}RR'$$

The identification of hydroperoxides formed by autoxidation of complex molecules, particularly organic molecules containing atoms other than carbon and hydrogen, is still in its infancy. Many cases not listed here are described in the review articles of Hawkins[2] and Criegee.[3b] The latter discusses, for example, the peroxidic products obtained by oxidation of phenolic and enolic compounds and by dehydrogenation of certain phenols and acids. It is anticipated that extensive developments in this field will occur in the next few years.

## III. Peroxides of Structure ROOR
## (Dialkyl and Diaralkyl Peroxides)

### *1. Dialkyl Peroxides*

A standard method for preparation of dialkyl peroxides is to react an alkyl sulfate with hydrogen peroxide in the presence of an

[68] (a) J. S. Beer, L. McGrath, A. Robertson, and A. B. Woodier, *Nature*, *164*, 362 (1949). (b) R. J. S. Beer, L. McGrath, and A. Robertson, *J. Chem. Soc.*, *1950*, 2118. (c) B. Witkop, *J. Am. Chem. Soc.*, *72*, 1428 (1950).

[69] (a) M. Busch and W. Dietz, *Ber.*, *47*, 2377 (1914). (b) R. Criegee and G. Lohaus, *ibid.*, *84*, 219 (1951). (c) K. H. Pausacker, *J. Chem. Soc.*, *1950*, 3478.

alkali.[70–72] This reaction leads to the formation of symmetrical peroxides:

$$(C_2H_5)_2SO_4 + HOOH \xrightarrow{NaOH} C_2H_5OOC_2H_5 + H_2SO_4$$

A method for preparing unsymmetrical peroxides is to react an alkyl sulfate with a hydroperoxide in the presence of alkali:

$$(C_2H_5)_2SO_4 + (CH_3)_3COOH \xrightarrow{NaOH} C_2H_5OOC(CH_3)_3 + C_2H_5(HSO_4)$$

Another method for preparing unsymmetrical dialkyl peroxides is to react the alkali metal salt of an alkyl hydroperoxide with an alcohol in the presence of sulfuric acid:[73–75]

$$(CH_3)_3COOK + CH_3OH \xrightarrow{H_2SO_4} (CH_3)_3COOCH_3$$

The reaction between the metal salts of hydroperoxides and alkyl halides can also be used:[76,77]

$$(CH_3)_3COOK + BrCH_2CH{=}CH_2 \longrightarrow (CH_3)_3COOCH_2CH{=}CH_2 + KBr$$

Alcohols that are reacted with hydrogen peroxide in the presence of strong sulfuric acid give mixtures of dialkyl peroxides and hydroperoxides:[12]

$$(CH_3)_3COH + HOOH \xrightarrow[H_2SO_4]{70\%} \underset{50\text{–}30\%}{(CH_3)_3COOC(CH_3)_3} + \underset{50\text{–}70\%}{(CH_3)_3COOH}$$

Symmetrical dialkyl peroxides can also be prepared by the oxidation of hydrocarbons with molecular oxygen using hydrogen bromide as a sensitizer. For example, di-*t*-butyl peroxide can be prepared by passing a vapor mixture of isobutane oxygen and hydrogen bromide in a 2:2:1 mole ratio through a glass tube at 158°C. for a contact time of three minutes. Following condensation, the mixture

[70] A. Baeyer and V. Villiger, *Ber.*, *33*, 3787 (1900).
[71] A. Rieche and W. Brumshager, *Ber.*, *62*, 218 (1929).
[72] A. Rieche and E. Hitz, *Ber.*, *62*, 218 (1929).
[73] N. A. Milas and L. H. Perry, *J. Am. Chem. Soc.*, *68*, 1938 (1946).
[74] A. Rieche, *Ber.*, *62*, 218 (1929).
[75] W. Bechmiller and L. Pfeuffer, *Ann.*, *537*, 178 (1939).
[76] U. S. Pat. 2,403,709 (to Shell Development Co.).
[77] T. W. Campbell and G. M. Coppinger, *J. Am. Chem. Soc.*, *73*, 1789 (1951).

is washed with water and 2 *N* sodium hydroxide. Based on the total isobutane used, 36 per cent di-*t*-butyl peroxide, 28 per cent *t*-butyl alcohol, 12.5 per cent *t*-butyl hydroperoxide, and 2 per cent of miscellaneous oxygenated products are obtained.[13,78]

For comparison, di-*t*-butyl peroxide can also be prepared by means of method (*a*).[12] In this case equimolar quantities of *t*-butyl alcohol (or isobutylene) are allowed to react in the cold with 70 per cent sulfuric acid. Hydrogen peroxide (30 per cent) is slowly added and a mixture of 50–70 per cent *t*-butyl hydroperoxide and 50–30 per cent di-*t*-butyl peroxide is obtained. The components may be separated by distillation, or by extraction of the hydroperoxide with alkali.

The stability of the dialkyl peroxides varies considerably with the lowest members being the least stable. Dimethyl peroxide is a gas at room temperature and is very explosive. Di-*t*-butyl peroxide on the other hand is unusually stable to heat, shock, acids, and alkalies. (See Appendix 2.)

*Some Properties of Di-t-butyl Peroxide.* Some of the chemical properties of di-*t*-butyl peroxide which are also valuable in proving its structure, are listed below:[12,79]

1. Di-*t*-butyl peroxide is reduced to sodium *t*-butylate by sodium in xylene. In contrast, diethyl peroxide is unaffected by this treatment.

2. Catalytic hydrogenation at room temperature with platinum oxide catalyst is ineffective, but reduction to two moles of *t*-butyl alcohol is effected at 126°C. under 1250 p.s.i. hydrogen pressure using Raney nickel as a catalyst.

3. Reaction of the peroxide at 0°C. with hydrogen bromide yields up to 64 per cent of 1,2-dibromo-2-methylpropane.

4. The peroxide is quite stable in the presence of strong bases. Concentrated hydrochloric acid, which decomposes di-*t*-butyl ether, does not affect the peroxide. Slow decomposition takes place in concentrated sulfuric acid.

5. The peroxide liberates iodine from acidified potassium iodide solution very slowly, and therefore the usual iodometric methods of peroxide estimation cannot be applied. It has, however, been re-

[78] U. S. Pats. 2,383,919; 2,395,523; 2,403,758; 2,403,771; 2,403,772; 2,434,-888, 2,446,797 (to Shell Development Co.).

[79] N. A. Milas and C. N. Winnick, *J. Am. Chem. Soc.*, *71*, 748 (1949).

ported that concentrated hydriodic acid can be used to estimate di-*t*-butyl peroxide.[80]

6. Pyrolysis of the peroxide at 200–300°C. gives two main products, acetone and ethane.

7. The peroxide is relatively safe to handle since it decomposes very slowly at ordinary temperatures. At temperatures above 100°C. it decomposes into radicals at a rate which makes it very suitable as a catalyst for high temperature polymerizations and other radical catalyzed reactions.

The physical constants of di-*t*-butyl peroxide have been reported by the Shell Development Company.[81]

Colorless liquid showing unusual stability not customarily associated with organic peroxides.

|  |  |
|---|---|
| Molecular weight | 146.22 |
| Specific gravity, 20/4°C. | 0.7940 |
| Refractive Index, 20/D | 1.3890 |
| Melting point, °C. | −40.0 |
| Boiling point, °C. | 111 at 760 mm. |
| Flash point (Tag open cup), °F. | 65 |
| Vapor pressure: | |
| 0°C. | 5.62 mm. |
| 20°C. | 19.51 mm. |
| 40°C. | 55.14 mm. |
| 60°C. | 133.2 mm. |
| 80°C. | 284.0 mm. |
| 111°C. | 760.0 mm. |
| Heat of vaporization (calc., at b. p.), $H_v$ = | 9.6 kcal./mole |
| Heat of combustion (liquid, 25°C.) | 1273.0 ± 1.2 kcal./mole |

Ultraviolet absorption (optical density,[a] 1 cm. cell, Beckman spectrophotometer, 10 g./liter solution in isooctane):

|  |  |
|---|---|
| 3400 A. | 0.017 |
| 3000 A. | 0.137 |
| 2800 A. | 0.285 |
| 2600 A. | 0.469 |
| 2400 A. | 0.603 |

[a] Optical density = log (1/transmission).

Solubility in water is about 0.01% by weight. The peroxide is completely miscible with most organic solvents.

[80] F. H. Dickey, J. H. Raley, F. F. Rust, R. S. Tresede, and W. E. Vaughan, *Ind. Eng. Chem.*, *41*, 1673 (1949).

[81] Shell Development Co., Emeryville, California, Report No. 8-9987, August, 1947.

## 2. *Diaralkyl Peroxides* (*Hexaarylethane Peroxides*)

In his initial attempts to prepare hexaphenylethane, Gomberg neglected to exclude atmospheric oxygen and thus prepared the peroxide of hexaphenylethane by the following reaction:

$$\underset{\text{(Air)}}{O_2} + (C_6H_5)_3CBr \xrightarrow{\text{(Ag)}} (C_6H_5)_3COOC(C_6H_5)_3$$

The substance prepared in this way was a white high melting solid which was only slightly soluble in the usual organic solvents. In later studies Gomberg prepared pure hexaphenylethane from triphenylmethyl halide and metallic zinc or mercury, carrying out the reaction in an atmosphere of carbon dioxide in order to exclude molecular oxygen.[82]

$$(C_6H_5)_3CBr \xrightarrow[\text{(Zn)}]{\text{air excluded}} (C_6H_5)_3CC(C_6H_5)_3$$

Hexaphenylethane is also a white solid, as is its peroxide, but it is highly soluble in organic solvents. In solution it rapidly absorbs oxygen from the air to give the peroxide discussed above. The structure proof of the peroxide of hexaphenylethane was accomplished by preparing it independently from triphenylmethyl chloride and sodium peroxide:

$$(C_6H_5)_3CCl + Na_2O_2 \longrightarrow (C_6H_5)_3COOC(C_6H_5)_3$$

A wide variety of other diaralkyl peroxides have been prepared, all having the general structure (I), where $R_1$ through $R_6$ are aryl

$$\begin{matrix} R_1 & & R_4 \\ R_2{-}C & OO & C{-}R_5 \\ R_3 & & R_6 \end{matrix}$$

**(I)**

groups. The most widely used procedure for obtaining these peroxides is to treat the corresponding tertiary halide with a finely divided metal such as zinc, silver, or mercury, in the presence of air or oxygen.

The hexaarylethanes when dissolved in nonpolar solvents dissociate to varying extents to give triarylmethyl radicals:

$$(Ar)_3C{-}C(Ar)_3 \rightleftharpoons 2(Ar)_3C\cdot$$

[82] M. Gomberg, *Ber.*, *33*, 3150 (1900); *J. Am. Chem. Soc.*, *22*, 1757 (1900).

These solutions are deeply colored. In the presence of molecular oxygen, the color rapidly fades and the peroxide is formed. Since oxygen itself may be regarded as a diradical, it is believed that the mechanism of formation of the peroxide follows the following sequence of reactions:[83–85]

$$R{-}R \rightleftharpoons 2R\cdot$$

$$R\cdot + O_2 \longrightarrow RO_2\cdot$$

$$RO_2\cdot + R{-}R \longrightarrow ROOR + R\cdot$$

If a hydrogen atom donor such as pyrogallol is present in a solution of hexaphenylethane, the oxidation with molecular oxygen gives triphenylmethyl hydroperoxide rather than the disubstituted peroxide. If we denote the hydrogen atom donor as SH, the formation of the hydroperoxide occurs through the following step:

$$RO_2\cdot + SH \longrightarrow ROOH + S\cdot$$

or more specifically:

$$(C_6H_5)_3COO\cdot + C_6H_3(OH)_3 \longrightarrow (C_6H_5)_3COOH + C_6H_3(OH)_2O\cdot$$

### *3. Alkyl Polyperoxides Derived from Vinyl Monomers*

When vinyl monomers such as styrene, methyl methacrylate, or vinyl acetate are heated or exposed to ultraviolet light in the presence of air, polyperoxides of varying molecular weights result. This appears to have first been noted by Staudinger[86] in the case of diphenylethylene. If 1,1-diphenylethylene is exposed to air in the presence of ultraviolet light, a polymeric substance is formed which upon analysis shows two atoms of oxygen for every diphenylethylene unit. This substance explodes when heated and appears to have the following structure:

$$CH_2{=}C(C_6H_5)_2 + O_2 \xrightarrow[\text{light}]{\text{u.v.}} {+}OCH_2{-}C(C_6H_5)_2O{+}_x$$

[83] K. Ziegler, P. Orth, and K. Weber, *Ann.*, *504*, 131 (1933).

[84] R. C. Mithoff and G. E. K. Branch, *J. Am. Chem. Soc.*, *52*, 255 (1930).

[85] K. Ziegler and L. Ewald, *Ann.*, *504*, 162 (1933).

[86] H. Staudinger, *Ber.*, *58*, 1075 (1925).

The polymeric peroxide gave good yields of benzophenone and formaldehyde when decomposed by heating. This can be formally represented as follows:

$$\left[ OCH_2C(C_6H_5)_2O \right]_x \xrightarrow{\Delta} \cdot OCH_2C(C_6H_5)_2O \cdot \longrightarrow O{=}CH_2 + (C_6H_5)_2C{=}O$$

Barnes[87,88] noted that, when methyl methacrylate is exposed to light in the absence of a continuous source of oxygen, the expected polymethyl methacrylate is rapidly formed:

$$CH_2{=}C(CH_3)(C{=}O)OCH_3 \xrightarrow[\text{light}]{\text{u.v.}} \left[ -CH_2-C(CH_3)(C{=}O\,OCH_3)- \right]_x$$

If the test tube containing methyl methacrylate is connected to a source which maintains a constant oxygen pressure and then exposed to light, the formation of polymer is strongly inhibited. A polymeric product finally does form, but upon analysis it proved to be the polyperoxide of methyl methacrylate:

$$CH_2{=}C(CH_3)(C{=}O)OCH_3 + O_2 \xrightarrow[\text{light}]{\text{u.v.}} \left[ -O-CH_2C(CH_3)(C{=}O\,OCH_3)-O- \right]_x$$

Polyperoxides of styrene and vinyl acetate have also been prepared using both thermal and photochemical activation.[88]

Bovey and Kolthoff[89] observed that the induction period in emulsion polymerization of styrene could in many cases be attributed to traces of oxygen which had to be consumed before the polymerization began. However, if a constant pressure of oxygen were supplied, and if the emulsion polymerization was then carried out for a very long period of time, a polyperoxide of styrene was formed:

[87] C. E. Barnes, *J. Am. Chem. Soc.*, *67*, 217 (1945).
[88] C. E. Barnes, R. M. Elofson, and G. D. Jones, *J. Am. Chem. Soc.*, *72*, 210 (1950).
[89] F. A. Bovey and I. M. Kolthoff, *J. Am. Chem. Soc.*, *69*, 2143 (1947).

$$CH_2{=}C(H)(C_6H_5) + O_2 \longrightarrow \left[ -O-CH_2-C(H)(C_6H_5)-O- \right]_x$$

In all these cases the formation of the polyperoxide may be considered to be a copolymerization of the monomer (1,1-diphenylethylene, styrene, methyl methacrylate, vinyl acetate) with oxygen. The copolymer is a 1:1 copolymer because of the very great reactivity of oxygen to hydrocarbon free radicals and because an oxygenated radical $RO_2\cdot$ cannot add oxygen but will add, though slowly, to a vinyl monomer. The rate of copolymerization of styrene with oxygen in the experiments of Bovey and Kolthoff was only about 1/1000 times the normal rate of emulsion polymerization of styrene in the absence of oxygen.

Among the proofs used for assigning the structure of styrene polyperoxide is the fact that it can be hydrogenated using Adams' catalyst to yield phenyl glycol:

$$\left[ -OCH_2-C(H)(C_6H_5)-O- \right]_x \xrightarrow{[H]} HOCH_2-CHOH(C_6H_5)$$

On heating, styrene polyperoxide decomposes mainly to formaldehyde and benzaldehyde:

$$\left[ -O-CH_2-C(H)(C_6H_5)-O- \right]_x \longrightarrow \cdot OCH_2C(H)(C_6H_5)O\cdot \longrightarrow O{=}CH_2 + C_6H_5C(H){=}O$$

The polymerization degrees of these polyperoxides appear to be fairly small (between 10 and 30 units) as estimated by cryoscopic and other methods.[88,89]

## 4. *Transannular Peroxides*

### (a) *Ascaridole*

The first compound that was shown to be a transannular peroxide is ascaridole (1,4-epidioxy-2-*p*-menthene) a substance which can be isolated from chenopodium oil.[90,91] Naturally occurring ascaridole is separated from the other constituents by distillation under reduced

[90] O. Wallach, *Ann.*, *392*, 59 (1912).

[91] E. K. Nelson, *J. Am. Chem. Soc.*, *33*, 1404 (1911); *35*, 84 (1913).

pressure (4–5 mm. at 83°C.). Ascaridole decomposes explosively when heated at 130°C. under atmospheric pressure.

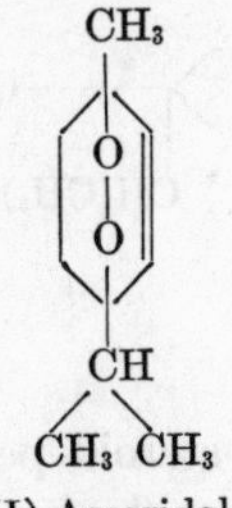

(I) Ascaridole

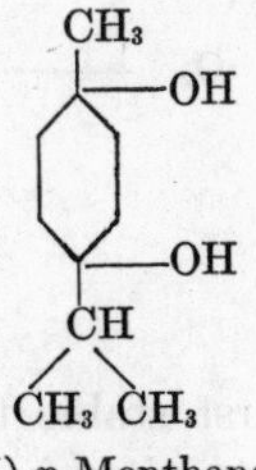

(II) *p*-Menthane-1,4-diol

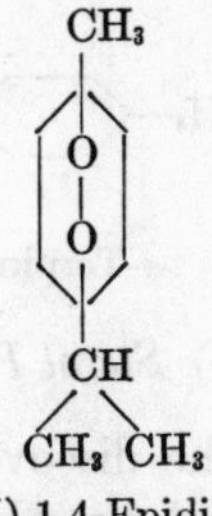

(III) 1,4-Epidioxy-*p*-menthane

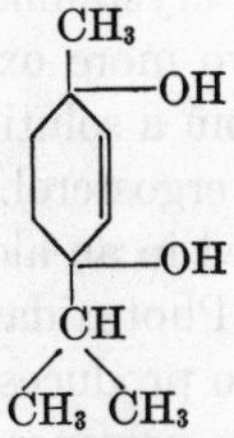

(IV) 2-*p*-Menthene-1,4-diol

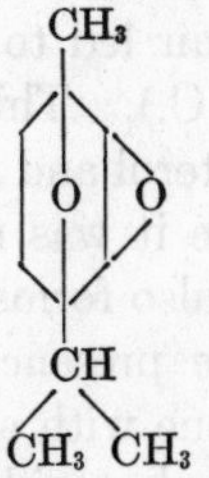

(V) Ether epoxide of *p*-menthane (1,4,2,3-diepoxy-*p*-menthane)

Among the structure proofs for formula (I) for ascaridole are the following: Hydrogenation of ascaridole using a colloidal platinum catalyst proceeds rapidly to form *p*-menthane-1,4-diol (II).[92] Under milder conditions of hydrogenation using a palladium catalyst, a mixture of compounds containing mainly 1,4-epidioxy-*p*-menthane (III)[93] and to a lesser extent 2-*p*-menthene-1,4-diol (IV)[94] is obtained. When heated in an inert solvent, ascaridole is almost completely transformed into the ether epoxide V.[94,95]

The conversion of α-terpinene to ascaridole has been reported to occur by irradiation of a dilute solution in the presence of oxygen and chlorophyll. α-Phellandrene and 1,3-cyclohexadiene also undergo the analogous reaction.[96b] However, when Farmer[96a] at-

[92] H. Paget, *J. Chem. Soc.*, *1938*, 829.

[93] F. Richter and W. Priesting, *Ber.*, *64*, 878 (1931).

[94] H. Thoms and W. Dobke, *Arch. Pharm.*, *128*, 268 (1930).

[95] E. H. Farmer, *Trans. Faraday Soc.*, *42*, 228 (1946).

[96] (a) E. H. Farmer, *I. R. I. Transactions*, *21*, No. 2 (1946). (b) G. O. Schenck and H. Ziegler, *Naturwiss.*, *32*, 157 (1944); *38*, 356 (1951).

tempted to synthesize ascaridole by heating α-terpinene with molecular oxygen, he obtained a polymeric peroxide instead of (I).

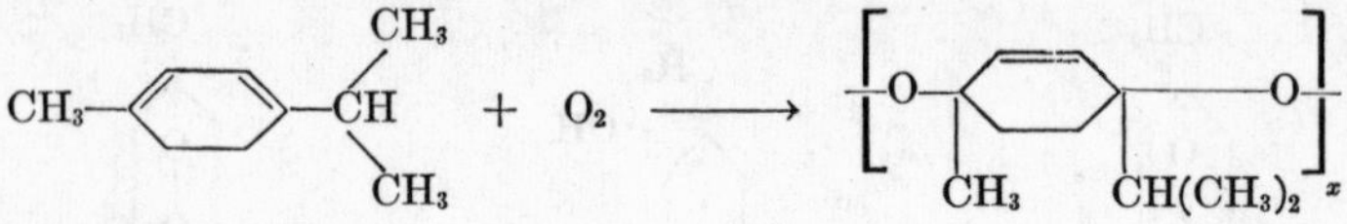

$CH_3$ $CH$ $CH_3$ $CH_3$ + $O_2$ ⟶ [—O— —O—] $CH_3$ $CH(CH_3)_2$ $x$

α-Terpinene

(*b*) *Sterol Peroxides*

The discovery of the first stable transannular steroid peroxide resulted directly from work on vitamin D.[97,98] It was observed that irradiation of an alcoholic solution of ergosterol in the presence of eosin and air led to the formation of a stable crystalline compound (m.p. 178°C.). This compound contained two more oxygen atoms than ergosterol and since it liberated iodine from a solution of potassium iodide it was regarded as a peroxide of ergosterol. Dehydroergosterol also forms a peroxide when irradiated in an alcoholic solution in the presence of eosin and oxygen. Photoxidation of 2,4-cholestadiene with a 200-watt Mazda bulb also produces a peroxide, but if the photoxidation is carried out in the presence of sunlight (which has more ultraviolet light) a ketone is produced. The structures of these peroxides have been rather completely proven, the details being presented in the review article by Bergmann and McLean.[99] The structures of the three sterols mentioned above and their corresponding peroxides are shown below.

Other steroids of structure similar to ergosterol have given crystalline peroxides upon photoxidation in the presence of a sensitizer.[99] These are probably transannular peroxides also, but their structures have not been fully proved as yet.

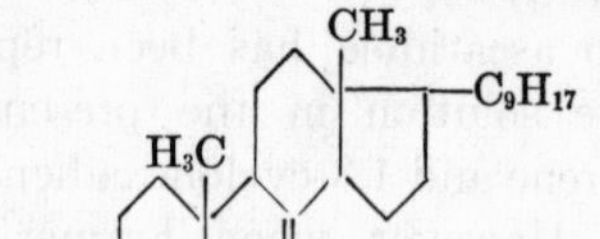

$CH_3$ $C_9H_{17}$ $H_3C$ HO

Ergosterol

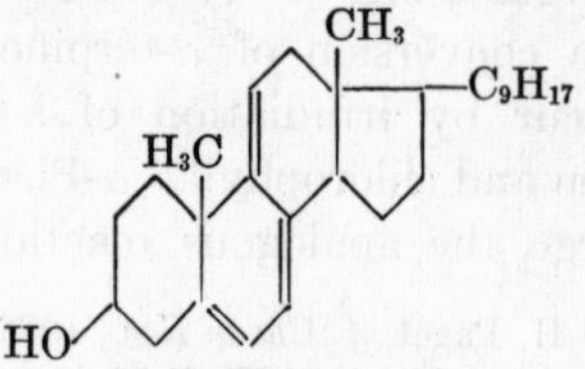

$CH_3$ $C_9H_{17}$ $H_3C$ HO

Dehydroergosterol

[97] A. Windaus and O. Linsert, *Ann.*, *465*, 157 (1928).
[98] A. Windaus, W. Bergmann, and A. Luttringhaus, *Ann.*, *472*, 195 (1929).
[99] W. Bergmann and M. J. McLean, *Chem. Reviews*, *28*, 367 (1941).

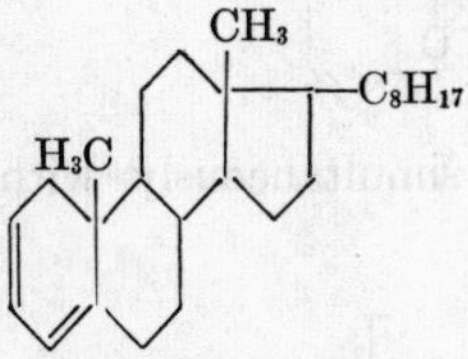

CH3, C8H17, H3C

2,4-Cholestadiene

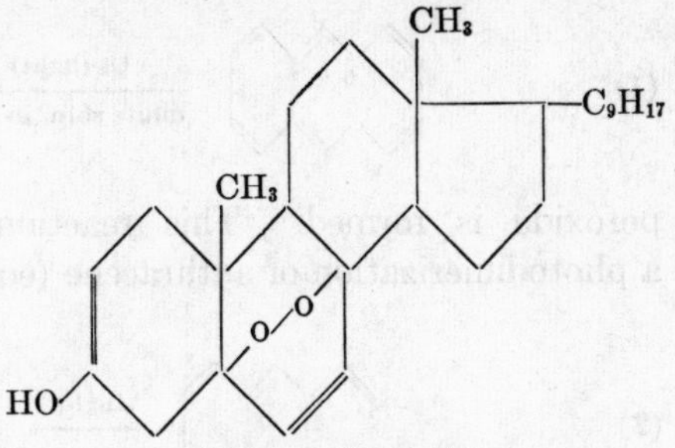

CH3, C9H17, CH3, O, O, HO

Ergosterol peroxide

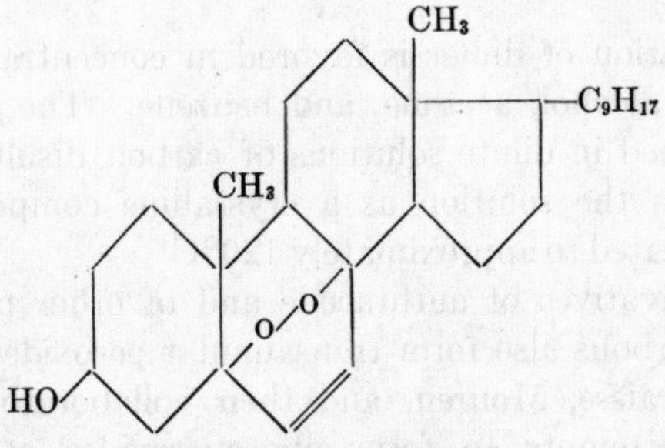

CH3, C9H17, CH3, O, O, HO

Dehydroergosterol peroxide

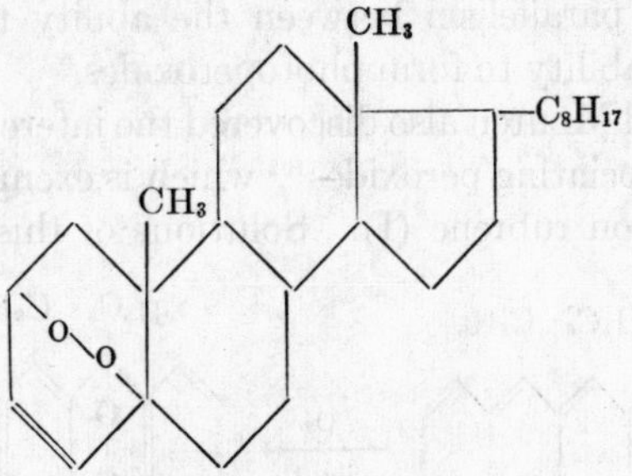

CH3, C8H17, CH3, O, O

2,4-Cholestadiene peroxide

### (c) *Transannular Peroxides of Anthracene and Related Compounds: Reversibly Dissociating Peroxides*

When anthracene is dissolved in carbon disulfide[100] and the solution is exposed to ultraviolet light and air (eq. 1), a transannular

[100] C. Dufraisse and M. Gerard, *Compt. rend.*, *201*, 428 (1935); *202*, 1859 (1936).

(1) 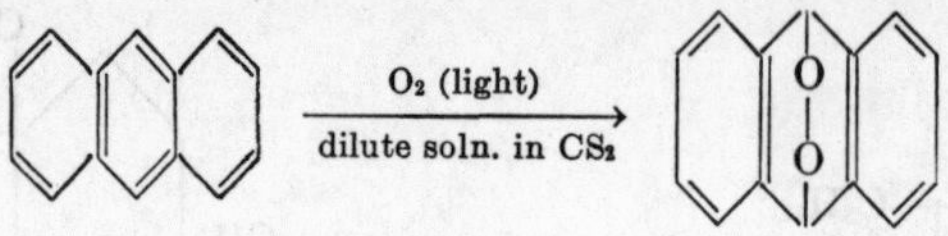 $\xrightarrow[\text{dilute soln. in } CS_2]{O_2 \text{ (light)}}$

peroxide is formed. This reaction occurs simultaneously with a photodimerization of anthracene (eq. 2).

(2) $\xrightarrow{\text{light}}$ $[\ ]_2$

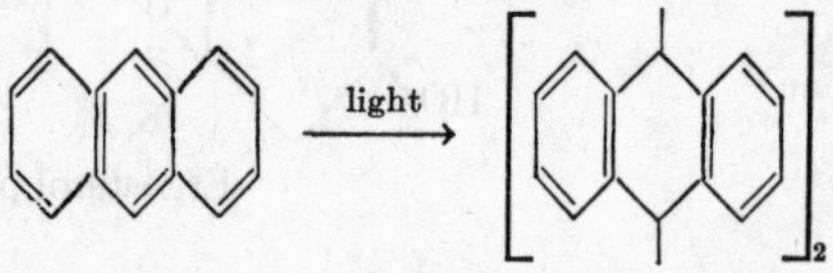

The formation of dimer is favored in concentrated solutions of anthracene in alcohol, acetone, and benzene. The peroxide is preferentially formed in dilute solutions of carbon disulfide. It can be recovered from the solution as a crystalline compound which explodes when heated to approximately 120°C.

Many derivatives of anthracene and of other polynuclear aromatic hydrocarbons also form transannular peroxides, as was established by Dufraisse, Moureu, and their collaborators.[99,101] On the other hand, attempts to form photoperoxides of phenanthrene, naphthalene, or acridine derivatives have been unsuccessful. There appears to be a parallelism between the ability to add maleic anhydride and the ability to form photoperoxides.

Dufraisse and Moureu also discovered the interesting phenomenon of reversibly dissociating peroxides[102] which is exemplified by the case of the hydrocarbon rubrene (I). Solutions of this red hydrocarbon

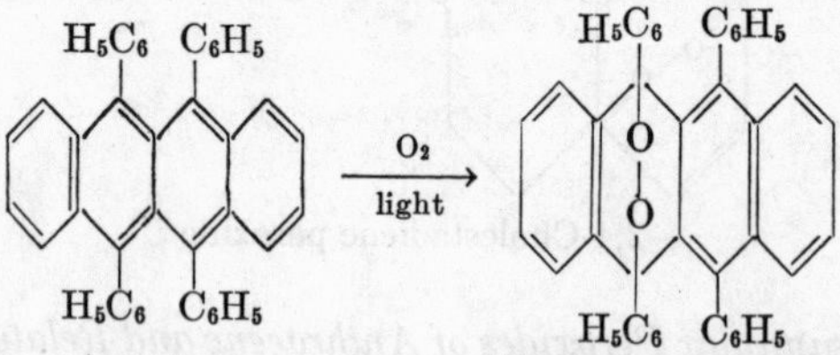

$H_5C_6$ $C_6H_5$ ... $H_5C_6$ $C_6H_5$ $\xrightarrow[\text{light}]{O_2}$ $H_5C_6$ $C_6H_5$ ... O O ... $H_5C_6$ $C_6H_5$

(I) Rubrene

(II) Rubrene peroxide (5,6,11,12-Tetraphenyl-5,12-epidioxy-naphthacene)

[101] A. Etienne, *Traité de chimie organique, 17*, 1299 (1944), an extensive review article.

[102] C. Moureu, C. Dufraisse, and P. M. Dean, *Compt. rend., 182*, 1440, 1584 (1926).

rapidly lose their color and their fluorescence when they are exposed to air in the presence of sunlight. Concentration of such a decolorized solution leads to a precipitation of a crystalline compound having the properties of a peroxide (II).

Upon heating rubrene peroxide *in vacuo,* partial (80 per cent) reversible dissociation takes place into rubrene and oxygen. Since a small amount of carbon dioxide is also evolved, it is clear that part of the peroxide undergoes degradation in addition to its reversible decomposition.

Hydrogenation of rubrene peroxide yields a compound which is identified as (III). This is one of the main proofs of the correctness of structure II for rubrene peroxide.

$C_6H_5$ OH $C_6H_5$

$C_6H_5$ OH $C_6H_5$

(III)

A very large number of photoperoxides of anthracene derivatives have been prepared. Among these, the ones that possess the property of reversible dissociation have at least one of the 9,10 positions of the anthracene molecule substituted by an aryl group, and if both positions are substituted the dissociation proceeds more easily, as in:

(1) $C_6H_5$, O, O, $C_6H_5$ $\underset{\text{light}}{\overset{\text{heat}}{\rightleftarrows}}$ $C_6H_5$, $C_6H_5$ + $O_2$

In addition to the photoperoxides of anthracene, rubrene, and their derivatives, Dufraisse and co-workers have prepared photoperoxides of benzanthracenes and pentacenes. In all cases the mesopositions of the fundamental anthracene grouping is attacked by oxygen to give the transannular peroxide.

(*d*) *Peroxides of Indene and Partially Hydrogenated Naphthalenes*

Hock and co-workers[58,59] recently prepared some new transannular peroxides by autoxidation of indene (I) and 1,2-dihydronaphthalene (II). These hydrocarbons and their corresponding peroxides are shown below.

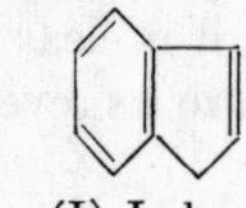

(I) Indene 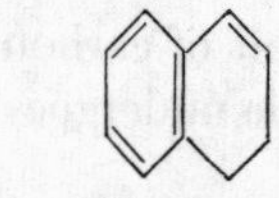 (II) 1,2-Dihydronaphthalene

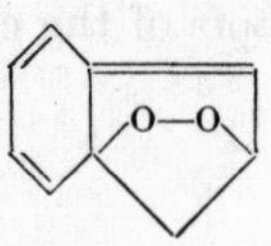

(III) 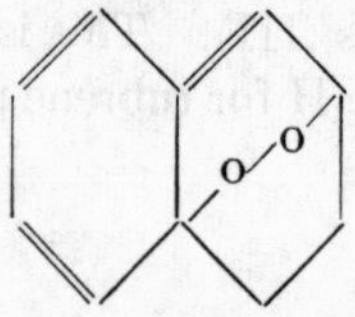 (IV)

The peroxide of indene (III) identified as 2,8-*endo*peroxyisoindene (2,3*a*-epidioxyisoindene) is quite unstable and therefore can be isolated only in small amounts and with great difficulty. It tends to rearrange to 3-oxoisochroman (V).

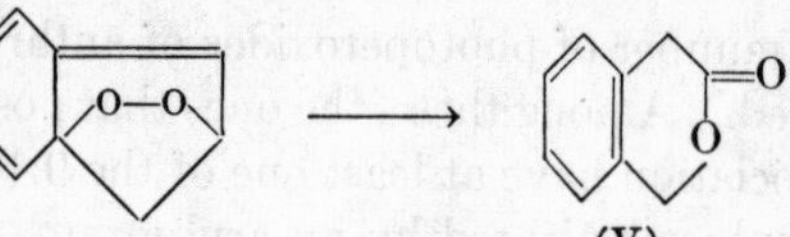

(V)

It is to be noted that the hydrocarbons (I) and (II) have a double bond in an aliphatic ring conjugated with a double bond in an aromatic ring. This is the distinguishing feature of this series of *endo*-peroxides. On the other hand certain hydrocarbons that have this structural feature form hydroperoxides, as does 1-methyl-1,2-dihydronaphthalene (VI).

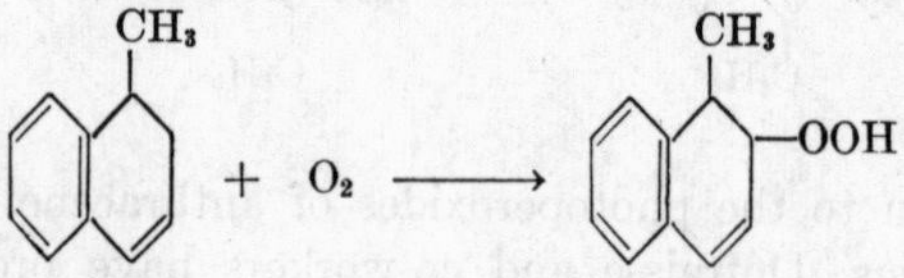

$CH_3$ + $O_2$ ⟶ $CH_3$ —OOH

(VI)

It is interesting to note that (VI) forms a hydroperoxide, whereas (II) which is closely related structurally adds oxygen to the conjugated dienic system to form an *endo*peroxide. This is probably due to the fact that the 2 position in (VI) is activated for hydroperoxide formation by both the double bond *and* the methyl group.

### (e) *Peroxides of Conjugated Olefins*

In the previous section it was shown that substances such as 1,2-dihydronaphthalene or indene which have a double bond conjugated with an aromatic ring tend to add molecular oxygen at the terminals of the diene system. The same generalization holds true for nonaromatic conjugated dienes and polyenes. In many cases polyperoxides are formed; in other cases it has been postulated that cyclic peroxides are formed. The structural work in this field is not far advanced because of the complexity of the products.

The simplest dienes including butadiene, isoprene, and 2,3-dimethylbutadiene are known to form polymeric peroxides by addition of oxygen in 1,2 or 1,4 positions (or at both positions).[103–105] In the case of 2,3-dimethylbutadiene the addition of oxygen at the 1,2 position apparently predominates since the resultant polymeric peroxide (eq. 2) decomposes thermally to formaldehyde and isopropenyl methyl ketone:[103b]

$$CH_2{=}C(CH_3){-}C(CH_3){=}CH_2 + O_2 \longrightarrow \left[ {-}O{-}CH_2{-}C(CH_3)(C(CH_3){=}CH_2){-}O{-} \right]_x \quad (2)$$

The peroxidic product obtained from isoprene is a resinous material and decomposes slightly above 0°C.[103a,105]

2,4-Dimethyl-1,3-pentadiene forms a peroxide which on heating to 80°C. decomposes to the dimer, $C_{14}H_{24}$. However, if the peroxide is heated to 100–120°C. a violent decomposition occurs with the formation of formaldehyde, formic acid, and acetone. It has been suggested[106] that this peroxide has one of the two structures (I) or (II).

[103] (a) W. Kern, H. Jokusch, and A. Wolfram, *Makromol. Chem.*, *3*, 223 (1949). (b) W. Kern and J. Stallman, *ibid.*, *7*, 199 (1951).
[104] D. A. Scott, *Chem. Zentral.*, *I*, 2428 (1941).
[105] K. Bodendorf, *Arch. Pharm.*, *271*, 1 (1933).
[106] R. Jacquemain, *Compt. rend.*, *215*, 200 (1942).

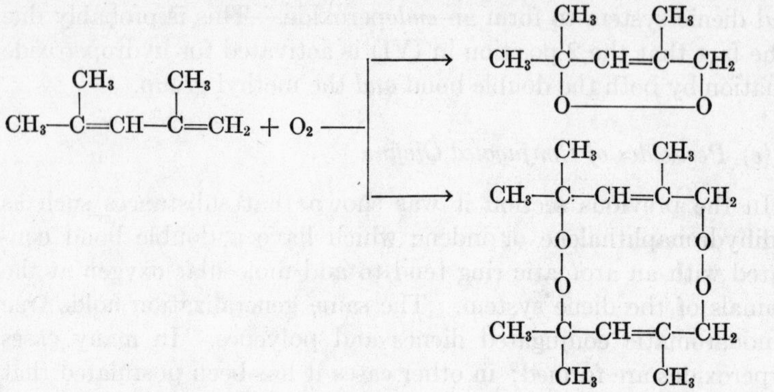

$$CH_3-\overset{CH_3}{C}=CH-\overset{CH_3}{C}=CH_2 + O_2 \longrightarrow \text{(I)} \; CH_3-\overset{CH_3}{C}-CH=\overset{CH_3}{C}-CH_2 \text{ (O–O bridge)}; \text{(II)} \text{ polymeric peroxide}$$

Other conjugated dienes and polyenes whose peroxides have been prepared and reported in the literature are the following: methyl sorbate[95] (III), methyl eleostearate[95] (IV), $\alpha$-terpinene[96,105] (V), $\alpha$-phellandrene[105] (VI), dimethylfulvene[107] (VII), cyclopentadiene[108] (VIII), and 1,3-cyclohexadiene[95,105,108] (IX). In the case

$$CH_3-CH=CH-CH=CH-\overset{O}{\overset{\|}{C}}OCH_3 \qquad CH_3(CH_2)_3(CH=CH)_3(CH_2)_7\overset{O}{\overset{\|}{C}}OCH_3$$

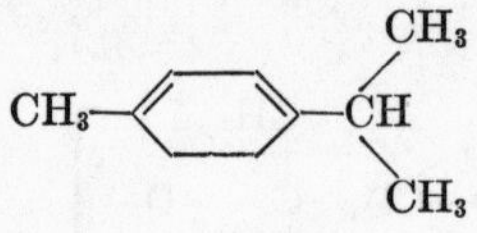

(V) 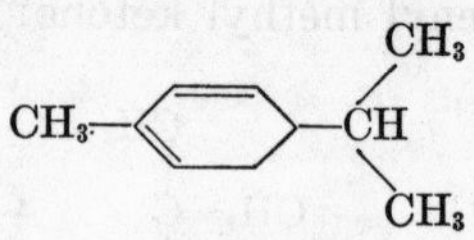 (VI)

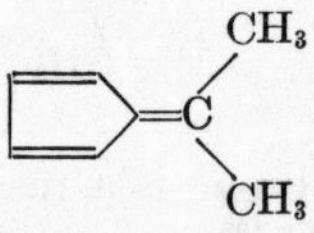

(VII) 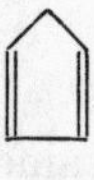 (VIII)  (IX)

of cyclohexadiene it has recently been reported[108] that a portion of the oxidized product contains the simple monomeric peroxide (X).

(X)

[107] C. Engler and W. Frankenstein, *Ber.*, *34*, 2933 (1901).
[108] H. Hock and F. Depke, *Ber.*, *84*, 349 (1951).

An interesting reaction occurs, when furan (XI) is oxidized in the presence of ultraviolet light and chlorophyll. An oxygen molecule adds across the double bonds of the diene structure to yield the monomeric ether peroxide (XII).[108a]

$$\text{(XI)} + O_2 \xrightarrow[\text{chlorophyll}]{\text{u.v. light}} \text{(XII)}$$

The polymeric products that are formed upon oxidation of conjugated olefins may be more complex than is indicated by the simple polymeric formulae. It has been reported by Overholt and Elm that extensive polymer formation occurs during the oxidation of methyl eleostearate after only very small amounts of oxygen have been absorbed.[109] These results indicate that oxidation can produce carbon-carbon polymerization. Carbon-carbon bond scissions probably also occur. Many details of the oxidation of eleostearic acid (one of the main components in tung oil) have been presented by Morell and co-workers.[110]

During the later stages of air oxidation of conjugated olefins many complex products are formed, as may be expected. Some of these are probably secondary products formed from the peroxides. Studies of the changes in refractive index of highly oxidized conjugated olefins have also indicated that polymeric products are formed with linkages other than the peroxide link.[111]

## IV. Peroxides of Structure RC(=O)OOH (Peroxy Acids)

Organic peroxy acids (peracids) are the monoacyl derivatives of hydrogen peroxide. The structural formula RC(=O)OOH is probable, but has never been proved by rigorous methods such as x-ray diffraction. An extensive review of the preparation, properties, and reactions of organic peroxy acids which gives approximately 700 references to the literature has recently been prepared by Swern.[5]

[108a] G. O. Schenck, *Angew. Chemie, 64*, 12 (1952).
[109] J. L. Overholt and J. C. Elm, *Ind. Eng. Chem., 32*, 378 (1940).
[110] R. S. Morell *et al., Trans. Faraday Soc., 38*, 362 (1942); *Paint Technology, 7*, 130, 169, 187 (1942).
[111] A. B. Miller and E. Claxton, *Ind. Eng. Chem., 20*, 43 (1928).

There are two major methods for preparing organic peroxy acids which are quite analogous to methods (*a*) and (*b*) for preparing hydroperoxides discussed in section II. The first method is by reaction of an organic acid with concentrated hydrogen peroxide in the presence of sulfuric acid or other inorganic catalysts:

$$RC(=O)\text{—}OH + HOOH \underset{}{\overset{H_2SO_4}{\rightleftharpoons}} RC(=O)\text{—}OOH + HOH$$

The second method is by reaction of the corresponding aldehyde with molecular oxygen:

$$RCHO + O_2 \longrightarrow RC(=O)\text{—}OOH$$

## 1. Aliphatic Peroxy Acids

The preparation of aliphatic peroxy acids is exemplified by the synthesis of peroxyformic acid, first described by D'Ans and coworkers.[112] This was accomplished by heating 98 per cent hydrogen peroxide with formic acid in the presence of 1 per cent sulfuric acid as catalyst. The reaction is reversible and approaches equilibrium within two hours:

$$HC(=O)\text{—}OH + HOOH \overset{H_2SO_4}{\rightleftharpoons} \underset{\text{Peroxyformic acid}}{HC(=O)\text{—}OOH} + H_2O$$

Other catalysts that may be employed include nitric acid, phosphoric acid, ammonium sulfate, sodium bisulfate, and potassium nitrate. When equimolar proportions of formic acid and hydrogen peroxide are used under the conditions described above, a 48 per cent solution of peroxyformic acid results. By using excess hydrogen peroxide, large catalyst concentrations, and employing fractional distillation under reduced pressure, a 90 per cent solution of peroxyformic acid in water can be prepared. The pure substance has not been prepared as yet. Peroxyformic acid solutions show typical peroxide properties, such as liberating iodine from potassium iodide.

[112] J. D'Ans, German Pat. 251,802 (1911). J. D'Ans and W. Frey, *Ber.*, *45*, 1845 (1912); *Z. anorg. Chem.*, *84*, 145 (1914); J. D'Ans and A. Kneip, *Ber.*, *48*, 1136 (1915).

The solutions are unstable, losing oxygen moderately rapidly even at 0°C. Concentrated solutions (60 per cent or higher) are explosive when heated, and also explode at room temperature in the presence of suitable catalysts. Peroxyformic acid is more volatile than formic acid, and its vapors are irritating to the skin.

Peroxyacetic acid is a much more tractable compound, and has been more extensively studied than other peracids. It can be prepared by reacting equimolar quantities of acetic acid with 98 per cent hydrogen peroxide in the presence of 1 per cent sulfuric acid. At 14.6°C. this reaction proceeds to equilibrium in 12–16 hours giving a 50 per cent solution of peroxyacetic acid:

$$CH_3\overset{\overset{\displaystyle O}{\|}}{C}{-}OH + HOOH \xrightleftharpoons{H_2SO_4} \underset{\text{Peroxyacetic acid}}{CH_3\overset{\overset{\displaystyle O}{\|}}{C}{-}OOH} + H_2O$$

If acetic anhydride is used instead of acetic acid under the above conditions, equilibrium is reached more rapidly. At 40°C. acetic acid reacts with 30 per cent hydrogen peroxide to give peroxyacetic acid solutions even in the absence of catalyst.

Freshly distilled, *dry* acetaldehyde reacts with molecular oxygen at temperatures as low as −10 or −20°C. to give peroxyacetic acid. The reaction rate is accelerated by ultraviolet light and by salts of cobalt, iron, and chromium. It is strongly retarded by water and manganese salts. Vapor phase oxidation of acetaldehyde will also yield peroxyacetic acid under proper conditions:[5]

$$CH_3CHO + O_2 \longrightarrow CH_3\overset{\overset{\displaystyle O}{\|}}{C}{-}OOH$$

Among the other procedures for preparation of peroxyacetic acid are the reaction of acetic acid with ozone, the reaction of ketene with hydrogen peroxide, and the hydrolysis of diacetyl peroxide:[113,114]

$$CH_3\overset{\overset{\displaystyle O}{\|}}{C}{-}OH + O_3 \longrightarrow CH_3\overset{\overset{\displaystyle O}{\|}}{C}{-}OOH + O_2$$

$$CH_2{=}C{=}O + HOOH \longrightarrow CH_3\overset{\overset{\displaystyle O}{\|}}{C}{-}OOH$$

[113] E. Galitzenstein and M. Mugdan, U. S. Pat. 1,179,421 (1916).

[114] Buffalo Electrochemical Co., Inc., *Peraceiic Acid Data Sheet*, 1 (1947).

$$CH_3\overset{O}{\overset{\|}{C}}—OO—\overset{O}{\overset{\|}{C}}CH_3 + H_2O \longrightarrow CH_3\overset{O}{\overset{\|}{C}}—OOH + CH_3\overset{O}{\overset{\|}{C}}—OH$$

Peroxyacetic acid can also be prepared by reacting acetic acid with oxygen in the presence of unfiltered ultraviolet radiation.[5] This may, however, occur through the intermediate formation of ozone.

Pure peroxyacetic acid ($d_{4°}^{15°}$ = 1.226, m.p. 0.1°C., b.p. 105°C.) has been prepared, but the commercially available material is a 40 per cent solution in acetic acid. Peroxyacetic acid is relatively insensitive to shock, but explodes violently when heated to 110°C. In the absence of catalysts, even concentrated solutions of peroxyacetic acid are fairly stable at room temperature, and show little loss of active oxygen after several weeks. One hundred parts per million of sodium pyrophosphate added to peroxyacetic acid solutions acts as an effective stabilizer.

Among the other aliphatic peracids that have been prepared are peroxypropionic, peroxybutyric, peroxyisovaleric, peroxyheptanoic, peroxycaproic, peroxycrotonic, peroxytrichloroacetic, and peroxylactic acids.

## 2. *Aromatic Peroxy Acids*

The most widely studied aromatic peroxy acid is peroxybenzoic acid. One of the principal methods for preparing this substance is by basic hydrolysis of benzoyl peroxide followed by acidification.[115] The benzoyl peroxide is dissolved in a methyl alcohol–chloroform mixture and the base used is sodium methoxide:[116]

$$\phi\overset{O}{\overset{\|}{C}}—O—O—\overset{O}{\overset{\|}{C}}\phi \xrightarrow{CH_3ONa} \phi\overset{O}{\overset{\|}{C}}—OONa \xrightarrow{\text{acidification}} \underset{\text{Peroxybenzoic acid}}{\phi\overset{O}{\overset{\|}{C}}—OOH}$$

Yields of up to 85 per cent can be obtained. Peroxybenzoic acid is a white crystalline solid which melts at 41°C. It is stable at room temperature, but decomposes smoothly to benzoic acid and gases containing oxygen when it is heated to 80–100°C.

[115] A. Baeyer and V. Villiger, *Ber.*, *33*, 858, 1569 (1900). (b) G. Braun, *Organic Syntheses*, Wiley, New York, Coll. Vol. I, 1932, p. 431.
[116] I. M. Kolthoff, T. S. Lee, and M. A. Mairs, *J. Polymer Sci.*, *2*, 220 (1947).

Peroxybenzoic acid can also be formed from the oxidation of benzaldehyde with molecular oxygen:

$$C_6H_5CHO + O_2 \longrightarrow C_6H_5\overset{\overset{\displaystyle O}{\|}}{C}—OOH$$

Yields of peroxybenzoic acid up to 63 per cent are obtained when benzaldehyde is dissolved in acetone and treated with molecular oxygen in the presence of sunlight.[117]

Among the other aromatic peroxy acids that have been prepared are monoperoxyphthalic, diperoxyphthalic, peroxycinnamic, *p*-methoxyperoxybenzoic, and *p*- and *m*-nitroperoxybenzoic acids.

## V. Peroxides of Structure RC(=O)OOR′ (Peroxy Esters)

The peroxides whose structure is of the type RC(=O)OOR′ are commonly known as peroxy esters or peresters. These substances, however, cannot be prepared by esterification of a peroxy acid. They are acylated derivatives of *hydroperoxides* formed by reacting a hydroperoxide with an acid chloride or an acid anhydride:

$$R'OOH + R\overset{\overset{\displaystyle O}{\|}}{C}—Cl \xrightarrow{\text{pyridine}} R\overset{\overset{\displaystyle O}{\|}}{C}—OOR'$$

Upon hydrolysis, the peroxy acids are converted to the corresponding organic acid and hydroperoxide, and *not* to a peroxy acid and an alcohol.

Ethyl peroxyacetate, which is the derivative of ethyl hydroperoxide and acetic acid, has been reported.[118] Most of the peroxy esters thus far reported are derivatives of *t*-butyl hydroperoxide. Tertiary butyl peroxybenzoate and peroxyacetate and ditertiary butyl diperoxyphthalate[119a] have been prepared commercially for use as polymerization catalysts. Various para substituted *t*-butyl peroxybenzoates have also been prepared.[119b]

[117] P. A. A. van der Beek, *Rec. trav. chim.*, *47*, 286 (1928).
[118] A. Baeyer and V. Villiger, *Ber.*, *34*, 738 (1901).
[119a] N. A. Milas and D. M. Surgenor, *J. Am. Chem. Soc.*, *68*, 642 (1946).
[119b] A. T. Blomquist and I. A. Berstein, *J. Am. Chem. Soc.*, *73*, 5546 (1951).

## VI. Peroxides of Structure RC(=O)OO(O=)CR (Diacyl and Diaroyl Peroxides)

### 1. *Diaroyl Peroxides*

Benzoyl peroxide is the most common member of the diaroyl peroxides and is sold commercially in extensive quantities. It is a white, crystalline solid (m.p. 103 °C.) which decomposes explosively on heating to 106 °C., but at ordinary temperatures it is relatively safe to handle. Its characteristic use is as a catalyst for vinyl polymerization and other free radical catalyzed reactions, although it also has a large number of miscellaneous uses.

Benzoyl peroxide was prepared from benzoyl chloride and an alkaline solution of hydrogen peroxide by Pechmann and Vanino.[120] A convenient procedure (eq. 1, 2) for preparing benzoyl peroxide from benzoyl chloride and sodium peroxide was reported by Gambarjan.[121]

In Gambarjan's original procedure, a mixture of 100 grams of benzoyl chloride and 200 cc. of acetone was added to a solution of 40 grams of sodium peroxide in 400 cc. of ice water. To keep the reaction under control, slow addition with stirring and occasional addition of ice were both necessary. A precipitate of benzoyl peroxide formed which could be separated by filtration giving 71 per cent of the theoretical yield.

(1) $2\ C_6H_5C(=O)Cl + HOOH \xrightarrow{NaOH} C_6H_5C(=O)-O-O-C(=O)C_6H_5$

Benzoyl peroxide

(2) $2\ C_6H_5C(=O)Cl + Na_2O_2 \longrightarrow C_6H_5C(=O)-O-O-C(=O)C_6H_5$

The preparation of bis(*p*-nitrobenzoyl) peroxide has been described.[122] In this case a chilled water solution of sodium peroxide is prepared, and a solution of *p*-nitrobenzoyl chloride in toluene is slowly added with vigorous stirring (eq. 3). The precipitate is then filtered and washed with cold water.

[120] H. Pechmann and L. Vanino, *Ber.*, *27*, 1511 (1894).
[121] S. Gambarjan, *Ber.*, *42*, 4004 (1909); *B58*, 1775 (1925).
[122] C. C. Price and E. Krebs, *Org. Syntheses*, *23*, 65 (1943).

$$(3)\quad 2\ NO_2C_6H_4COCl + Na_2O_2 \longrightarrow NO_2C_6H_4C(=O){-}O{-}O{-}C(=O)C_6H_4NO_2$$

The description of the preparation and properties of a wide variety of substituted benzoyl peroxides has been given by Swain *et al.*[123]

If diaroyl chlorides such as phthalyl chloride are treated with sodium peroxide, polymeric peroxides (eq. 4) are formed.[124, 125]

$$(4)\quad Cl{-}C(=O){-}C_6H_4{-}C(=O){-}Cl + Na_2O_2 \longrightarrow \left[{-}O{-}C(=O){-}C_6H_4{-}C(=O){-}O{-}\right]_x$$

It has been reported that ozone oxidizes benzaldehyde to a 15 per cent yield of benzoyl peroxide,[126] although the main products are benzoic acid and perbenzoic acid.

## 2. *Diacyl Peroxides*

The most widely studied diacyl peroxide is diacetyl peroxide:

$$CH_3C(=O){-}O{-}O{-}C(=O){-}CH_3$$

In the hands of Fieser, Kharasch, and others it has become a very useful agent in organic synthesis.[127] It is, however, a quite dangerous explosive compound. The peroxides of the higher fatty acids are much more stable.

Diacyl peroxides are formed when anhydrides of carboxylic acids or acid chlorides act on sodium peroxide, barium peroxide or hydro-

[123] C. G. Swain, W. H. Stockmayer, and J. T. Clarke, *J. Am. Chem. Soc.*, *72*, 5426 (1950).

[124] H. v. Pechmann and L. Vanino, *Ber.*, *27*, 1511 (1894).

[125] H. A. Shah, F. Leonard, and A. V. Tobolsky, *J. Polymer Sci.*, *7*, 537 (1951).

[126] C. S. Marvel and V. Nichols, *J. Org. Chem.*, *6*, 96 (1941).

[127] (a) W. A. Waters, *The Chemistry of Free Radicals*, Oxford Univ. Press, London, 1949. (b) L. F. Fieser *et al.*, *J. Am. Chem. Soc.*, *70*, 3174 (1948); *69*, 2338 (1947); *64*, 2060 (1942). (c) M. S. Kharasch, *et al.*, *ibid.*, *65*, 15 (1943); *J. Org. Chem.*, *10*, 386 (1945).

gen peroxide, in a solvent such as ether. A relatively safe procedure for the preparation of crystalline diacetyl peroxide has been recently described by Shanley.[128]

Kharasch and co-workers[129] prepared di-*n*-butyryl peroxide by the reaction of *n*-butyryl chloride, dissolved in ether, with sodium peroxide (eq. 5). 40 grams of the acid chloride and 200 cc. of absolute ether were placed in a 500 cc. flask fitted with a stirrer and surrounded by an ice–salt mixture. After the temperature had fallen to 0°C., 20 grams of sodium peroxide was added slowly. Excess acid chloride was carefully decomposed by the slow addition of ice. The ether layer was separated and dried, and the peroxide recovered by evaporating the ether.

$$(5)\qquad 2C_4H_9\overset{\overset{\displaystyle O}{\|}}{C}—Cl + Na_2O_2 \longrightarrow C_4H_9\overset{\overset{\displaystyle O}{\|}}{C}—O—O—\overset{\overset{\displaystyle O}{\|}}{C}—C_4H_9$$

Diacyl peroxides may also be obtained as one of the products of the electroreduction (eq. 6) of the potassium salts of carboxylic acids (the Kolbe reaction).[127a]

$$(6)\qquad RCOO^- + e \longrightarrow R\overset{\overset{\displaystyle O}{\|}}{C}—O\cdot$$

$$2R\overset{\overset{\displaystyle O}{\|}}{C}—O\cdot \longrightarrow R\overset{\overset{\displaystyle O}{\|}}{C}—O—O—\overset{\overset{\displaystyle O}{\|}}{C}R$$

### 3. *Dialkyl Peroxydicarbonates*

Dialkyl peroxydicarbonates of the structure:

$$R—O—\overset{\overset{\displaystyle O}{\|}}{C}—O—O—\overset{\overset{\displaystyle O}{\|}}{C}—OR$$

are formally similar to the diacyl peroxides. These former substances can be most readily prepared[130,131a] by the reaction of alkyl chlorocarbonates and sodium peroxide (eq. 7).

[128] E. S. Shanley, *J. Am. Chem. Soc.*, *72*, 1419 (1950).

[129] M. S. Kharasch, S. S. Kane, and H. C. Brown, *J. Am. Chem. Soc.*, *63*, 526 (1941).

[130] H. Wieland, H. von Hove, and K. Barnes, *Ann.*, *446*, 31 (1926).

[131] (a) F. Strain, U. S. Pats. 2,370,588; 2,464,062 (issued to Pittsburgh Plate Glass Company. F. Strain *et al.*, *J. Am. Chem. Soc.*, *72*, 1254 (1950). (b) S. G. Cohen and D. B. Sparrow, *ibid.*, *72*, 611 (1950).

$$\text{(7)}\quad 2R{-}O{-}\overset{\overset{\displaystyle O}{\|}}{C}{-}Cl + Na_2O_2 \longrightarrow RO{-}\overset{\overset{\displaystyle O}{\|}}{C}{-}O{-}O{-}\overset{\overset{\displaystyle O}{\|}}{C}{-}OR + 2NaCl$$

Many dialkyl peroxydicarbonates have been prepared and studied as initiators of vinyl polymerization.[131b]

## VII. Peroxy Derivatives of Aldehydes and Ketones

There exists a formal structural analogy between alcohols, ethers, acids, etc. which may be regarded as organic oxides, and hydroperoxides, dialkyl peroxides, peroxy acids, etc. which are regarded as organic peroxides:

| | | | |
|---|---|---|---|
| $C_2H_5OH$ | Alcohol | $C_2H_5OOH$ | Hydroperoxide |
| $C_2H_5OC_2H_5$ | Dialkyl ether | $C_2H_5OOC_2H_5$ | Dialkyl peroxide |
| $C_2H_5\overset{\overset{O}{\|}}{C}{-}OH$ | Organic acid | $C_2H_5\overset{\overset{O}{\|}}{C}{-}OOH$ | Peroxy acid |
| $C_2H_5\overset{\overset{O}{\|}}{C}{-}OC(CH_3)_3$ | Ester | $C_2H_5\overset{\overset{O}{\|}}{C}{-}OOC(CH_3)_3$ | Peroxy ester |
| 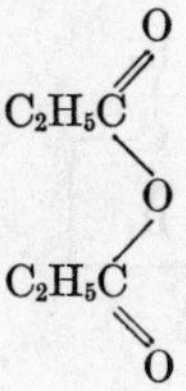 $(C_2H_5C(=O))_2O$ | Acid anhydride | 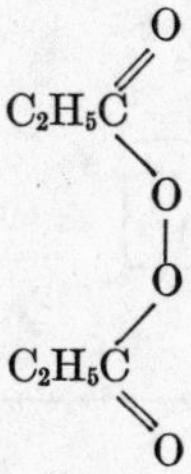 $C_2H_5C(=O){-}O{-}O{-}C(=O)C_2H_5$ | Diacyl peroxide |

A similar relationship also exists between the condensation products of aldehydes and ketones and their corresponding peroxy analogues:

| | | | |
|---|---|---|---|
| 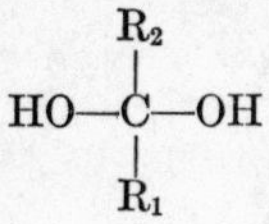 $HO{-}C(R_1)(R_2){-}OH$ | Hypothetical hydrated structure of an aldehyde or ketone | 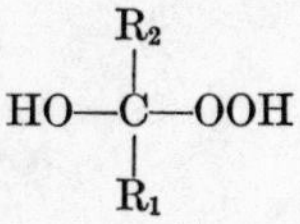 $HO{-}C(R_1)(R_2){-}OOH$ | Hydroxyalkyl hydroperoxide |
| | | 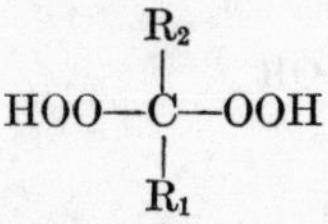 $HOO{-}C(R_1)(R_2){-}OOH$ | Hydroperoxyalkyl hydroperoxide |

*(continued)*

$HO-C(R_1)(R_2)-O-C(R_1)(R_2)-OH$

Bis(hydroxyalkyl)ether

$HO-C(R_1)(R_2)-OO-C(R_1)(R_2)-OH$

Bis(hydroxyalkyl)peroxide

$HOO-C(R_1)(R_2)-OO-C(R_1)(R_2)-OH$

$HOO-C(R_1)(R_2)-OO-C(R_1)(R_2)-OOH$

*Chain form*

$HO-C(R_1)(R_2)-O-[C(R_1)(R_2)-O]-C(R_1)(R_2)-OH$

Polyalkylidene oxide

*Chain form*

$(HOO)\ HO-C(R_1)(R_2)-OO-[C(R_1)(R_2)-OO]-C(R_1)(R_2)-OH\ (OOH)$

Polyalkylidene peroxide

*Ring form*

$\overline{C(R_1)(R_2)-O-[C(R_1)(R_2)-O]-C(R_1)(R_2)-O}$ (ring)

Polyalkylidene oxide

*Ring form*

$\overline{C(R_1)(R_2)-OO-[C(R_1)(R_2)-OO]-C(R_1)(R_2)-OO}$ (ring)

Polyalkylidene peroxide

$HO-C(R_1)(R_2)-OR$

Hemiacetal

$HO-C(R_1)(R_2)-OOR$

Alkyl (1-hydroxyalkyl) peroxide

$HOO-C(R_1)(R_2)-OOR$

$RO-C(R_1)(R_2)-OR$

Acetal

$ROO-C(R_1)(R_2)-OOR$

Peroxy acetal

### 1. *Condensation of Aldehydes and Ketones with Hydrogen Peroxide*

The numerous products that can be obtained as reaction products of ketones and aldehydes with hydrogen peroxide are illustrated by the case of cyclohexanone and hydrogen peroxide.[132] All but one of the following products have been isolated.

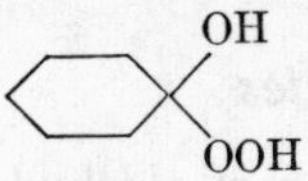

OH / OOH
(I)
1-Hydroxycyclohexyl hydroperoxide
m.p. = 76–78°

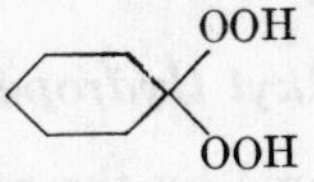

OOH / OOH
(II)
Cyclohexylidene hydroperoxide
(not yet isolated)

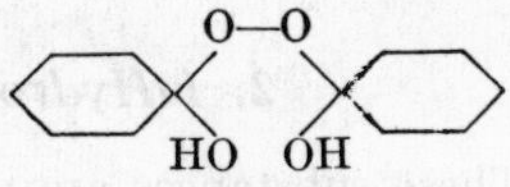

O—O / HO OH
(III)
Bis(1-hydroxycyclohexyl) peroxide
m.p. = 68–70°

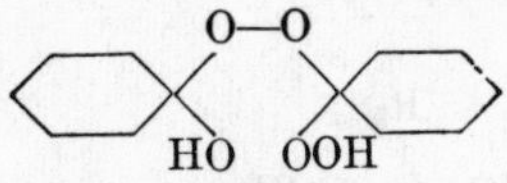

O—O / HO OOH
(IV)
1-Hydroxy-1′-hydroperoxycyclohexyl peroxide, m.p. = 76°

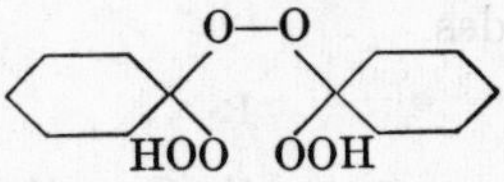

O—O / HOO OOH
(V)
Bis(hydroperoxycyclohexyl) peroxide, m.p. = 82–83°

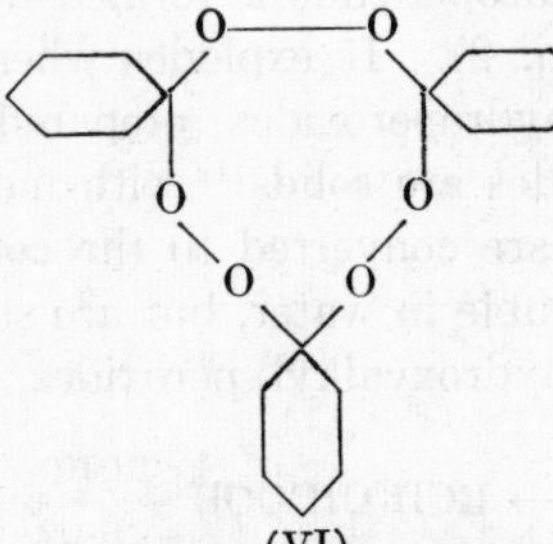

O—O / O O / O O
(VI)
Trimeric cyclohexanone peroxide
m.p. = 93°

Compounds I and III were also prepared by Milas *et al.*[133] by reacting cyclohexanone with an ethereal solution of $H_2O_2$. The formation of III is favored by using an excess of ketone. Compound IV was prepared by Criegee *et al.*[132] by reacting cyclohexanone with a 30 per cent aqueous solution of hydrogen peroxide in the presence of

[132] R. Criegee, W. Schnorrenberg, and J. Becke, *Ann.*, *565*, 7 (1949).
[133] N. A. Milas, S. A. Harris, and P. C. Panagiotakos, *J. Am. Chem. Soc.*, *61*, 2430 (1939).

concentrated HCl as catalyst. Compound V is obtained in the same way if larger amounts of the 30 per cent $H_2O_2$ are used. Compound VI is obtained in the same manner as compound IV except that the reaction is carried out at a somewhat higher temperature. Compound VI can also be prepared directly from compound IV. The structure proof of all of these peroxides is given in the paper by Criegee *et al.*

### *2. 1-Hydroxyalkyl Hydroperoxides*

These substances are prepared by the reaction of aldehydes or ketones with hydrogen peroxide (eq. 1) in nonaqueous media such as ether.[133–135] If the reaction is attempted in aqueous media, there is a tendency to form bis(hydroxyalkyl) peroxides or polyalkylidene peroxides.

$$(1)\qquad R_2R_1C{=}O + H_2O_2 \longrightarrow HO{-}C(R_2)(R_1){-}OOH$$

Hydroxymethyl hydroperoxide is formed from anhydrous formaldehyde and $H_2O_2$ (eq. 2). It explodes when heated in a flame. The 1-hydroxyalkyl hydroperoxides prepared from the straight chain $C_7$ to $C_{12}$ aldehydes are solids[134] with melting points between 40° and 67°C. They are converted to the corresponding acids on fusion. They are insoluble in water, but are slowly decomposed by water to give the bis(1-hydroxyalkyl) peroxides.

$$(2)\qquad RCHO + H_2O_2 \longrightarrow RCH(OH)OOH \xrightarrow[H_2O]{RCHO} RCH(OH)OOCH(OH)R$$

Criegee and Dietrich have obtained a tetrahydroperoxide derivative of cyclodecane by reacting (eq. 3) 1,6-cyclodecanedione with hydrogen peroxide.[136]

$$(3)\qquad \text{1,6-cyclodecanedione} + H_2O_2 \longrightarrow \text{(HOO)}_2\text{-bicyclic}(\text{OOH})_2$$

[134] A. Rieche, *Ber.*, *64*, 2328 (1931).
[135] A. Rieche and R. Meister, *Ber.*, *68*, 1465 (1935).
[136] R. Criegee and H. Dietrich, *Ann.*, *560*, 135 (1948).

### 3. *Bis(1-hydroxyalkyl) Peroxides*

These peroxides are prepared by the reaction of hydrogen peroxide with aldehydes or ketones.[1–3] Their formation is favored over that of the 1-hydroxyalkyl hydroperoxides if an excess of aldehyde or ketone is used or if the reaction is carried out in an aqueous medium (eq. 1).

$$(1)\quad R_1R_2C{=}O + H_2O_2 \rightleftharpoons HO{-}CR_1R_2{-}OOH \rightleftharpoons HO{-}CR_1R_2{-}OO{-}CR_1R_2OH$$

The first member of the series, $CH_2(OH)OOCH_2OH$ (prepared by reacting formaldehyde with $H_2O_2$), is an explosive solid. The subsequent members of the series CHR(OH)OOCH(OH)R (up to $R = C_7H_{15}$), are nonexplosive distillable liquids.[1] The series from $R = C_7H_{15}$ to $R = C_{12}H_{25}$ have also been prepared[1] and are nonexplosive solids. In addition to the normal bis(1-hydroxyalkyl) peroxides derived from the normal series of aliphatic aldehydes, compounds I and II have been prepared from chloral and benzaldehyde.[137,138]

$$HO{-}CH(CCl_3){-}OO{-}CH(CCl){-}OH$$

(I)

$$HO{-}CH(C_6H_5){-}OO{-}CH(C_6H_5){-}OH$$

(II)

The bis(hydroxyalkyl) peroxides that are prepared from aldehydes can be reconverted to aldehyde and hydrogen peroxide by warming with water. This reaction is catalyzed by dilute acid or alkali.

Rieche has emphasized the relationship between bis(hydroxyalkyl) peroxides and ozonides. 2-Butene ozonide and a dimer of 2-butene ozonide can both be obtained (eq. 2) from bis(1-hydroxyethyl) peroxide by treating the latter with $P_2O_5$.[139,140]

[137] A. Baeyer and V. Villiger, *Ber.*, *33*, 2481 (1900).
[138] V. Nef, *Ann.*, *298*, 292 (1897).
[139] A. Rieche and R. Meister, *Ber.*, *65*, 1274 (1932).
[140] A. Rieche, R. Meister, H. Southoff, and H. Pfeiffer, *Ann.*, *533*, 187 (1942).

(2)

$$HO{-}CH(CH_3){-}OO{-}CH(CH_3){-}OH \xrightarrow{P_2O_5} CH_3{-}\overset{O-O}{CH \quad\quad CH}{-}CH_3 \ (\text{ring closed by } O)$$

$$HO{-}CH(CH_3){-}O{-}O{-}CH(CH_3){-}OH \xrightarrow{P_2O_5} \text{cyclic dimer: } (CH_3)(H)C{<}\overset{O-O}{}{>}C(H)(CH_3),\ \text{each C joined through } O \text{ to } C(H)(CH_3){-}O{-}O{-}C(H)(CH_3)$$

Furthermore the mild hydrolysis of 2-butene ozonide produces bis(1-hydroxyethyl) peroxide[140] (eq. 3) and the decomposition of ethylene ozonide by water gives bis(hydroxymethyl) peroxide[141] (eq. 4).

$$(3)\quad CH_3{-}\overset{O-O}{CH \quad\quad CH}{-}CH_3\ (\text{ring closed by } O) \xrightarrow{H_2O} HO{-}CH(CH_3){-}O{-}O{-}CH(CH_3){-}OH$$

$$(4)\quad H_2C\overset{O-O}{\quad\quad}CH_2\ (\text{ring closed by } O) \xrightarrow{H_2O} HO{-}CH_2{-}O{-}O{-}CH_2{-}OH$$

Rieche used this reaction as a means of proving the structure of ozonides—which he takes to be the one that is used in the above equations. He also believes that bis(1-hydroxyalkyl) peroxides may be intermediates in the decomposition of all ozonides.

On the other hand, Marvel and Nichols[142] failed to find bis(hydroxyalkyl) peroxides in their studies of the decomposition of the ozonides of aryl substituted ethylenes (*e.g.*, styrene, stilbene, tetraphenylethylene). Instead they found dimeric benzaldehyde peroxide or dimeric benzophenone peroxide. In addition they found that the decomposition of these ozonides was not accelerated by water. They suggest the following mechanism (eq. 5) for the decomposition of ozonides.

[141] E. Briner and P. Schnorf, *Helv. Chim. Acta, 12,* 154 (1929).
[142] C. S. Marvel and V. Nichols, *J. Org. Chem., 6,* **296** (1941).

$$R_2CO + R'CHO_2\text{—} \longleftarrow R_2C\text{—}CHR' \text{ (bridged by } O_3) \longrightarrow R_2CO_2\text{—} + R'CHO \quad (5)$$

$$\downarrow \text{ R'CH(O—O)(O—O)CHR' (cyclic)} \qquad \downarrow \text{ R}_2\text{C(O—O)(O—O)CR}_2 \text{ (cyclic)}$$

Bis(hydroxymethyl) peroxide has been prepared by the action of ozone (eq. 6) on dimethyl ether[143] as well as by synthesis from formaldehyde and hydrogen peroxide.

$$CH_3OCH_3 + O_3 \longrightarrow HO\text{—}CH_2\text{—}OO\text{—}CH_2\text{—}OH$$

### 4. *Polyalkylidene Peroxides*

In section VII-1 the preparation of trimeric cyclohexanone peroxide by reaction of cyclohexanone with 30 per cent $H_2O_2$ in the presence of dry HCl (without cooling) was discussed. This compound is classified as a polyalkylidene peroxide.

In analogy to the polymeric forms of formaldehyde (polyoxymethylenes) and acetaldehyde, which can exist in ring or chain form, the polyalkylidene peroxides can also exist in ring and chain forms. Some of the polymeric forms of formaldehyde and acetaldehyde are given below.

Ring of $H_2C$, O—$CH_2$, O, O—$CH_2$

Trioxane (trioxymethylene)

$$HOCH_2O[CH_2O]_xCH_2OH$$

Linear polyoxymethylene

Ring of $CH_3CH$, O—$C(H)CH_3$, O, O—$C(H)CH_3$

Paraldehyde

$$HO\text{—}CH(CH_3)\text{—}O\text{—}[CH(CH_3)\text{—}O]_x\text{—}CH(CH_3)\text{—}OH$$

Polyethylidene oxide
(linear polyacetaldehyde)

[143] F. G. Fischer, *Ann.*, *476*, 244 (1929).

Some of the ring forms of the polyalkylidene peroxides whose structures are reasonably well established are also given below (trimeric cyclohexanone peroxide was discussed in section VII-1).

(I)
Dimeric benzaldehyde peroxide
m.p. = 202°

(II)
Dimeric benzophenone peroxide
m.p. = 212.5°

(III)
Dimeric acetone peroxide
m.p. = 132°

(IV)
Trimeric acetone peroxide
m.p. = 98°

Structure I was prepared and characterized by Baeyer and Villiger.[144] It is formed by reacting benzaldehyde with Caro's acid ($H_2SO_5$) or by reacting styrene or stilbene with ozone.[142] Structure II was obtained in over 50 per cent yield by Marvel and Nichols by reacting tetraphenylethylene with ozone.[142]

Structure III was obtained by Baeyer and Villiger by treating acetone with solid $H_2SO_5$ in ether solution (eq. 1). Its structure was established[1,2,132,145] by elemental analysis, molecular weight determination, catalytic hydrogenation, and iodine titration.

$$(1)\quad 2\,(CH_3)_2C{=}O + H_2SO_5 \longrightarrow (CH_3)_2C\langle{}^{O-O}_{O-O}\rangle C(CH_3)_2$$

Dimeric acetone peroxide can also be obtained from the ozonides of compounds with a terminal isopropylidene group (*e.g.*, mesityl oxide, $(CH_3)_2C{=}CHCOCH_3$).[1]

[144] A. Baeyer and V. Villiger, *Ber.*, *33*, 2484 (1900).
[145] A. Baeyer and V. Villiger, *Ber.*, *32*, 3628, 3692 (1899); *33*, 124 (1900).

Trimeric acetone peroxide was first prepared by Wolffenstein[146] by reacting acetone with aqueous hydrogen peroxide at room temperature for a long period of time (eq. 2). The reaction is accelerated by the addition of concentrated HCl, care being taken to keep the reaction mixture cool.[1,147]

$$(2) \qquad 3\ (CH_3)_2C{=}O \xrightarrow[HCl]{H_2O_2} \text{cyclo-}[(CH_3)_2C{-}O{-}O{-}C(CH_3)_2{-}O{-}O{-}C(CH_3)_2{-}O{-}O{-}]$$

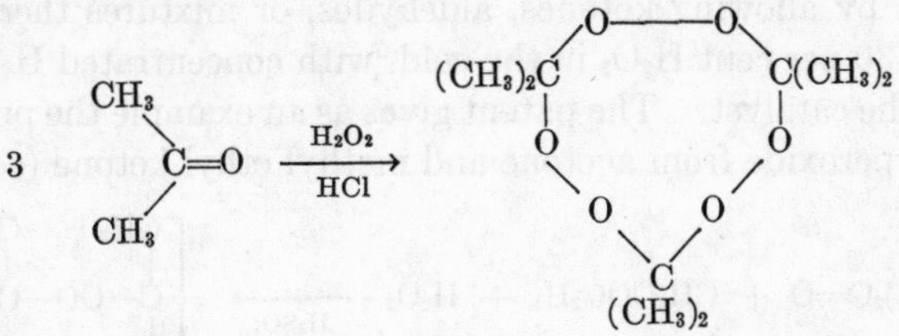

Since this structure was first announced it has been the subject of considerable skepticism, particularly because it liberates iodine from iodide very slowly. However, Rieche[1] and Criegee[132] have both reinvestigated this material and accepted its structure.

Kharasch and Gladstone[148] found that old samples of diisopropyl ether contained large quantities of trimeric acetone peroxide (m.p. 98°C.). The peroxide evidently arises by an autoxidation of the ether with molecular oxygen (eq. 3).

$$(3) \qquad H{-}C(CH_3)_2{-}O{-}C(CH_3)_2{-}H + O_2 \longrightarrow \text{trimeric acetone peroxide}$$

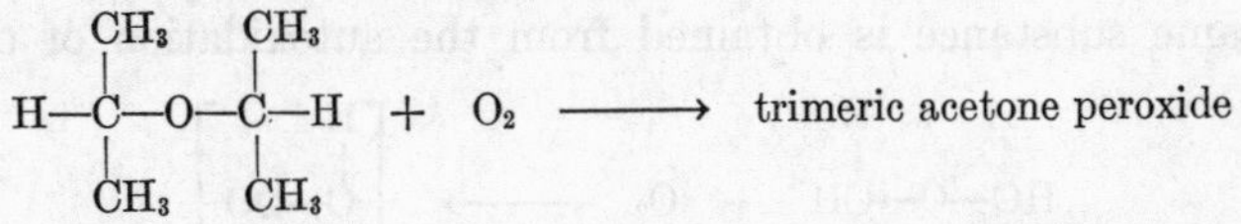

Attempts have been made to explain the mechanism of this autoxidation; the first step is assumed to be a hydroperoxide formation.[149,150]

Other (probably) dimeric ketone peroxides (*e.g.*, from diethyl ketone and diisopropyl ketone) have been prepared by reacting these substances with Caro's acid.[1]

Inasmuch as dimeric and trimeric ketone peroxides containing 6 and 9 atoms in the ring, respectively, have been prepared, it would appear that larger rings and linear polymers (with OH or OOH terminals)

[146] K. Wolffenstein, *Ber.*, *28*, 2265 (1895).
[147] A. Baeyer and V. Villiger, *Ber.*, *33*, 124, 858 (1900).
[148] M. S. Kharasch and M. Gladstone, *J. Chem. Educ.*, *16*, 498 (1939).
[149] A. Rieche and K. Koch, *Ber.*, *75*, 1016 (1942).
[150] K. I. Ivanov, V. K. Savinova, and E. G. Mikhailova, *J. Gen. Chem.* (*U. S. S. R.*), *16*, 65, 1003, 1015 (1940).

and with peroxy bonds along the chain could also be synthesized. Dilthey *et al.*[151] have found that higher ketones yield polymeric peroxides on treatment with hydrogen peroxide or with Caro's acid. A patent for the production of polymeric polyperoxides (for use as catalysts in ethylene polymerization) has been issued.[152] These are prepared by allowing ketones, aldehydes, or mixtures thereof to react with 30 per cent $H_2O_2$ in the cold, with concentrated $H_2SO_4$ being used as the catalyst. The patent gives as an example the preparation of a polyperoxide from acetone and methyl ethyl ketone (eq. 4).

$$(4)\quad (CH_3)_2C{=}O + CH_3COC_2H_5 + H_2O_2 \xrightarrow[H_2SO_4]{} \left[-\overset{CH_3}{\underset{CH_3}{C}}-OO-\overset{CH_3}{\underset{C_2H_5}{C}}-OO-\right]_x$$

Ethylidene peroxide is a highly explosive substance formed from hydroxyethyl hydroperoxide (eq. 5) by treatment with $P_2O_5$.[134] This

$$(5)\quad HO-\overset{H}{\underset{CH_3}{C}}-OOH \xrightarrow[P_2O_5]{} \left[-\overset{H}{\underset{CH_3}{C}}-OO-\right]_x$$

substance is probably a complex polymer (either linear or cyclic). The same substance is obtained from the autoxidation of diethyl

$$(6)\quad H\overset{H}{\underset{CH_3}{C}}-O-\overset{H}{\underset{CH_3}{C}}H + O_2 \longrightarrow \left[-\overset{H}{\underset{CH_3}{C}}-OO-\right]_x$$

ether (eq. 6). It has also been obtained by heating butene ozonide *in vacuo* (eq. 7).[153]

$$(7)\quad CH_3-\overset{H}{C}\overset{O-O}{\underset{O}{\diagdown\diagup}}\underset{H}{C}-CH_3 \longrightarrow \left[-\overset{H}{\underset{CH_3}{C}}-OO-\right]_x$$

## 5. *Alkyl 1-Hydroxyalkyl Peroxides*

These peroxides are prepared by reaction of a hydroperoxide with an excess of an aldehyde or ketone in the presence of an acid cata-

[151] W. Dilthey, M. Inckel, and H. Stephan, *J. prakt. Chem.*, *154*, 219 (1940).
[152] U. S. Pat. 2,511,480 (M. Roedel to E. I. du Pont de Nemours & Co.).
[153] A. Rieche and R. Meister, *Ber.*, *64*, 2335 (1931); *72*, 1933 (1939).

lyst[154–156] (eq. 1). Ether may be used as the solvent. Methyl

$$(1)\qquad \underset{R_1}{\overset{R}{|}}\!\!C{=}O + ROOH \xrightarrow[{[H^+]}]{} HO{-}\underset{R_1}{\overset{R_2}{C}}{-}OOR$$

hydroperoxide, for example, reacts with formaldehyde to form methyl hydroxymethyl peroxide, $CH_3OOCH_2OH$ (eq. 1). An excess of the hydroperoxides leads to the diperoxy compound (section 6).

Alkyl 1-hydroxyalkyl peroxides are somewhat less explosive than dialkyl peroxides and more stable than the corresponding hemiacetals. In general they are liquids which are sufficiently stable to be distilled.

## 6. *Peroxy Acetals*

If an aldehyde or ketone is allowed to react with an *excess* of hydroperoxide in the presence of an acidic catalyst, a diperoxy compound, which may be termed a peroxy acetal is formed:[157–159]

$$\underset{R_1}{\overset{R_2}{C}}{=}O + 2ROOH \xrightarrow[{[H^+]}]{} ROO{-}\underset{R_1}{\overset{R_2}{C}}{-}OOR$$

This reaction occurs more readily with ketones than with aldehydes. The hydroperoxide most widely used in this reaction thus far is *t*-butyl hydroperoxide. Among the carbonyl compounds that have been reacted with *t*-butyl hydroperoxide to form peroxy acetals are: acetone, methyl ethyl ketone, methyl propyl ketone, diethyl ketone, ethyl isobutyl ketone, benzaldehyde, and cyclohexanone.[159]

[154] A. Rieche, *Ber.*, *63*, 2642 (1930).
[155] U. S. Pats. 2,400,041; 2,455,569 (to Shell Development Co.).
[156] British Pat. 444,544.
[157] U. S. Pat. 2,455,569 (to Shell Development Co.).
[158] F. H. Dickey, J. H. Raley, F. F. Rust, R. S. Tresede, and W. E. Vaughan, *Ind. Eng. Chem.*, *41*, 1673 (1949). See also W. E. Vaughan *et al.*, *ibid.*, *41*, 1679 (1949).
[159] F. H. Dickey, F. F. Rust, and W. E. Vaughan, *J. Am. Chem. Soc.*, *71*, 1432 (1949).

## VIII. Analytical Methods for Determination of Organic Peroxides

### 1. *Iodometric Methods for Determination of Hydroperoxides and Diacyl and Diaroyl Peroxides*

As a typical example, one may cite the reaction between benzoyl peroxide and sodium or potassium iodide:

$$(C_6H_5CO)_2O_2 + 2KI \longrightarrow 2C_6H_5COOK + I_2$$

Inasmuch as benzoyl peroxide is insoluble in water, the above reaction proceeds very slowly in aqueous media. However, in solvents in which both reagents are soluble the reaction goes quantitatively and rapidly. Usually the estimation of peroxide is achieved by titrating the liberated iodine with standard thiosulfate solution. Among the solvents that may be used are acetone, acetic acid, and isopropyl alcohol.

The following procedure was employed by Swain *et al.*[123] for assaying various substituted benzoyl peroxides to within 0.5 per cent:

1 cc. to 5 cc. aliquots of the peroxide samples were pipetted into 125-cc. glass-stoppered Pyrex flasks, and 20 cc. of pure acetone added. About 2 grams of crushed Dry Ice was added to the solution to insure a slightly acid solution and to avoid possible errors due to oxygen. The flasks were warmed to room temperature with the aid of a hot plate; 1 cc. of a half-saturated solution of sodium iodide in acetone was added and the contents of the flask swirled. The liberation of iodine was complete within a few seconds; and a gelatinous precipitate of the sodium salt of the corresponding benzoic acid was formed in some cases. After about 30 seconds, 10 cc. of carbonated water was added; and the homogeneous solution was immediately titrated with 0.01 *N* thiosulfate, made up with conductivity water. The end points were established by comparing the run with a blank, both illuminated by a white background and a strong light. Thorough shaking of the contents of the flask at or near the end point is essential for success, especially for heterogeneous systems likely to be encountered in the titration of peroxide decomposed in the presence of a vinyl monomer or in benzene or other water immiscible solvent.

Wagner, Smith, and Peters[160] have proposed an iodometric procedure which they claim to be accurate for hydroperoxides as well as diacyl and diaroyl peroxides:

Into a 250-cc. Erlenmeyer flask equipped with a gas inlet tube were introduced 40 cc. of dry isopropyl alcohol, 2 cc. of glacial acetic acid, and up to 10 cc.

[160] C. D. Wagner, R. H. Smith, and E. D. Peters, *Ind. Eng. Chem., Anal. Ed.*, *19*, 976 (1947).

(usually 5 cc.) of the sample, containing up to 2 milliequivalents of peroxides. The flask was connected to a reflux condenser and carbon dioxide gas passed through the mixture for 3 minutes. The carbon dioxide flow was stopped and the solution heated to reflux; 10 cc. of isopropyl alcohol saturated with sodium iodide through the condenser was added and the mixture was heated at gentle reflux for $15 \pm 0.5$ minutes. The $CO_2$ flow was resumed, the flask disconnected from the condenser, and the contents titrated immediately with 0.1 *N* sodium thiosulfate to the disappearance of the yellow color (0.01 *N* thiosulfate was used for very low peroxide concentrations).

This method is stated to give high accuracy for various types of hydroperoxides (cumene hydroperoxide, tetralin hydroperoxide, etc.) and also for diacyl peroxides such as benzoyl peroxide. The method does not work for dialkyl peroxides, ROOR, and also fails in the presence of substances containing conjugated double bonds. It also gives erratic results in the case of ascaridole. It appears to be generally true that cyclic peroxides (such as trimeric cyclohexanone peroxide) and transannular peroxides such as ascaridole react slowly and perhaps incompletely with iodide.

A modification of the method of Wagner *et al.* was used by Fordham and Williams[161] for the determination of cumene hydroperoxide. This method was originally suggested by the Hercules Powder Company.

The sample is added to 100 cc. of 99 per cent isopropanol in a glass-stoppered Erlenmeyer. 10 cc. of glacial acetic acid and 1 cc. of saturated potassium iodide solution are added and the mixture is refluxed gently (to avoid the loss of iodine) for three to four minutes. The condenser is washed with 10 cc. of isopropanol; 25 cc. of water is then added and the flask is stoppered. When the resulting solution has cooled somewhat, the liberated iodine is titrated with standard thiosulfate solution to the disappearance of the yellow color. Starch cannot be used as an indicator, but this is not a serious disadvantage unless the solution is objectionably colored. A blank is measured on the reagents. This procedure gives reproducible results that are independent of the time of refluxing up to ten minutes.

The normal iodometric methods do not work for dialkyl peroxides such as di-*t*-butyl peroxide or for peroxy acetals such as 2,2-bis(*t*-butylperoxy)butane.[162] The following method was developed by Vaughan and co-workers[80] to estimate di-*t*-butyl peroxides and probably most other dialkyl peroxides as well.

[161] J. W. L. Fordham and H. Leverne Williams, *Can. J. Research, B27*, 943 (1949).

[162] J. H. Raley, F. F. Rust, and W. E. Vaughan, *J. Am. Chem. Soc., 70*, 1336 (1948).

The sample dissolved in glacial acetic acid is mixed in an inert atmosphere with an equal volume of constant boiling aqueous hydrogen iodide (*circa* 56 per cent). The container is closed, the mixture heated at 60 °C. for 45 minutes, and the liberated iodine titrated with standard thiosulfate solution after dilution with oxygen-free water. By this method all other types of peroxides are determined and correction must be made for their presence. Other organic substances reactive with concentrated hydrogen iodide will interfere.

Even under optimum conditions iodometric methods such as the above are limited by the accuracy of the visual determination of the end point since starch end points cannot be used in semiaqueous media. This is especially aggravated when colored matter or suspended solids are present in the sample being analyzed. An electrometric method for determining end points has been reported by Abrahamson and Linschitz[163] using a principle developed by Foulk and Bawden.[164]

## 2. *Ferrous Ion Method for Determination of Organic Peroxides*

The ferrous ion method for the detection of organic peroxides is based on analogy with the following idealized reaction:

$$2Fe^{++} + HOOH \longrightarrow 2Fe^{+++} + 2OH^-$$

Even for hydrogen peroxide, the above reaction is not always stoichiometric and depends on the nature of the medium in which the reaction is being carried out. For organic peroxides the reaction is definitely not stoichiometric and in the absence of oxygen gives values that represent only a fraction of the true peroxide value.[165] However, under controlled conditions, and after calibration against an absolute method such as the iodometric method, it has an empirical usefulness, particularly for multiple analyses.

Several variations of the ferrous method have been used. (*a*) Reaction of the peroxide with ferrous thiocyanate to produce the red-colored ferric thiocyanate complex. This is then back-titrated with a titanous solution to the disappearance of the red color.[165] (*b*) Reaction of the peroxide with ferrous thiocyanate to produce the red-colored ferric thiocyanate complex which is estimated colorimetri-

[163] E. W. Abrahamson and H. Linschitz, *Anal. Chem.*, *24*, 1355 (1952).

[164] C. W. Foulk and A. T. Bawden, *J. Am. Chem. Soc.*, *48*, 2045 (1926).

[165] C. D. Wagner, R. H. Smith, and E. D. Peters, *Ind. Eng. Chem.*, *Anal. Ed.*, *19*, 980 (1947).

cally.[166] This method with slight modification as to solvent medium has been used by Bolland and by Farmer to estimate the peroxide content in oxidized natural rubber and other polyisoprenes.[167,168] This method has also been evaluated by Wagner *et al.*,[165] who found that it gave reasonably accurate results when applied to pure tetralin and *t*-butyl hydroperoxides in air, but gave very low values when carried out in nitrogen. (*c*) Reaction of the peroxide with an excess of ferrous ion. The unreacted ferrous ion is then reacted with *o*-phenanthroline, which produces a deep-red colored complex which can be determined colorimetrically. This method was developed by Laitinen and Nelson,[169] who state that it has important advantages when compared to the thiocyanate method. The ferrous ion-*o*-phenanthroline method is reported sensitive to peroxide concentrations down to 10 parts per million in systems such as autoxidized natural rubber dissolved in benzene. However, the reproducibility of the method is then quite poor.

The sole advantage of the ferrous ion methods is that they provide a means for estimating peroxides in systems having an active oxygen content too small for iodometric analysis.

### 3. *Other Methods*

Among the other methods for peroxide determination which have proved useful in particular cases one may note the following:

(*a*) The arsenious oxide method developed by Siggia[170] which is particularly applicable in media where the liberation of iodine from potassium iodide cannot be employed, as in some olefinic solvents.

(*b*) The stannous chloride method which has been carefully reexamined by Barnard and Hargrave[171] and found to be of high accuracy and precision. It is particularly useful when the peroxide is in

[166] C. A. Young, R. R. Vogt and J. A. Nieuwland, *Ind. Eng. Chem., Anal. Ed.*, *8*, 198 (1936).

[167] J. L. Bolland, A. Sundralingham, D. A. Sutton, and G. R. Tristam, *Trans. Inst. Rubber Ind.*, *17*, 29 (1941).

[168] E. H. Farmer and A. Sundralingham, *J. Chem. Soc.*, *1943*, 125.

[169] H. A. Laitinen and J. S. Nelson, *Ind. Eng. Chem., Anal. Ed.*, *18*, 422 (1946).

[170] S. Siggia, *Ind. Eng. Chem., Anal. Ed.*, *19*, 827 (1947). See also S. Siggia, *Quantitative Organic Analyses via Functional Groups*, Wiley, New York, 1949, p. 102.

[171] D. Barnard and K. R. Hargrave, *Anal. Chim. Acta*, *5*, 476 (1951).

the presence of organic sulfur compounds, and iodometric methods therefore fail.

(*c*) Polarographic methods have been applied to the analysis of organic peroxides. Neiman and Gerber[172] studied the electroreduction of methyl, ethyl, and cyclohexene hydroperoxides, diethyl peroxide, and trimeric acetone peroxide.

Lewis and co-workers[173,174] have described a method for the polarographic determination of organic peroxides in nonaqueous media. They applied this method to a study of the oxidation of fats. In the case of methyl linoleate they found that a linear relation exists between the peroxide number determined iodometrically and the polarographic value.

Reimers[175] has used the polarographic method to establish the fact that no hydrogen peroxide is produced during the autoxidation of ethers.

(*d*) It has been suggested that the infrared absorption bands at 870 and 840 cm.$^{-1}$ are characteristic for peroxides and hydroperoxides, respectively.[176,177]

(*e*) Chromatographic separation of peroxides, microtechniques for gas analysis of peroxides, and many special reactions of peroxides suitable for analytical procedures are discussed in the monograph by Eggersglüss.[7c]

[172] M. B. Neiman and M. I. Gerber, *Zhur. Anal. Khimie, 1,* 211 (1946).

[173] W. R. Lewis, F. W. Quackenbush and T. de Vries, *Anal. Chem., 21,* 762 (1949).

[174] W. R. Lewis and F. W. Quackenbush, *J. Am. Oil Chemists' Soc., 26,* 53 (1949).

[175] F. Reimers, *Quart. J. Pharm., 19,* 27 (1946).

[176] A. R. Philpotts and W. Thain, *Anal. Chem., 24,* 638 (1952).

[177] O. D. Shreve, M. R. Heether, H. B. Knight, and D. Swern, *Anal. Chem., 23,* 282 (1951).

## B. DECOMPOSITION OF ORGANIC PEROXIDES

### I. Introduction

Organic peroxides are relatively unstable compounds which can be decomposed by heat and light or by reaction with other substances. The decomposition of peroxides is widely utilized to catalyze many important reactions such as vinyl polymerization. In addition, peroxides are formed in the initial phase of the reaction of molecular oxygen with many hydrocarbons and act as autocatalysts for the subsequent autoxidation process. The decomposition products of peroxides are often complex and vary markedly with changes in the external environment. In this chapter, peroxide decomposition will be discussed mainly in terms of the above-mentioned subjects.

If one considers the organic peroxide, ROOR′, where R and R′ may be alkyl, acyl, or hydrogen, the most usual locus of initial cleavage is the O—O linkage. More generally, in the compound A:B in which the groups A and B are joined by a covalent linkage, the linkage can be ruptured in three, and only three, ways:

$$A^+ + :B^- \rightleftharpoons A:B \rightleftharpoons A: + B^+$$
$$A:B \rightleftharpoons A\cdot + B\cdot$$

If the molecule splits into ions of unlike charges the process is called an "heterolytic cleavage," whereas if the molecule splits into two radicals each having one electron from the original covalent bond the process is called an "homolytic cleavage." The dissociation of the bond is in all cases an endothermic process.

For almost all linkages, A:B, and particularly those having largely covalent character, the natural cleavage tendency in the gas phase will be the homolytic cleavage, since this will require the least energy.[1]

In solution, the dissociation of A:B may be either homolytic or

[1] M. G. Evans, *Trans. Faraday Soc.*, *42*, 101 (1946).

heterolytic. The heterolytic cleavage tendency is favored when the two groups A and B have very different electron attracting powers, and when the solvent in which A:B is dissolved has a high dielectric constant. Furthermore the solvation of the ions resulting from the heterolytic cleavage of A:B is always a factor which promotes this kind of cleavage. Reaction of this type can be generalized as follows:

$$A{:}B + 2S \longrightarrow S\bar{A}{:} + SB^+$$

The most incontrovertible way of establishing whether ions or radicals are formed by the dissociation of a compound A:B in a solvent is by direct physical tests. Ions which carry electric charge should be detectable by conductance experiments.[2] Radicals which contain unpaired electrons having a net magnetic moment of one Bohr magneton should be measurable by magnetic susceptibility measurements. For example, $AlCl_3$ dissolved in ethyl chloride gives conducting solutions,[2] whereas the hexaarylethanes, which largely dissociate into free radicals in nonpolar solvents such as toluene, have experimentally measurable magnetic moments from which the extent of dissociation can be calculated at least qualitatively.[3] Also, the hexaarylethanes form colored solutions on dissociation due to the characteristic light absorption of the free radicals, and consequently the transmission curves of the solutions can also be used to calculate the extent of dissociation.

On the other hand, many compounds, A:B, which dissociate into radicals or ions when dissolved in an appropriate solvent and subjected to thermal and photoenergy, produce such small quantities of radicals or ions that physical measurements of the type discussed above are not sufficiently sensitive to detect these fragments. Nevertheless this small quantity of the fragments of A:B may initiate chain reactions in the substrate in which A:B is dissolved. The over-all chemical reaction which is produced may be very extensive compared to the small amount of active fragments which are present at any time. The typical situation in the case of radical cleavage is that the radical fragments from A:B attack the solvent in which A:B is dissolved producing new radicals. The primary radicals from A:B and the derived radicals produced by reaction with the solvent can both react with A:B to decompose it further. Since this attack by radicals

[2] A. Wohl and E. Wertyporoch, *Ber.*, *B64*, 1357 (1931).

[3] P. W. Selwood and R. M. Dobres, *J. Am. Chem. Soc.*, *72*, 3860 (1950).

on A:B must produce a new radical, the process is clearly a chain reaction. This type of chain decomposition of A:B is referred to as "induced decomposition."

The radicals produced by homolytic cleavage of A:B in a solvent may produce many other chain reactions in the solvent (which acts as a substrate). Among the more important of these are polymerization, oxidation, and chlorination. However, whatever the nature of the reaction initiated by radicals may be, the ultimate fate of all radicals is a process of mutual destruction by recombination or disproportionation. The average lifetime of a radical from formation to destruction is generally (but not always) very short, and for this reason the total radical concentration in solution is very small in most instances except for unusual cases such as the hexaarylethanes.

### *1. Diagnostic Tests for Detection of Radical Decomposition of Peroxides*

Several of the diagnostic tests which can be used to ascertain whether a compound A:B is dissociating into radicals rather than ions will now be reviewed. In general the presence of radicals is deduced from the characteristic chain reactions that they produce.

#### *(a) Vinyl Polymerization*

When the decomposing compound A:B can initiate polymerization of a vinyl monomer such as ethylene, styrene, or methyl methacrylate, the presence of radicals among the primary decomposition products of A:B may be suspected. This is not a complete test because positive and negative ions may also initiate polymerization.[4] However, the composition of a copolymer initiated by the decomposition of A:B is a definitive test. For example, the polymerization of an equimolar mixture of styrene and methyl methacrylate initiated by radicals produces a copolymer containing exactly 51 mole per cent styrene. Positive ion initiated polymerization of this same mixture produces a polymer containing over 99 per cent styrene; negative ion initiated polymerization under these same conditions produces a polymer containing over 99 per cent methyl methacrylate.[5]

[4] H. Mark and A. V. Tobolsky, *The Physical Chemistry of High Polymeric Systems*, Interscience, New York-London, 1950.

[5] C. Walling, E. R. Briggs, W. Cummings, and F. R. Mayo, *J. Am. Chem. Soc.*, *72*, 48 (1950).

*(b) Addition of HBr to Olefins*

The so-called normal addition of HBr to olefins, which is probably initiated by a proton addition to the double bond, follows the Markownikoff rule, *i.e.*, the Br adds on the more highly substituted carbon atom:

$$CH_2{=}CHR + HBr \xrightarrow{\text{"normal"}} CH_3{-}CHRBr$$

If HBr is reacted with an olefin in the presence of a compound A:B which decomposes into radicals, the addition is anti-Markownikoff:[6,7]

$$CH_2{=}CHR + HBr \xrightarrow{\text{radicals}} CH_2Br{-}CH_2R$$

Similar rules apply for addition of mercaptans, aldehydes, etc., to double bonds.

*(c) Effect of Solvent on Rate of Decomposition*

When a substance decomposes by means of an heterolytic cleavage, the over-all rate of decomposition will bear a definite relation to the acidity or basicity of the solvent and to the dielectric constant of the solvent. The absence of any systematic relation between decomposition rate and the above-mentioned variables is diagnostic of an *homolytic* cleavage.

*(d) Induced Decomposition of A:B*

The total decomposition rate of A:B via an homolytic mechanism is often the sum of the spontaneous rate of cleavage into radicals A:B (which is a first order reaction) plus an induced decomposition rate (which is often of an order different from first order). The induced decomposition is a chain reaction in which the primary radicals A· and B·, or secondary radicals derived from A· or B· by dismutation or by reaction with the solvent, attack the substrate A:B and cause it to decompose into other radicals. The process is then repeated in a typical chain reaction fashion until the radicals disappear by mutual combination or disproportionation. The contribution of the spon-

[6] M. S. Kharasch, H. Engelmann, and F. R. Mayo, *J. Org. Chem.*, *2*, 288, 400 (1937).

[7] D. H. Hey and W. A. Waters, *Chem. Reviews*, *21*, 202 (1937). Also W. A. Waters, *The Chemistry of Free Radicals*, Oxford Univ. Press, 1946.

taneous (first order) cleavage to the total rate of decomposition can be obtained by kinetic analysis or by other means shortly to be discussed. Although the induced rate of decomposition is very markedly dependent upon the solvent, the spontaneous cleavage rate is relatively independent of solvent and is nearly the same in the pure liquid phase, in solution, or in the gas phase. The induced decomposition of a compound A:B may also be initiated by the spontaneous, homolytic cleavage of a more unstable substance. Thus azomethane in small amounts can be used to produce a rapid decomposition of acetaldehyde at temperatures at which pure acetaldehyde is quite stable. This situation arises because at these temperatures the primary cleavage of acetaldehyde is slow but its induced decomposition rate is large, provided there is a reasonably rapid supply of initiating radicals. Azomethane provides a rapid supply of methyl radicals at the temperatures in question, while pure acetaldehyde does not.[8]

(e) *Effect of Inhibitors*

There are certain substances which characteristically inhibit free radical initiated chain reactions, and in particular vinyl polymerization, oxidation with molecular oxygen, anti-Markownikoff addition of HBr to olefins, and radical induced decompositions. These substances include quinone, hydroquinone, and other polyhydroxy derivatives of benzene, primary, and secondary aromatic amines, nitroaromatics, nitrous acid, nitric oxide, iodine, and oxygen. For gas phase decompositions, even toluene and propylene serve to inhibit the induced decomposition of many substances. It must be realized, however, that not all of these substances act as inhibitors for all radical chain reactions.

(f) *Reaction with Stable Free Radicals*

The radicals produced by the compound A:B during homolytic cleavage may react rapidly with stable free radicals such as triphenylmethyl or 2,2-diphenylpicrylhydrazyl. The rate of reaction of radicals with 2,2-diphenylpicrylhydrazyl may be conveniently followed by measuring the disappearance of the highly colored hydrazyl by a photometric technique.[9]

[8] K. J. Laidler, *Chemical Kinetics*, McGraw-Hill, New York, 1950, Chapter 9.

[9] C. E. H. Bawn and S. F. Mellish, *Trans. Faraday Soc.*, *47*, 1216 (1951).

(g) *Primary Products of Decomposition*

The primary products of decomposition are often different for homolytic and heterolytic cleavages. For example cumene hydroperoxide decomposes largely into acetophenone and methyl alcohol in nonpolar solvents by homolytic cleavage of the O—O bond, whereas this same substance decomposes quantitatively into phenol and acetone in certain very strongly acidic media where the initial cleavage is heterolytic.[10]

(h) *Reaction Products with the Solvent*

If the substance A:B is decomposed in an aromatic solvent, fragments of A:B are often found substituted on the aromatic ring. Where this substitution does not follow the directing influences of the groups already attached to the benzene nucleus, this is indicative of an initial homolytic cleavage of A:B.

(i) *Removal of Metallic Mirrors*

Radicals produced by gas phase homolytic decompositions have the ability to remove metallic deposits of lead, antimony, etc. by forming volatile products such as $Pb(CH_3)_4$. It is of historical interest that this so-called Paneth technique was one of the first methods used to establish firmly the existence of radicals in gas phase decompositions.[7,8]

(j) *Catalysis of Orthohydrogen–Parahydrogen Conversion*

Due to their paramagnetic properties, free radicals have the ability to catalyze the conversion of orthohydrogen to parahydrogen. This has been used as a diagnostic test for free radicals in the gas phase.[7,8]

(k) *Effect of Ultraviolet Light*

If the decomposition rate of A:B, but not its decomposition products, is markedly altered by the absorption of ultraviolet light, this may be regarded as diagnostic of a homolytic cleavage of A:B.

[10] M. S. Kharasch and J. G. Burt, *J. Org. Chem.*, *16*, 150 (1951). H. Hock and S. Lang, *Ber.*, *77*, 257 (1944).

In succeeding portions of this chapter the homolytic decompositions of peroxides will be treated in greater detail than the heterolytic decompositions, since the former are more frequent and more important from the point of view of initiation of chain reactions such as polymerization and oxidation. Sections II and III will treat the homolytic decompositions of di-*t*-butyl peroxide and benzoyl peroxide, respectively. Section IV will consider bimolecular decomposition of peroxides by a one-electron transfer mechanism. Section V will treat certain aspects of heterolytic cleavage, chiefly by way of contrast with homolytic processes.

## II. Decomposition of Di-*t*-butyl Peroxide and Related Peroxides

### 1. Gas Phase Decomposition of Di-t-butyl Peroxide

Di-*t*-butyl peroxide is a colorless liquid boiling at 111°C. at 760 mm. The compound has a rather surprising stability toward heat, acids, and bases. Its relatively slow decomposition into radicals by a primary cleavage makes it very suitable as a catalyst for high temperature polymerizations and other radical initiated reactions carried out in the range of 100–180°C.

The pioneering work on this peroxide (DTBP) was carried out mainly by Milas and Surgenor,[11a] George and Walsh,[11b] and Vaughan, Rust, Raley, and co-workers.[11c,d] Pyrolysis of DTBP in the gas phase at temperatures between 120–300°C. yields mostly acetone and ethane, particularly in vessels containing large glass surfaces (*i.e.*, packed with glass wool). In large, unpacked vessels about 5–10 per cent of methane, methyl ethyl ketone, and higher ketones are also found.

Vaughan and co-workers[11d] showed that the decomposition of DTBP in the gas phase between 140–160° is a first order reaction, with a half-life independent of the initial pressure of the peroxide. The decomposition of the peroxide clearly produces radicals as will be demonstrated in the subsequent discussion, but Vaughan *et al.*

[11] (a) N. A. Milas and D. M. Surgenor, *J. Am. Chem. Soc.*, *68*, 205, 643 (1946); (b) P. George and A. D. Walsh, *Trans. Faraday Soc.*, *42*, 94 (1946). (c) W. E. Vaughan and F. F. Rust, U. S. Pat. 2,403,771 (July 9, 1946) and earlier patents. (d) J. H. Raley, F. F. Rust, and W. E. Vaughan, *J. Am. Chem. Soc.*, *70*, 88, 1336 (1948).

thought that in the gas phase there was no important induced decomposition resulting from radical attack on the peroxide. These workers expressed the reaction as follows:

(1) $(CH_3)_3COOC(CH_3)_3 \xrightarrow{k_d} 2(CH_3)_3CO\cdot$

(2) $2(CH_3)_3CO\cdot \longrightarrow 2CH_3COCH_3 + 2CH_3\cdot$

(3) $2CH_3\cdot \longrightarrow C_2H_6$

In other words, one mole of DTBP produced two moles of acetone and one mole of ethane. The first step is rate-controlling and, according to Vaughan *et al.*, the first order rate constant for this step in the vapor phase is:

(4) $k_d(\text{DTBP}) = 3.2 \times 10^{16} \exp\{-39.1 \text{ kcal}/RT\}$ gas phase

(Vaughan *et al.*)

Vaughan *et al.* found that typical radical inhibitors such as propylene, oxygen, and nitric oxide did not affect the rate of decomposition of DTBP in the gas phase, and this result, in addition to the first order character of the reaction, led them to believe that there was no important radical induced decomposition of the peroxide. On the other hand, Szwarc and Roberts found that the rate of decomposition was reduced approximately 30 per cent in the presence of large amounts of toluene.[12] They concluded that there is a small amount of radical induced decomposition in the vapor phase, which toluene in large amounts serves to repress. They therefore measured the decomposition rate of DTBP in the vapor phase between 120° and 160°C. in the presence of excess toluene and redetermined $k_d$ as follows:

(5) $k_d$ (DTBP) lies between $4 \times 10^{14}$ and $7 \times 10^{14} \exp\{-36.0 \text{ kcal.}/RT\}$

(Szwarc and Roberts)

In view of these somewhat disparate results, a number of authors have carried out independent studies to determine $k_d$ (DTBP).[13]

[12] M. Szwarc and J. S. Roberts, *J. Chem. Phys.*, *18*, 561 (1950); *19*, 683 (1951).

[13] (a) R. K. Brinton and D. H. Volman, *J. Chem. Phys.*, *20*, 25 (1952). (b) M. T. Jaquiss, J. S. Roberts, and M. Szwarc, *J. Am. Chem. Soc.*, *74*, 6005 (1952) (c) F. Lossing and A. W. Tickner, *J. Chem. Phys.*, *20*, 907 (1952).

Lossing and Tickner[13c] have developed a method for measuring the partial pressure of methyl radicals in thermally decomposing gases, using a modified mass spectrometer. This enabled them to determine $k_d$ (DTBP) up to temperatures of 500°C. They find their results at higher temperatures to be concordant with those of Szwarc[12] and Vaughan[11d] at lower temperatures. The expression for $k_d$ that best fits all the data is:

$$(6) \quad k_d\,(\text{DTBP}) = 7 \times 10^{15} \exp\{-38.0\ \text{kcal.}/RT\}$$

(Lossing and Tickner)
116–350°C.

This is also in agreement (or at least does not disagree) with the other recent data.[13a,b]

To explain the small amounts of methane, methyl ethyl ketone, etc. formed in large unpacked vessels in the absence of inhibitors, the following reactions are postulated

$$(7) \quad CH_3\cdot + CH_3COCH_3 \longrightarrow CH_3COCH_2\cdot + CH_4$$

$$(8) \quad CH_3\cdot + CH_3COCH_2\cdot \longrightarrow CH_3COC_2H_5$$

These reactions can occur only after primary decomposition of the peroxide has produced appreciable quantities of acetone in the system. The carbonyl group of acetone activates the hydrogen atoms on the adjacent methyl groups so that these are attacked by the methyl radicals much more readily than are the corresponding hydrogen atoms of DTBP.

It is interesting to compare the decomposition of diethyl peroxide in the gas phase with that of DTBP. Rebbert and Laidler[14] found that the main processes in the gas phase are:

$$C_2H_5OOC_2H_5 \xrightarrow{k_d} 2C_2H_5O\cdot$$

$$C_2H_5O\cdot \longrightarrow CH_3\cdot + CH_2O$$

$$2CH_3\cdot \longrightarrow C_2H_6$$

By use of toluene as an inhibitor (method of Szwarc) they found that

$$(9) \quad k_d\,(\text{diethyl peroxide}) = 2.1 \times 10^{13} \exp\{-31.7\ \text{kcal.}/RT\}$$

($k_d$ is given in reciprocal seconds in equations 4–6 and 9. In all cases

[14] R. E. Rebbert and K. J. Laidler, *J. Chem. Phys.*, *20*, 574 (1952).

throughout this chapter time will be given in seconds and concentrations in moles per liter unless otherwise specified.)

## 2. *Thermal and Photochemical Decomposition of Pure Di-t-butyl Peroxide in the Liquid Phase*

In the liquid phase decomposition of pure DTBP, whether activated thermally or photochemically, the induced decomposition of the peroxide becomes very important because of the high concentration of peroxide available to attack by methyl and *t*-butoxy radicals. Bell, Rust, and Vaughan[15] showed that when the pure peroxide is decomposed thermally at 110°C. or photochemically at 17°C. the main reactions that occur are (1) to (5).

$$(1)\quad (CH_3)_3COOC(CH_3)_3 \xrightarrow[\text{or } h\nu]{\text{heat}} 2(CH_3)_3CO\cdot$$

$$(2)\quad (CH_3)_3CO\cdot \longrightarrow CH_3COCH_3 + CH_3\cdot$$

$$(3)\quad (CH_3)_3CO\cdot + (CH_3)_3COOC(CH_3)_3 \longrightarrow (CH_3)_3COH + (CH_3)_3COOC(CH_3)_2CH_2\cdot$$

$$(4)\quad CH_3\cdot + (CH_3)_3COOC(CH_3)_3 \longrightarrow CH_4 + (CH_3)_3COOC(CH_3)_2CH_2\cdot$$

$$(5)\quad (CH_3)_3COOC(CH_3)_2CH_2\cdot \longrightarrow (CH_3)_3CO\cdot + (CH_3)_2\underset{\diagdown O \diagup}{C\!-\!\!-\!CH_2}$$

TABLE B-1
Products of Thermal Decomposition of Pure Di-*t*-butyl Peroxide in Liquid Phase[15]
(30.5 hours, 110°C., peroxide charged 100 g., peroxide recovered 30.4 g.)

| Product | Moles per 100 moles peroxide decomposed | Moles per 100 moles *t*-butoxy units |
|---|---|---|
| *t*-Butyl alcohol | 49.6 | 24.8 |
| Acetone | 65.5 | 32.8 |
| Isobutylene oxide | 69.8 | 39.4 |
| Polymer | trace | trace |
| Methane | 62.5 | 31.3 |
| Ethane | 1.9 | 1.0 |
| *Total* | *184.9* | *92.5* |

[15] E. R. Bell, F. F. Rust, and W. E. Vaughan, *J. Am. Chem. Soc.*, *72*, 337 (1950).

The products that are obtained from the thermal and photodecomposition of the pure liquid peroxide are entirely in accord with the above mechanisms. In Tables B-1 and B-2 are shown the percentages of the products that are obtained in typical thermal and photo runs.[15] Due to the large amount of induced decomposition, the total rate of decomposition of pure liquid peroxide is larger than would be obtained under comparable conditions in the gas phase or in solution.

TABLE B-2

Products of Photolysis of Pure Di-*t*-butyl Peroxide in Liquid Phase[15]

(212 hours, 17°C., illumination type-AH-5 lamp, "stripped," 10 cm. distant, peroxide charged 86.5 g., peroxide recovered 66.9 g.)

| Product | Moles per 100 moles peroxide decomposed | Moles per 100 moles *t*-butoxy units |
|---|---|---|
| *t*-Butyl alcohol | 109.0 | 54.5 |
| Acetone | 7.2 | 3.6 |
| Isobutylene oxide | 41.0 | 20.5 |
| Polymer | 36.6 | 18.3 |
| Methane | 2.8 | 1.4 |
| Ethane | 0.1 | 0.05 |
| *Total* | *196.7* | *98.4* |

## 3. *Photochemical Decomposition of Gaseous Di-t-butyl Peroxide*

The photochemical decomposition of gaseous DTBP at pressures less than atmospheric and temperatures ranging from 25° to 75°C. has been investigated by Dorfman and Salsburg.[16] Acetone and ethane are the major products of the photodecomposition, and smaller amounts of *t*-butyl alcohol and methane are also found. Methane is a major product only at very low light intensities. It is assumed that under the experimental conditions the primary quantum yield for fission of the O—O bond is unity since the wavelength used (2600 A.) has an energy of 100 kcal./mole, whereas the bond strength is about 34 kcal./mole. The total quantum yield of acetone plus *t*-butyl alcohol at room temperature was very nearly 2.0, which is the theoretical value that would be obtained if there was no chain reaction de-

[16] L. M. Dorfman and Z. W. Salsburg, *J. Am. Chem. Soc.*, *73*, 255 (1951).

composition. It was concluded that at room temperature no chain decomposition of the peroxide occurs, but at higher temperatures (75°C.) the data seemed to indicate the possible existence of short reaction chains.

### *4. Decomposition of Di-t-butyl Peroxide in Solvents*

The decomposition of DTBP in the gas phase is a relatively clean-cut reaction, as was shown above. This is also true of the decomposition of this peroxide in solvents. The important fact is that the overall rate of decomposition is a first order reaction which occurs at nearly the same rate in all solvents, and which is also nearly equal to the decomposition rate in the gas phase under comparable conditions.[17] This implies that in all these cases the cleavage of the O—O bond is the rate determining step whether in the gas phase or in solvents as diverse as tri-*n*-butylamine and cumene. On the other hand, the main products of decomposition of the peroxide in solvents are quite different from those obtained in the gas phase. Inasmuch as the solvents can donate a hydrogen atom to the *t*-butoxy radicals, *t*-butyl alcohol is found as a major product. The important reactions which occur during the decomposition in solvents SH are:

(1) $$(CH_3)_3COOC(CH_3)_3 \longrightarrow 2(CH_3)_3CO\cdot$$

(2) $$(CH_3)_3CO\cdot \longrightarrow CH_3COCH_3 + CH_3\cdot$$

(3) $$(CH_3)_3CO\cdot + SH \longrightarrow (CH_3)_3COH + S\cdot$$

(4) $$CH_3\cdot + SH \longrightarrow CH_4 + S\cdot$$

Raley, Rust, and Vaughan[17] found that the decomposition of the peroxide in cumene, *t*-butylbenzene, and tri-*n*-butylamine in the temperature range 125–140°C. was first order up to conversions as high as 85 per cent. They found that the activation energy for the first order specific rate constant was approximately 38 kcal./mole and the frequency factor approximately $10^{16}$ sec.$^{-1}$. They had previously found that for the gas phase decomposition:

$$k_d = 3.2 \times 10^{16} \exp \{-39.1 \text{ kcal.}/RT\} \text{ sec.}^{-1}$$

The relative amounts of *t*-butyl alcohol and acetone formed at different temperatures provide important information regarding the

[17] J. H. Raley, F. F. Rust, and W. E. Vaughan, *J. Am. Chem. Soc., 70,* 1336 (1948).

relative rate at which the *t*-butoxy radicals transfer with the solvent as compared to the rate at which they dismute to form acetone. For example at 125° in cumene, every mole of di-*t*-butyl peroxide produces 1.61 moles of *t*-butyl alcohol and 0.39 mole of acetone, whereas at 145°, 1.23 moles of the alcohol and 0.77 mole of acetone are formed from every mole of peroxide. From these measurements it is possible to obtain the difference in activation energy between the transfer step (eq. 3) and the dismutation step (eq. 2). In all the solvents studied, relatively more acetone was always found at higher temperatures, demonstrating that the activation energy, $E_2$, for dismutation is higher than the activation energy, $E_3$, for radical transfer. It was shown that:

$$E_2 - E_3 = 16 \text{ kcal. for cumene solvent}$$

$$E_2 - E_3 = 11 \text{ kcal. for } t\text{-butylbenzene solvent}$$

### 5. *Dismutation of Alkoxy Radicals*

The dismutation of the *t*-butoxy radical involves the fission of a carbon-carbon bond and is of considerable theoretical interest. It was estimated that the heat of reaction for the dismutation of the *t*-butoxy radical to acetone and methyl is endothermic to the extent of about 5 kcal./mole.[17] It appears that for tertiary alkoxy radicals the largest group attached to the carbon atom is preferentially lost as a radical. This was demonstrated by Milas and Surgenor,[11a] who showed that when di-*t*-amyl peroxide is decomposed in the vapor phase over glass wool the products are mainly *n-butane* and acetone with smaller amounts of ethane, propane, and methyl ethyl ketone. The reaction proceeds essentially as follows:

$$(CH_3)_2(C_2H_5)COOC(C_2H_5)(CH_3)_2 \longrightarrow 2(CH_3)_2(C_2H_5)CO\cdot$$

$$(CH_3)_2(C_2H_5)CO\cdot \longrightarrow CH_3COCH_3 + C_2H_5\cdot$$

$$C_2H_5\cdot + C_2H_5\cdot \longrightarrow C_4H_{10}$$

In more extensive studies by Rust, Seubold, and Vaughan,[18] the relative stability of a series of alkoxy radicals in which primary, secondary, and tertiary alkyl groups are involved was established by preparing a series of unsymmetrical alkyl-*t*-butyl peroxides and

[18] F. F. Rust, F. H. Seubold, and W. E. Vaughan, *J. Am. Chem. Soc.*, *72*, 338 (1950).

decomposing them under uniform conditions in the presence of cyclohexene at 195°C. The cyclohexene was used so that the alkoxy radicals formed would have the choice between reacting with the very active cyclohexene or dismuting. The initial product of cleavage was in all cases the *t*-butoxy radical and the other alkoxy radical from the unsvmmetrical peroxide. The *t*-butoxy radical can transfer with the cyclohexene or dismute, and the other alkoxy radical can do likewise. By chemical and physical (infrared and mass spectrometer) analysis of the decomposition products it was possible to determine the relative amount of dismutation versus transfer for the other alkoxy radical. An order of stability (with respect to dismutation) could therefore be established for various alkoxy radicals.

The unsymmetrical dialkyl peroxides that were prepared for this study were methyl *t*-butyl peroxide, ethyl *t*-butyl peroxide, isopropyl *t*-butyl peroxide, isobutyl *t*-butyl peroxide, *n*-butyl *t*-butyl peroxide, and di-*t*-butyl peroxide.

The reactions of the *t*-butoxy radical and the isopropoxy radical derived by decomposition of isopropyl *t*-butyl peroxide in the presence of cyclohexene, $C_6H_{10}$, are illustrated below: From *t*-butoxy and its products:

$$(1)\quad (CH_3)_3CO\cdot + C_6H_{10} \longrightarrow (CH_3)_3COH + C_6H_9\cdot$$

$$(2)\quad (CH_3)_3CO\cdot \longrightarrow (CH_3)_2CO + CH_3\cdot$$

$$(3)\quad CH_3\cdot + C_6H_{10} \longrightarrow CH_4 + C_6H_9\cdot$$

$$(4)\quad C_6H_9\cdot + C_6H_9\cdot \longrightarrow (C_6H_9)_2$$

$$(5)\quad CH_3\cdot + CH_3\cdot \longrightarrow C_2H_6$$

From isopropoxy and its products:

$$(6)\quad (CH_3)_2CHO\cdot + C_6H_{10} \longrightarrow (CH_3)_2CHOH + C_6H_9\cdot$$

$$(7)\quad (CH_3)_2CHO\cdot \longrightarrow CH_3CHO + CH_3\cdot$$

$$(8)\quad CH_3CHO + R\cdot \longrightarrow RH + CH_3\overset{\overset{\displaystyle O}{\|}}{C}\cdot$$

$$(9)\quad CH_3\overset{\overset{\displaystyle O}{\|}}{C}\cdot \longrightarrow CO + CH_3\cdot$$

$$(10)\quad (CH_3)_2CHO\cdot + R\cdot \longrightarrow (CH_3)_2CO + RH$$

where R· can be any radical present in the system.

Reactions (2) and (7) depict C—C bond rupture in an alkoxy radical. The relative stability of an alkoxy radical was defined as the ratio of the number of moles of alcohol produced by hydrogen atom abstraction to the sum of that quantity and the number of moles of products of decomposition of that radical. For example the relative stability of the isopropoxy radical would be defined as follows:

$$\frac{\text{Relative stability}}{\text{isoproxy radical}} = \frac{\text{moles } (CH_3)_2CHOH}{\text{moles } (CH_3)_2CHOH + \text{moles } CH_3CHO + \text{moles CO}}$$

The relative stability of the *t*-butoxy radical would be:

$$\frac{\text{Relative stability}}{t\text{-butoxy radical}} = \frac{\text{moles } (CH_3)_3COH}{\text{moles } (CH_3)_3COH + \text{moles } (CH_3)_2CO}$$

From studies of this nature the relative stability of alkoxy radicals was determined.[18] The results are summarized in Table B-3, with the alkoxy radicals listed in the order of decreasing stability

TABLE B-3

Estimated Bond Strength and Observed Relative Stabilities of Alkoxy Radicals[18]

| Alkoxy radical | Reference hydrocarbon | C—C bond strength in reference hydrocarbon[19] (kcal./mole) | Relative stability |
|---|---|---|---|
| H—¦—$CH_2O\cdot$ | No C—C bond | — | Nearly unity |
| $CH_3$—¦—$CH_2O\cdot$ | $CH_3$—¦—$CH_2CH_3$ | 85.0 | 0.86 |
| $CH_3CH_2CH_2$—¦—$CH_2O\cdot$ | $CH_3CH_2CH_2$—¦—$CH_2CH_3$ | 80.0 | 0.51 |
| $CH_3$—¦—$CH(CH_3)O\cdot$ | $CH_3$—¦—$CH(CH_3)CH_3$ | 78.0 | 0.25 |
| $CH_3CH(CH_3)$—¦—$CH_2O\cdot$ | $CH_3CH(CH_3)$—¦—$CH_2CH_3$ | 76 | 0.08 |
| $CH_3$—¦—$C(CH_3)_2O\cdot$ | $CH_3$—¦—$C(CH_3)_2CH_3$ | 75.5 | 0.08 |

[19] E. T. Butler and M. Polanyi, *Trans. Faraday Soc.*, *39*, 19 (1943).

reading from top down in the first column. It should be noted that the order of stability of the alkoxy radicals determined by this method is qualitatively in accord with the order of known bond strengths in straight and branched chain hydrocarbons.

## III. Decomposition of Benzoyl Peroxide and Related Peroxides

### *1. General Considerations Regarding Decomposition of Benzoyl Peroxide*

In contrast to the decomposition of di-*t*-butyl peroxide in solvents, which is a first order reaction whose rate is nearly the same in all solvents, the decomposition of benzoyl peroxide is much more complex. As was first shown by Brown, the kinetics of the decomposition in many solvents appears to be the sum of a first order reaction plus a reaction of another order.[20] Furthermore, the over-all rate of decomposition of the peroxide varies very greatly with the solvent and the products of decomposition are very different in diverse solvents. The decomposition products of pure benzoyl peroxide are carbon dioxide, biphenyl, and small amounts of phenyl benzoate and benzene.[21] These and many other products are found when the peroxide is decomposed in solution.

Except for some very special decompositions of benzoyl peroxide in the presence of such agents as $AlCl_3$ and HI, the decomposition of benzoyl peroxide in all solvents is to be regarded as resulting from an initial homolytic cleavage of the molecule into radicals.[7] The radicals may attack the solvent, and both primary and secondary radicals may then attack the peroxide, effecting a radical induced chain decomposition. The dismutation of the $C_6H_5COO\cdot$ radicals (probably during the process of radical transfer) leads to the formation of carbon dioxide. Recombination of radicals results in the termination of the chain reaction.

Some of the proofs of the homolytic character of the cleavage of benzoyl peroxide will be outlined below, and several of these will be elaborated in the subsequent discussion.

[20] D. J. Brown, *J. Am. Chem. Soc., 62,* 2657 (1940).
[21] H. Erlenmeyer and W. Schoenaur, *Helv. Chim. Acta, 19,* 338 (1936).

### (a) *Vinyl Polymerization*

If benzoyl peroxide is decomposed in the presence of vinyl monomers such as styrene or methyl methacrylate, it effects the polymerization of these monomers. It is in fact one of the most widely used catalysts for this purpose. The copolymer produced by benzoyl

TABLE B-4
Decomposition of Benzoyl Peroxide at 79.8°C.[22]

| Solvent | Per cent decomposition 10 min. | 1 hr. | 4 hrs. |
|---|---|---|---|
| Tetrachloroethylene | | 13.0 | 35.0 |
| Carbon tetrachloride | | 13.5 | 40.0 |
| Cyclohexene | | 14.0 | 39.5 |
| Methylbenzoate | | 14.5 | 41.4 |
| Anisole | | 14.0 | 43.0 |
| Chloroform | | 14.5 | 43.7 |
| Ethyl benzene | | 15.0 | 45.5 |
| Chlorobenzene | | 18.0 | 48.5 |
| Nitrobenzene | | 15.5 | 49.0 |
| Benzene | | 15.5 | 50.4 |
| Toluene | | 17.4 | 49.5 |
| Allyl acetate | | 17.0 | 52.3 |
| Styrene | | 19.0 | |
| Cumene | | 20.0 | 53.3 |
| Iodobenzene | | 18.0 | 55.8 |
| Carbon disulfide | | 19.0 | |
| Ethyl iodide | | 23.4 | 61.2 |
| Methylene chloride | | 24.5 | 62.2 |
| Ethyl chloride | | 26.0 | 64.7 |
| Bromobenzene | | 26.3 | 69.0 |
| *t*-Butylbenzene | | 28.5 | 69.5 |
| Acetone | | 28.5 | |
| Ethyl bromide | | 33.6 | 71.8 |
| Allyl bromide | | 37.2 | |
| Acetic anhydride | | 48.5 | |
| Cyclohexane | | 51.0 | 84.3 |
| Ethyl acetate | | 53.5 | 85.2 |
| Acetic acid | | 59.3 | 87.4 |
| Pyridine | | 77.3 | |
| Dioxane | | 82.4 | |
| Diethyl ether | 75.2 | | |
| Ethyl alcohol | 82.2 | | |
| *m*-Cresol | 87.7 | | |

peroxide in an equimolar mixture of styrene and methyl methacrylate is composed of 51 per cent styrene and 49 per cent methyl methacrylate. The quantitative aspects of the role of peroxides in vinyl polymerization will be reserved for Chapter C.

*(b) Addition of HBr to Olefins*

Benzoyl peroxide is a very effective catalyst for the anti-Markownikoff addition of HBr to olefins.[6,7]

*(c) Effect of Solvent on Rate of Decomposition*

There is a very large effect of solvent on the over-all rate of decomposition of benzoyl peroxide. This is apparent in Table B-4 (p. 73), where per cent decomposition of 0.197 *M* benzoyl peroxide in various solvents after 10 minutes, 1 hour, and 4 hours at 79.8° is tabulated.[22] The solvents are arranged in the approximate order of increasing decomposition rates. As can be seen from the table, the approximate order of increasing rate is: highly halogenated solvents < most aromatics < most aliphatics < ethers, alcohols, monohydric phenols. There is no relation between the over-all rate of decomposition and the acidity or polarity of the solvent.

*(d) Induced Decomposition of Benzoyl Peroxide*

The decomposition rate of benzoyl peroxide in solvents has been successfully interpreted as being due to the sum of a spontaneous cleavage which is first order with respect to the peroxide, plus an induced (radical chain) decomposition which may be of any order between 0.5 and 2.0.[22] The rate of spontaneous cleavage is nearly (but not exactly) the same in all solvents. The induced decomposition rate varies tremendously in different solvents

Certain substances such as hexaphenylethane which decompose into radicals very rapidly and extensively at room temperatures will accelerate the over-all decomposition rate of benzoyl peroxide when added to the solvent in which the peroxide is dissolved. This is an example of a free radical inducing the decomposition of the peroxide, just as the radicals from azomethane sensitize the decomposition of acetaldehyde.

[22] P. D. Bartlett and K. Nozaki, *J. Am. Chem. Soc.*, *68*, 1686 (1946); *69*, 2299 (1947).

### (e) *Effect of Inhibitors on Decomposition of Benzoyl Peroxide in Solvents*

Typical inhibitors of free radical chain reactions will lower the over-all rate of decomposition of benzoyl peroxide in a solvent such as dioxane or acetic anhydride.[22] These inhibitors include oxygen, hydroquinone, *p-t*-butylcatechol, *m*-dinitrobenzene, picric acid, and vinyl monomers such as vinyl acetate or methyl methacrylate. In fact, in certain cases the inhibitors will completely suppress the induced decomposition of the peroxide so that the measured rate of decomposition in the presence of these inhibitors may be taken as equal to the rate of spontaneous cleavage. This method has been used as a quantitative measure of spontaneous cleavage rates by employing 3,4-dichlorostyrene or methyl methacrylate[23a] and 2,2-diphenylpicrylhydrazyl[24] as the inhibitors. In other cases the use of an appropriate solvent eliminates the induced decomposition.[23b]

### (f) *Reaction Products with the Solvent*

The reaction products which are formed when benzoyl peroxide decomposes in solvents can be interpreted in terms of radical mechanisms. When benzoyl peroxide is decomposed in substituted benzenes, fragments of the catalyst are always found attached to the ortho or para positions of the solvent molecules, even if the substituent on the aromatic solvent is normally meta directing. This is a very strong argument in favor of the radical nature of the reaction between peroxide and solvent.[7]

### (g) *Decomposition of Benzoyl Peroxide by Ultraviolet Light*

The rate of decomposition of benzoyl peroxide in solvents is markedly increased by the absorption of ultraviolet light, but the products of decomposition are not greatly altered.

## 2. *Spontaneous Decomposition of Benzoyl Peroxide and Related Peroxides*

The viewpoint that the over-all decomposition of benzoyl peroxide is the sum of a spontaneous cleavage and a radical induced chain

[23] (a) C. G. Swain, W. T. Stockmayer, and J. T. Clarke, *J. Am. Chem. Soc.*, *72*, 5426 (1950). (b) A. T. Blomquist and A. J. Buselli, *ibid.*, *73*, 3883 (1951).
[24] C. E. H. Bawn and S. F. Mellish, *Trans. Faraday Soc.*, *47*, 1216 (1951).

reaction was put forth independently by Bartlett and Nozaki[22] and by Cass.[25a] The former showed that the disappearance of peroxide can be expressed as follows:

$$(1) \qquad -\frac{d(\mathrm{P})}{dt} = k_d[\mathrm{P}] + k_i[\mathrm{P}]^x$$

where $-d(\mathrm{P})/dt$ represents the rate of decomposition of the peroxide, $k_d$ the specific rate of spontaneous cleavage, $k_i$ the specific rate of induced decomposition, and $x$ the order of the induced reaction which may vary between 0.5 and 2.0.

By analyzing the data for rate of disappearance of peroxide at various initial concentrations of peroxide, it is possible to deduce the values of $k_d$, $k_i$, and $x$. In some cases, however, it is possible that the term for induced decomposition should, in fact, be regarded as the sum of several terms each arising from a different mechanism of induced decomposition and radical chain termination and each having a characteristic order of its own. In such cases the analysis of the decomposition data becomes hopelessly complex. However, several authors have obtained values for the specific rate of spontaneous cleavage of benzoyl peroxide by kinetic analysis of the type discussed above. These values agree fairly well with the results obtained by the inhibitor method. The results obtained by both methods will therefore be tabulated at the end of this section.

In the cases where the order of the induced decomposition term ($x$ in eq. 1) is larger than unity, a simple method for obtaining $k_d$ can be used. The "apparent first order rate constant" for the over-all decomposition of peroxide can be obtained for several different initial concentrations of peroxide and extrapolated to zero concentration. This value may be taken to be $k_d$.[25b]

The suppression of the induced decomposition reaction by inhibitors was used by Swain, Stockmayer, and Clarke[23a] to isolate the rate of spontaneous cleavage of the O—O bond in benzoyl peroxide and a series of substituted benzoyl peroxides. As an example of the effect of inhibitors, the half-life of 0.05 $M$ benzoyl peroxide in dioxane at 80° is 23 minutes. In the presence of 0.2 $M$ styrene, 3,4-dichlorostyrene, 1,4-diphenylbutadiene, and acrylonitrile the half-life is 275

[25] (a) W. E. Cass, *J. Am. Chem. Soc., 68*, 1976 (1946). (b) B. Barnett and W. E. Vaughan, *J. Phys. & Colloid Chem., 51*, 926, 944 (1947).

minutes, and in the presence of 0.2 $M$ methyl methacrylate the half-life is approximately 300 minutes. These inhibitors of the induced decomposition are the best found by these authors, and are approximately *equally* effective in suppressing the chain decomposition of the peroxides. This strongly indicates that the rate of decomposition of peroxides in the presence of these inhibitors is essentially equal to the rate of spontaneous homolytic cleavage. The rate measured in this fashion might also include other types of cleavage, such as ionic cleavage; however, the fact that the inhibitor method gives nearly equal rates of decomposition in all inert solvents which do not vary systematically with the dielectric constant of the solvent clearly indicates that only the homolytic cleavage is being measured. The fact that the inhibitor method may be more reliable than kinetic analysis for obtaining $k_d$ is indicated by the observation that it sometimes gives a smaller value for $k_d$ than can be obtained by kinetic analysis in the same solvent under identical conditions.[23a] It was concluded that 3,4-dichlorostyrene in 0.2 $M$ concentration was the most generally effective inhibitor for studying the spontaneous decomposition of benzoyl peroxide and numerous substituted benzoyl peroxides in various solvents.

Bawn and Mellish[24] have also employed the inhibitor technique in independent studies of the rate of spontaneous decomposition of benzoyl peroxide in various solvents. The inhibitor employed by these authors was the stable free radical, 2,2-diphenylpicrylhydrazyl:

$$\text{(I)}\quad 2,4,6\text{-}(NO_2)_3C_6H_2\text{—}\dot{N}\text{—}N(C_6H_5)_2$$

This stable radical combines directly and stoichiometrically with the radicals produced in the spontaneous cleavage of benzoyl peroxide. The rate of spontaneous cleavage of the peroxide can therefore be measured by following the disappearance of the inhibitor. Since the hydrazyl is a highly colored substance, its disappearance can be conveniently followed by a colorimetric technique.

The unimolecular cleavage of benzoyl peroxide varies somewhat with the solvent, though this variation is very much smaller than the variation of the rate of induced decomposition among different solvents. For the six solvents studied, Bawn and Mellish did not find

TABLE B-5

Specific Rate Constant for the Spontaneous Decomposition of Benzoyl Peroxide

| Solvent | Temp., °C. | $k_d$ (sec.$^{-1}$) | Ref. |
|---|---|---|---|
| Benzene | 60 | $1.95 \times 10^{-6}$ | a |
| Benzene | 80 | $3.28 \times 10^{-5}$ | a |
| Benzene | 80 | $4.3 \times 10^{-5}$ | b |
| Benzene | $T$(°K.) | $6.0 \times 10^{14} \exp\{-30.7 \text{ kcal.}/RT\}$ | a |
| Benzene | $T$(°K.) | $1.0 \times 10^{14} \exp\{-29.9 \text{ kcal.}/RT\}$ | f |
| Benzene | $T$(°K.) | $3.0 \times 10^{13} \exp\{-29.6 \text{ kcal.}/RT\}$ | g |
| Acetic anhydride | 60 | $5.55 \times 10^{-6}$ | a |
| Acetic anhydride | 80 | $7.5 \times 10^{-5}$ | b |
| Dioxane | 80 | $4.42 \times 10^{-5}$ | b |
| Dioxane | $T$(°K.) | $1.7 \times 10^{14} \exp\{-30.0 \text{ kcal.}/RT\}$ | b |
| Carbon tetrachloride | 80 | $2.08 \times 10^{-5}$ | a |
| Carbon tetrachloride | 80 | $3.03 \times 10^{-5}$ | b |
| Toluene | 80 | $3.28 \times 10^{-5}$ | a |
| Nitrobenzene | 80 | $3.28 \times 10^{-5}$ | a |
| *t*-Butylbenzene | 80 | $3.28 \times 10^{-5}$ | a |
| Cyclohexene | 80 | $1.93 \times 10^{-5}$ | a |
| Ethyl iodide | 80 | $4.03 \times 10^{-5}$ | a |
| Cyclohexane | 80 | $6.36 \times 10^{-5}$ | a |
| Ethyl acetate | 80 | $8.99 \times 10^{-5}$ | a |
| Acetic acid | 80 | $8.15 \times 10^{-5}$ | a |
| Acetic anhydride | 80 | $7.51 \times 10^{-5}$ | a |
| Ethyl acetate | 45 | $1.09 \times 10^{-6}$ | c |
| Vinyl acetate | 45 | $1.09 \times 10^{-6}$ | c |
| Vinyl acetate | 25 | $3.9 \times 10^{-8}$ | d |
| Vinyl acetate | $T$(°K.) | $2.65 \times 10^{13} \exp\{-28.3 \text{ kcal.}/RT\}$ | d |
| Styrene | 60 | $2.1 \times 10^{-6}$ | a |
| Styrene | 60 | $2.25 \times 10^{-6}$ | a |
| Styrene | 60 | $2.83 \times 10^{-6}$ | e |
| Acetophenone | 80 | $4.32 \times 10^{-5}$ | h |
| Acetophenone | $T$(°K.) | $2.2 \times 10^{14} \exp\{-30.2 \text{ kcal.}/RT\}$ | h |

(a) K. Nozaki and P. D. Bartlett, *J. Am. Chem. Soc.*, *68*, 1686 (1946).
(b) C. G. Swain, W. Stockmayer, and T. Clarke, Jr., *J. Am. Chem. Soc.*, *72*, 5426 (1950).
(c) K. Nozaki and P. D. Bartlett, *J. Am. Chem. Soc.*, *68*, 2377 (1946).
(d) C. G. Swain and P. D. Bartlett, *J. Am. Chem. Soc.*, *68*, 2381 (1946).
(e) F. R. Mayo, R. A. Gregg, and M. S. Matheson, *J. Am. Chem. Soc.*, *73*, 1691 (1951).
(f) P. F. Hartman, H. G. Sellers, and D. Turnbull, *J. Am. Chem. Soc.*, *69*, 2416 (1947).
(g) C. E. H. Bawn and S. F. Mellish, *Trans. Faraday Soc.*, *47*, 1216 (1951).
(h) A. T. Blomquist and A. J. Buselli, *J. Am Chem. Soc.*, *73*, 3883 (1951).

any systematic effect of the structure of the solvent on the rate of spontaneous cleavage. Swain *et al.* believe that the rate of spontaneous cleavage increases slightly with increasing polarity of the solvent. The magnitude of this effect can be gauged from the following data: the spontaneous decomposition is approximately 20 per cent faster in toluene than in carbon tetrachloride, and about 70 per cent faster in acetonitrile than in carbon tetrachloride.

In Table B-5 a summary is presented of the measured specific rates of spontaneous cleavage of benzoyl peroxide in numerous solvents as obtained from several literature sources.

Various authors have also studied the effect of substituents on one or both phenyl rings of benzoyl peroxide upon the rate of spontaneous decomposition. Qualitatively speaking, it was found that electron-repelling substituents on one or both of the phenyl rings increase the rate of unimolecular spontaneous decomposition, whereas electron-attracting groups retard the reaction. The stability of the radicals formed after cleavage is not an important factor in determining the rates of spontaneous cleavage of the substituted benzoyl peroxides. The explanation deduced from the experimental facts is as follows: the two benzoate groups in benzoyl peroxide are dipoles which are attached to one another in such a way as to repel each other:[23a]

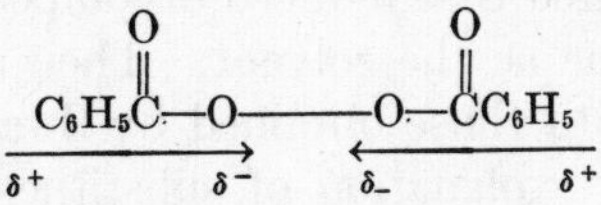

$$\overset{\delta+}{C_6H_5}\overset{O}{\overset{\|}{C}}-\overset{\delta-}{O}\longrightarrow\longleftarrow\overset{\delta-}{O}-\overset{O}{\overset{\|}{C}}\overset{\delta+}{C_6H_5}$$

The peroxide cleaves into free radicals because this relieves the electrostatic repulsion between the two benzoate groups. Electron-donating groups such as *p*-methoxy attached to either or both of the phenyl rings increase the negative charge on the two central oxygen atoms, enhance the electrostatic repulsion, and accelerate the rate of spontaneous fission. Electron-attracting groups such as cyano or nitro attached to one or both phenyl groups decrease the negative charge on the central oxygen atoms, reduce the electrostatic repulsion, and therefore lower the rate of spontaneous cleavage.

A quantitative treatment of the effect of substituents on the rate of spontaneous cleavage of substituted benzoyl peroxides was given by Swain *et al.*[23a] in terms of the Hammett equation.[26] This equation is:

$$\log (k/k_0) = \rho\sigma$$

where $k$ is a rate constant for a phenyl compound containing a meta or para substituent; $k_0$ is the corresponding rate constant for the unsubstituted compound; $\sigma$ is a constant characteristic of the substituent only, for which values have been tabulated by Hammett[26] for a wide variety of substituents; $\rho$ is a constant characteristic of the reaction. In order to apply this equation to peroxide decomposition data, the logarithm of the ratio of the rate constant for a substituted benzoyl peroxide to the rate constant for benzoyl peroxide is plotted against $\sigma_1 + \sigma_2$, the sum of the tabulated substituent constants for the groups in the peroxide. A reasonably good straight line is obtained, from the slope of which the reaction constant is evaluated as equal to $-0.38$ (at 80°C.). Table B-6 summarizes the rate constants for spontaneous cleavage in dioxane at 80° for numerous substituted benzoyl peroxides. The values of $\log(k/k_0)$ and $\sigma_1 + \sigma_2$ for these peroxides are also included.

Blomquist and Buselli[23b] made a similar and independent study of the spontaneous thermal decomposition of substituted benzoyl peroxides. They showed that induced decomposition was eliminated by using acetophenone as the solvent. Their results are generally in good agreement with those obtained by Swain, Stockmayer, and Clarke and a similar explanation of substituent effects was given. However, they find that the plot of log $k/k_0$ versus $\sigma_1 + \sigma_2$ has a minimum; i.e., for sufficiently large values of $\sigma_1 + \sigma_2$ as occur in the nitrobenzoyl peroxides, the value of $k/k_0$ starts to increase again. By studying the first order rate constants at various temperatures these authors showed that both the energy of activation and the frequency factor were affected in a systematic manner by the substituents such that higher activation energies were correlated with higher frequency factors. The Hammett relationship is exact only for those series of reactions for which potential energy terms alone are affected by the change of substituents. This requires that the frequency factor of the rate constants be the same for all members

[26] L. P. Hammett, *Physical Organic Chemistry*, McGraw-Hill, New York, 1940, Chap. VII.

of the series, and hence the Hammett equation is only approximate for the substituted benzoyl peroxides.[23b]

TABLE B-6

Rate Constants at 80°C. for Spontaneous Cleavage of Substituted Dibenzoyl Peroxides in Dioxane[23a]*

| Substituents | $k_1 \times 10^3$ (min.$^{-1}$) | log $(k/k_0)$ | $\sigma_1 + \sigma_2$ |
|---|---|---|---|
| *p,p'*-Dimethoxy | 7.06 | 0.447 | −0.536 |
| *p*-Methoxy | 4.54 | 0.255 | −0.268 |
| *p,p'*-Dimethyl | 3.68 | 0.164 | −0.340 |
| *p,p'*-Di-*t*-butyl | 3.65 | 0.161 | −0.394 |
| *m,m'*-Dimethoxy | 3.45 | 0.137 | +0.230 |
| *m*-Methoxy | 2.89 | 0.059 | 0.115 |
| *p*-Methoxy-*m'*-bromo | 2.66 | 0.023 | 0.221 |
| *m,m'*-Dimethyl | 2.64 | 0.019 | −0.138 |
| Benzoyl peroxide | 2.52 | 0.000 | 0.000 |
| *p,p'*-Dichloro | 2.17 | −0.065 | +0.454 |
| *p,p'*-Dibromo | 1.94 | −0.113 | 0.464 |
| *m*-Cyano | 1.64 | −0.187 | 0.517 |
| *m,m'*-Dichloro | 1.58 | −0.203 | 0.746 |
| *m,m'*-Dibromo | 1.54 | −0.215 | 0.782 |
| *p,p'*-Dicyano | 1.22 | −0.314 | 1.30 |
| *m,m'*-Dicyano | 1.02 | −0.393 | 1.03 |

* Comparable values can be obtained from the article by Blomquist and Buselli.[23b]

*Decomposition of t-Butyl Perbenzoate*

In view of the detailed studies which have been made on the kinetics of the decomposition of benzoyl peroxide and di-*t*-butyl peroxide, it is interesting to compare the decomposition of *t*-butyl perbenzoate, $C_6H_5C({=}O)OOC(CH_3)_3$.[27] The decomposition of this peroxide in various solvents parallels that of benzoyl peroxide very closely, proceeding at nearly the same rate in all the aromatic solvents employed, and at much faster and widely different rates in the aliphatic solvents. The decomposition of *t*-butyl perbenzoate is much slower than benzoyl peroxide at ordinary temperatures; very roughly, *t*-butyl perbenzoate decomposes as fast at 110°C. as benzoyl peroxide does at 80°C.

[27] A. T. Blomquist *et al.*, *J. Am. Chem. Soc.*, *73*, 3408, 3412, 5546 (1951).

In aromatic solvents the increase in the over-all first order rate constant with increasing peroxide concentration is small but real and appears to be caused by free radical attack on undecomposed peroxide, since it was eliminated by acetanilide, a known free radical inhibitor. At the lowest peroxide concentration used (0.02 *M*), the first order rate constant $k$ for decomposition of *t*-butyl perbenzoate in *p*-chlorotoluene was calculated to be:

$$k = 1.3 \times 10^{16} \exp\{-34.3 \text{ kcal.}/RT\}$$

The value of $k$ given above is probably very nearly equal to $k_d$ since in this solvent the induced decomposition is not large, and it is minimized by the low peroxide concentration.

It was suggested[27] that the variation in the rate of decomposition of *t*-butyl perbenzoate from solvent to solvent is the result of an attack on the peroxide by *solvent* radicals of varying reactivity arising from chain transfer to solvent, this induced reaction being superimposed on a unimolecular cleavage which proceeds at essentially the same rate in a large number of solvents.

The rate of *t*-butyl perbenzoate decomposition in a number of solvents is increased by trichloroacetic acid but not by dichloroacetic, suggesting a strong acid is necessary to make any portion of the decomposition proceed by an ionic path.

Finally, substituents on the phenyl ring in *t*-butyl perbenzoate affect the rate of spontaneous decomposition in a manner entirely similar to that already discussed for benzoyl peroxide. A kinetic study was made of the thermal decomposition of *t*-butyl perbenzoate and four *p*-substituted *t*-butyl perbenzoates in phenyl ether.[27] The decompositions in this solvent were all first order and the rates were unaffected by the presence of inhibitors. It was therefore concluded that induced decomposition of these peroxy esters is negligible in this solvent. Energies and entropies of activation for the five peroxy esters were tabulated. The first order rate constant for decomposition of *t*-butyl perbenzoate in phenyl ether was calculated to be:

$$k_d \text{ (}t\text{-butyl perbenzoate in phenyl ether)} = 5 \times 10^{16} \exp\{-37.5 \text{ kcal.}/RT\}$$

The rates of decomposition of the five peroxy esters studied were closely correlated by means of the Hammett relationship, as in the case of the substituted benzoyl peroxide. However, since the activation energies *and* frequency factors were both affected by the substituents, it is clear that the Hammett relationship cannot hold exactly.

### 3. *Products of Reaction and Chain Decomposition of Benzoyl Peroxide in Solvents*

Once the primary cleavage of the peroxide (P) into two benzoate radicals (R·) has occurred, a number of typical radical reactions can take place. The solvent (S) enters into these reactions and fragments of the solvent molecule are found in high yield among the decomposition products of the peroxide. A study of the decomposition products in various solvents has made it possible to offer a reasonable chain mechanism for the over-all decomposition of the peroxide in most solvents:

(1) Spontaneous cleavage $\quad P \xrightarrow{k_d} 2R\cdot$

(2) Transfer of radical activity to solvent
$R\cdot + S \xrightarrow{k_2} S\cdot$ [for unsaturated or aromatic solvents]
$R\cdot + SH \longrightarrow S\cdot + RH$
$R\cdot + SH \longrightarrow S\cdot + \phi H + CO_2$
$R\cdot + SX \longrightarrow S\cdot + RX$
$R\cdot + SX \longrightarrow S\cdot + \phi X + CO_2$

(3) Induced decomposition by R·
$R\cdot + P \xrightarrow{k_3} R\cdot + R\phi + CO_2$
$R\cdot + P \longrightarrow R\cdot + \phi_2 + 2CO_2$

(4) Induced decomposition by S·
$S\cdot + P \xrightarrow{k_4} R\cdot + RS$
$S\cdot + P \longrightarrow R\cdot + \phi S + CO_2$

(5) Termination
$R\cdot + R\cdot \xrightarrow{k_5}$ products of combination and disproportionation
$R\cdot + S\cdot \xrightarrow{k_6}$ products of combination and disproportionation
$S\cdot + S\cdot \xrightarrow{k_7}$ products of combination and disproportionation

In the above equations it is indicated that transfer may involve either a hydrogen or a halogen atom.

Carbon dioxide is almost always found among the products of decomposition of benzoyl peroxide in solvents. This is also true of other aroyl and acyl peroxides. The formation of carbon dioxide may arise as follows:

$$\text{(1a)} \qquad \phi\overset{\overset{\displaystyle O}{\|}}{C}\text{—O}\cdot \longrightarrow \phi\cdot + CO_2$$

However, the evidence (at least in the analogous case of acetyl peroxide) is that reactions of the type (1a) probably do not occur,[28] and that carbon dioxide is evolved in the reactions (2), (3), and (4) of the chain mechanism given above. It is interesting to note that the amount of $CO_2$ evolved during the chain decomposition of benzoyl peroxide in ether is small, and becomes negligible in phenols.

In order to specify completely the chain mechanism for benzoyl peroxide decomposition given above, it is necessary to state the mode of attack by which the benzoate radical (R·) reacts with the solvent (S). From a study of the products of decomposition of benzoyl peroxide in numerous solvents, Cass (private communication to the authors) arrived at the conclusions listed in Table B-7.

TABLE B-7

Mode of Attack by Primary Radicals from Benzoyl Peroxide on Numerous Solvents

| Solvent | Radical attacks |
|---|---|
| Aliphatic hydrocarbons | |
| Saturated | Hydrogen |
| Unsaturated | Double bond, α-methylenic hydrogen |
| Chlorinated | Chlorine, hydrogen |
| Vinyl monomers | Double bond |
| Alcohols | α-Methylenic hydrogen (where available) |
| Aldehydes | Aldehydic hydrogen |
| Acids | α-Methylenic hydrogen |
| Ethers | " " |
| Phenols | Phenolic hydrogen |
| Aromatic compounds | Adds to double bond causing substitution in *o,p* positions |

The initial attack of R· upon aromatic solvents requires further elaboration. When benzoyl peroxide is decomposed in aromatic solvents the following products are found.[29,30]

[28] F. G. Edwards and F. R. Mayo, *J. Am. Chem. Soc.*, *72*, 1265 (1950).
[29] H. Gelissen and P. H. Hermans, *Ber.*, *58*, 476, 764 (1925).
[30] D. H. Hey, *J. Chem. Soc.*, *1934*, 1966.

## TABLE B-8

Products of Decomposition of Benzoyl Peroxide in Various Solvents*

| Solvent | Products (moles/mole peroxide decomposed) | Ref. |
|---|---|---|
| 1. Saturated aliphatic hydrocarbons (cyclohexane, $C_6H_{12}$) | $CO_2$(0.96), acids(1.0), $\phi COOH(\sim 0.35)$, $o,p$-$C_6H_{11}C_6H_4COOH(>0.18)$, $\phi H$ $(\sim 0.5)$, $\phi C_6H_{11}(\sim 0.1)$, $\phi COO\phi(\sim 0.03)$, tricyclic acids | a, b (for decompns. in heptane and octane consult c and d) |
| 2. Unsaturated aliphatic hydrocarbons (cyclohexene, $C_6H_{10}$) | $CO_2$(0.3), $\phi COOH$(0.31), $\phi H$, $C_6H_{12}$, $\phi COOR$(1.35), $\phi COOC_6H_9$(0.13), $\phi COOC_6H_{11}$(0.70), $\phi COOC_6H_{10}C_6H_9$ $(\sim 0.11)$, $\phi COOC_6H_{10}C_6H_{11}$(0.04), $C_6H_9C_6H_9$(0.15), $C_6H_{11}C_6H_9$(0.06) | a, e |
| 3. Chlorinated aliphatic hydrocarbons (chloroform and carbon tetrachloride | In $CHCl_3$: $CO_2$, $COCl_2$, $Cl_3CC_6H_4COCl$, $\phi H$, $C_2Cl_6$, $\phi_2$<br>In $CCl_4$: $CO_2$, $COCl_2$, $Cl_3CC_6H_4COCl$, $C_2Cl_6$, $\phi Cl$ | f |
| 4. Alcohols (2-methylpropanol, $C_4H_9OH$) | $CO_2$(0.7), $\phi H$(0.24), aldehyde(0.24), $\phi COOH$, $C_4H_9OC_6H_4COOH$, $\phi C_6H_4$-$COOH$, $\phi COOC_4H_9(<0.16)$ | g |
| 5. Acids (acetic, $CH_3COOH$) | $CO_2$(0.94), $\phi H$(0.41), $o,p$-$HOOCCH_2$-$C_6H_4COOH$(0.18), $\phi COOH$(0.12), $\phi_2$(0.01), $p$-$\phi C_6H_4COOH$(0.09) | h, i |
| 6. Ethers (diethyl ether and diethyl Cellosolve) | In $C_2H_5OC_2H_5$: $CO_2$(0.2), $\phi COOH$ (0.80) $\phi COOCH(CH_3)OC_2H_5$ (0.95)<br>In $C_2H_5OCH_2CH_2OC_2H_5$: (*a*) $\phi COOCH(CH_3)OCH_2CH_2OC_2H_5$ (*b*) $\phi COOCH(OC_2H_5)CH_2OC_2H_5$ $(a)/(b) \simeq 3$ | <br>j |
| 7. Aromatic compounds (benzene and $\phi Z$, where Z = $CH_3$—, $\phi$—, Cl—, $NO_2$—, —$COOC_2H_5$) | In $C_6H_6$: $CO_2 + \phi COOH + \phi_2$ (main products), $\phi COO\phi$, $\phi C_6H_4\phi$, resin<br>In $\phi Z$: $CO_2$, $\phi COOH$, $o,p$-$ZC_6H_4\phi$, $\phi H$, $\phi COOC_6H_4Z$, $p$-$\phi C_6H_4COOH$, $o,p$-$ZC_6H_4C_6H_4\phi$, etc. | <br>k, l, m, n |
| 8. Pyridine | $CO_2$, $\phi H$, $\phi COOH$, $\alpha,\gamma$-$\phi C_5H_4N$, $\phi C_6H_4$-$COOH$, $C_5H_4NC_6H_4\phi$ | o |

* Courtesy of W. E. Cass.

(a) P. H. Hermans and J. VanEyk, *J. Polymer Sci.*, *1*, 407 (1946).
(b) H. Gelissen and P. H. Hermans, *Ber.*, *69*, 662 (1926).
(c) J. Boeseken and A. Gaster, *Rec. trav. chim.*, *49*, 102 (1930).
(d) J. Boeseken and S. J. Wildschutz, *Rec. trav. chim.*, *51*, 168 (1932).
(e) E. H. Farmer and S. E. Michael, *J. Chem. Soc.*, *513* (1942).
(f) J. Boeseken and H. Gelissen, *Rec. trav. chim.*, *43*, 869 (1924).
(g) H. Gelissen and P. H. Hermans, *Ber.*, *58*, 765 (1925).
(h) H. Gelissen and P. H. Hermans, *Ber.*, *58*, 770 (1925).
(i) M. S. Kharasch, E. V. Jensen and W. H. Urry, *J. Org. Chem.*, *10*, 386 (1945).
(j) W. E. Cass, *J. Am. Chem. Soc.*, *69*, 500 (1947).
(k) H. Gelissen and P. H. Hermans, *Ber.*, *58*, 285, 476, 764 (1925).
(l) W. Dietrich, *Helv. Chim. Acta*, *8*, 149 (1925).
(m) H. Wieland, S. Schapiro, and H. Metzger, *Ann.*, *513*, 93 (1934).
(n) D. H. Hey, *J. Chem. Soc.*, *1934*, 1966.
(o) J. Overhoff and G. Tilman, *Rec. trav. chim.*, *48*, 993 (1929).

$$(\phi COO)_2 + \phi Z \longrightarrow CO_2 + \phi COOH + o,p\text{-}ZC_6H_4\phi$$
$$\phi H + \phi COOC_6H_4Z + p\text{-}\phi C_6H_4COOH$$
$$o,p\text{-}ZC_6H_4C_6H_4\phi, \text{ etc.}$$
$$Z = CH_3;\ \phi—;\ Cl—;\ NO_2—;\ —COOC_2H_5$$
(Some meta substitution is also found)

The reactions which give the main products are probably the following:

$$\phi\overset{O}{\overset{\|}{C}}O\cdot + C_6H_5Z \longrightarrow \phi\overset{O}{\overset{\|}{C}}O\text{—}C_6H_5Z(H)\cdot$$

$$\phi\overset{O}{\overset{\|}{C}}O\cdot + C_6H_5Z \longrightarrow \phi\text{—}C_6H_5Z(H)\cdot + CO_2$$

$$\phi\text{—}C_6H_5Z(H)\cdot + \phi\overset{O}{\overset{\|}{C}}O\cdot \longrightarrow \phi\text{—}C_6H_4Z + \phi\overset{O}{\overset{\|}{C}}OH$$

etc.

The products of decomposition of benzoyl peroxide in numerous solvents with references to the original literature are given in Table B-8. In several cases the number of moles of product arising from each mole of peroxide is given in parentheses. These products are all consistent with the chain mechanism given in the beginning of this section and with the point of radical attack postulated in Table B-7.

The chain mechanism can also be used to obtain the kinetic equation for the *over-all* rate of decomposition of peroxide. If one selects a particular type of induced decomposition ($k_3$ or $k_4$) and a particular type of termination, the over-all rate of peroxide decomposition is given by equation (6).

$$-d[\mathrm{P}]/dt = k_d[\mathrm{P}] + k_i[\mathrm{P}]^x \qquad (6)$$

TABLE B-9

Calculated Kinetic Order for Induced Term with Respect to Peroxide Concentration[22,23a]

| Type of termination | Type of induced decomposition: R· + P ($k_3$) | S· + P ($k_4$) |
|---|---|---|
| R· + R· | 1.5 | 0.5 |
| R· + S· | 2.0 | 1.0 |
| S· + S· | 2.0 | 1.5 |

where $k_d[P]$ represents the rate of spontaneous decomposition and $k_i[P]^x$ represents the rate of induced decomposition. Table B-9 shows the calculated kinetic order for the induced rate of decomposition (*i.e.*, the value of $x$ in eq. 6).[23]

In a completely inert solvent with which the R· radicals cannot react (perhaps a perfluorocarbon), the significant type of induced decomposition would be R· + P and the significant type of termination would be R· + R·. The reaction would therefore be as follows

$$P \xrightarrow{k_d} 2R\cdot \tag{7}$$

$$R\cdot + P \xrightarrow{k_3} R\cdot + \phi R + CO_2 \tag{8}$$

$$R\cdot + R\cdot \xrightarrow{k_5} \phi R + CO_2 \tag{9}$$

This gives rise to the expression (10) for the total rate of disappearance of peroxide using the steady state method.

$$-d[P]/dt = k_d[P] + k_3(k_d/k_5)^{1/2}[P]^{3/2} \tag{10}$$

On the other hand, if the primary R· radicals are rapidly converted to S· radicals and if the reactions $k_4$ and $k_7$ are the important induced decomposition step and termination step, respectively, the total rate of disappearance of peroxide is given by equation (11).

$$-d[P]/dt = k_d[P] + k_4(k_d/k_7)^{1/2}[P]^{3/2} \tag{11}$$

Finally, if the primary R· radicals are rapidly converted to S· radicals and if the termination step occurs between unlike radicals (*i.e.*, reactions $k_4$ and $k_6$ predominate), the total rate of disappearance of peroxide is given by equation (12).

$$-d[P]/dt = k_d[P] + (k_d k_2 k_4/k_6)^{1/2}[S]^{1/2}[P] \tag{12}$$

It is quite possible that the above mechanism is valid in solvents such as ethers where the induced decomposition rate is very great.[22] It is interesting to note in this case that the *overall* rate of peroxide decomposition is first order even though spontaneous and induced decompositions are operative.

### *4. Cleavage of Benzoyl Peroxide by the Triphenylmethyl Radical*

Hexaphenylethane in benzene solutions dissociates to a considerable extent into triphenylmethyl radicals. When these solutions are added to benzoyl peroxide (either dry or in benzene solution) a rather rapid reaction occurs at room temperature yielding tetraphenylmethane, benzoic acid, and trityl benzoate.[31] This reaction has been reinvestigated by Hammond *et al.*,[32] who showed that these products accounted quantitatively for the decomposition of the peroxide and the loss of triphenylmethyl radical. In particular, it was verified that no carbon dioxide was evolved. A reaction scheme that accounts for the observed course of the reaction is:[32]

$$\text{(1)} \quad T\cdot + Bz_2O_2 \longrightarrow BzOT + BzO\cdot$$
$$\text{(2)} \quad T\cdot + BzO\cdot \longrightarrow BzOT$$
$$\text{(3)} \quad BzO\cdot + ArH \longrightarrow BzOH + Ar\cdot$$
$$\text{(4)} \quad Ar\cdot + T\cdot \longrightarrow ArT$$

where $T\cdot$ represents the trityl (triphenylmethyl) radical, $Bz_2O_2$ represents benzoyl peroxide, ArH represents benzene, BzOH represents benzoic acid, and $BzO\cdot$ represents the benzoate radical.

It is as yet not clear why benzoyl peroxide decomposition in benzene produces $CO_2$, while the same decomposition in the presence of trityl radical produces no $CO_2$. It may be that in the case of the trityl induced decomposition, the BzO radicals are very short lived, and that instead of reacting by equation (3) (which may allow them to split $CO_2$) they react with the solvent simultaneously with $T\cdot$ in a concerted attack:

$$\text{(5)} \quad BzO\cdot + ArH + T\cdot \longrightarrow BzOH + ArT$$

Reaction (5) is, of course, equivalent stoichiometrically to (3) plus (4).

It should be noted that reaction (1) is clearly a case of radical induced decomposition.

### *5. Thermal Decomposition of Cumene Hydroperoxide and Related Hydroperoxides*

The thermal decomposition of cumene hydroperoxide ($Ph(Me)_2$-COOH) in numerous solvents has been studied by several authors.[33-35]

[31] H. Wieland, T. Ploetz, and H. Indest, *Ann.*, *532*, 166 (1937).

[32] G. S. Hammond, J. T. Rudesill, and F. J. Modic, *J. Am. Chem. Soc.*, *73*, 3929 (1951).

[33] J. W. L. Fordham and H. L. Williams, *Can. J. Research*, *B27*, 943 (1949).

[34] V. Stannett and R. B. Mesrobian, *J. Am. Chem. Soc.*, *72*, 4125 (1950).

[35] M. S. Kharasch, A. Fono, and W. Nudenberg, *J. Org. Chem.*, *16*, 113 (1951).

In attempting to interpret the decomposition of cumene hydroperoxide (CHP) in hydrocarbon solvents the following facts must be taken into account.[35] (*a*) The various workers in the field disagree as to the kinetic order of the decomposition reaction. Kharasch *et al.*[35] state that the decomposition is nearly but not exactly first order; Fordham and Williams[33] state that the reaction can be considered as the sum of a first order spontaneous cleavage plus a three-halves order induced decomposition. Stannett and Mesrobian[34] claim that the reaction can best be described as bimolecular (peroxide concentration times solvent concentration) plus three-halves order induced decomposition. (*b*) The rate of decomposition varies markedly from solvent to solvent.[34,35] (*c*) The rate of decomposition of cumene hydroperoxide is appreciably slower than that of di-$\alpha$-cumyl peroxide, $Ph(Me)_2COOC(Me)_2Ph$, or *t*-butyl cumene peroxide or of di-*t*-butyl peroxide. (*d*) The rate of thermal decomposition of cumene hydroperoxide is not altered by addition of di-$\alpha$-cumyl peroxide, which cleaves into radicals at a faster rate than CHP. (*e*) The rate of decomposition of CHP is markedly increased at low temperatures by the addition of acetyl peroxide; one of the products of this reaction is di-$\alpha$-cumyl peroxide. (*f*) Free radicals must be formed during the reaction to account for the nature of the products, and also because the decomposition of CHP initiates vinyl polymerization. The products of reaction in certain solvents are listed in Table B-10.

Because of item (*d*), Kharasch argues that the primary radicals from CHP do not attack the hydroperoxide very rapidly. However, secondary radicals produced by transfer with the solvent or by dismutation certainly induce the decomposition of CHP.[33,34] In addition, it has been shown that growing polymer radicals such as polystyryl radicals or polymethyl methacrylate radicals transfer with CHP, and thereby induce its decomposition.[36,37] Furthermore, according to item (*e*), the primary and/or secondary radicals derived from acetyl peroxide do induce the decomposition of CHP.

It has been shown that at 60° the rate of initiation of polymer chains produced by cumene hydroperoxide is very nearly the same in both styrene and methyl methacrylate.[37] This would indicate that the primary cleavage of CHP into radicals in these two quite diverse

[36] D. H. Johnson and A. V. Tobolsky, *J. Am. Chem. Soc.*, *74*, 938 (1952).
[37] B. Baysal and A. V. Tobolsky, *J. Polymer Sci.*, *8*, 529 (1952).

TABLE B-10

Products of Thermal Decomposition of Cumene Hydroperoxide (0.1 Mole) in Various Solvents (0.8 Mole)[35]
(except for high boiling residues, yields are expressed in mole per cent)

| Solvent temp., °C. | $CH_4$ | $O_2$ | $CH_3COC_6H_5$ | $C_6H_5(CH_3)_2COH$ | $C_6H_5OH$ | $(CH_3)_2CO$ | High boiling residue (grams) |
|---|---|---|---|---|---|---|---|
| Decane (140°) | 30.0 | 0.0 | 20.0 | 54.0 | 0.7 | 0.7 | 6.2 |
| Cumene (128°) | 32.0 | 0.0 | 30.0 | 90.0 | 6.0 | 4.0 | 4.5 |
| Cumene (158°) | 46.0 | 0.0 | 39.0 | 78.0 | 6.0 | 6.0 | 4.0 |
| Ethylbenzene (158°) | 24.0 | — | — | — | 7.0 | — | — |
| Diisopropylcarbinol (140°) | 34.0 | — | 34.0 | 59.0 | — | — | 1.0 |
| α-Cumyl alcohol (170°) | 63.0 | 7.0 | — | — | — | — | — |

monomers occurred at nearly the same rate. In addition, this primary cleavage of CHP is found to be first order.[36,37]

These results would make it appear likely that the decomposition of CHP in hydrocarbon solvents is similar in over-all character to the decomposition of benzoyl peroxide in solvents; *i.e.*, there is a primary homolytic first order cleavage (which may occur at nearly the same rate in most solvents) followed by an induced decomposition which is largely responsible for the large differences in over-all decomposition rate among the various solvents.[33]

The value of the specific rate constant for the spontaneous first order cleavage of CHP into radicals in benzene–styrene mixtures was found to be:[33]

$$k_d\ (\text{CHP}) = 2.7 \times 10^{12} \exp\{-30.4\ \text{kcal.}/RT\} \quad (1)$$

To explain the major products listed in Table B-10 for the decomposition of CHP in cumene (RH), the following basic steps are postulated (although many more than these are certainly involved):

$$C_6H_5(CH_3)_2COOH \longrightarrow C_6H_5(CH_3)_2CO\cdot + \cdot OH \quad (2)$$

$$C_6H_5(CH_3)_2CO\cdot + RH \longrightarrow C_6H_5(CH_3)_2COH + R\cdot \quad (3)$$

$$C_6H_5(CH_3)_2CO\cdot \longrightarrow C_6H_5COCH_3 + CH_3\cdot \quad (4)$$

$$CH_3\cdot + RH \longrightarrow CH_4 + R\cdot \quad (5)$$

$$R\cdot + C_6H_5(CH_3)_2COOH \longrightarrow ROH + C_6H_5(CH_3)_2CO\cdot \quad (6)$$

$$R\cdot + R\cdot \longrightarrow R\text{—}R \quad (7)$$

The dismutation which produces acetophenone may occur mainly during collision or reaction of RO· with a solvent or hydroperoxide molecule, *e.g.*:

$$C_6H_5(CH_3)_2CO\cdot + RH \longrightarrow C_6H_5COCH_3 + CH_4 + R\cdot \quad (8)$$

Equation (8) is obviously a combination of (4) and (5).

The formation of acetophenone and methane are regarded as diagnostic of a homolytic cleavage of CHP; the products of the acid catalyzed (heterolytic) cleavage of CHP are phenol and acetone (see section V).

The formation of acetophenone in equation (4) is worthy of special emphasis. Kharasch and co-workers state that in the radical RR′R″CO·, the relative tendency of the group to participate in the cleavage of the R—C bond increases in the order: phenyl, methyl,

ethyl, hydrogen.[38a] This is in accord with equation (4). If all three groups are aryl, the RR′R″CO· radical tends to rearrange rather than dismute (see section IV).

Kharasch *et al.*[35] believe that, side by side with the radical reaction discussed here, two other types of reaction also occur during the decomposition of CHP in hydrocarbon solvents. The first is an intramolecular splitting of water:

$$C_6H_5(CH_3)_2COOH \longrightarrow CH_3(C_6H_5)\overset{}{C}\!\!-\!\!CH_2 + H_2O \quad \text{(epoxide: C and } CH_2 \text{ bridged by O)} \tag{9}$$

The expoxide was not isolated, but its presence was inferentially demonstrated.[35]

Second, in order to explain the small amounts of phenol and acetone found during CHP decomposition in cumene, it was assumed that a polar (heterolytic) cleavage of CHP was occurring to a very small extent.

The rapid decomposition of CHP in tertiary alcohols and the presence of oxygen among the reaction products is also believed due in part to a heterolytic reaction mechanism.[35,38b,c]

### (a) *Decomposition of t-Butyl Hydroperoxide*

The decomposition of *t*-butyl hydroperoxide has been studied in both the gaseous and the liquid phase.[39] The gas phase studies were carried out at 260°C. in the presence of an excess of cyclohexene. The products found included acetone, *t*-butyl alcohol, methane, methanol, carbon monoxide, water, and a 13 per cent yield of cyclohexanol. The most reasonable way to explain the formation of this last product is in terms of a fission of the O—O linkage followed by an addition of the hydroxyl radical to the cyclohexene.

The over-all reaction mechanism for the decomposition of *t*-butyl hydroperoxide can therefore be portrayed as:[39]

$$(CH_3)_3COOH \longrightarrow (CH_3)_3CO\cdot + \cdot OH$$
$$(CH_3)_3CO\cdot \longrightarrow (CH_3)_2CO + CH_3\cdot$$

[38] (a) M. S. Kharasch, A. Fono, and W. Nudenberg, *J. Org. Chem.*, *15*, 763 (1950). (b) M. S. Kharasch, A. Fono, W. Nudenberg, and B. Bischof, *ibid.*, *17*, 207 (1952). (c) M. S. Kharasch, F. S. Arimoto, and W. Nudenberg, *ibid.*, *16*, 1556 (1951).

[39] E. R. Bell, J. H. Raley, F. F. Rust, F. H. Seubold, and W. E. Vaughan, *Faraday Soc. Discussion*, *10*, 246 (1951).

$$X\cdot + (CH_3)_3COOH \longrightarrow XH + (CH_3)_3COO\cdot$$
$$R\cdot + (CH_3)_3COO\cdot \longrightarrow (CH_3)_3COOR$$
$$(CH_3)_3COOR \longrightarrow (CH_3)_3CO\cdot + RO\cdot$$
$$2(CH_3)_3COO\cdot \longrightarrow 2(CH_3)_3CO\cdot + O_2$$

where X = RO·, HO·, $(CH_3)_3CO\cdot$, $CH_3\cdot$, and R = $CH_3\cdot$ or a radical derived from the solvent.

The combination of two $RO_2\cdot$ radicals to give two RO· radicals and molecular oxygen is particularly noteworthy.

A quantitative kinetic study of the liquid phase decomposition of *t*-butyl hydroperoxide in *n*-octane was made in the temperature range 150–180°C. The reaction proved to be a combination of a unimolecular fission plus a chain process of higher order. For each initial concentration of peroxide the decomposition could be approximately fitted by a "first order rate constant" which increased markedly with the initial concentration of peroxide. The true unimolecular rate constant was obtained by extrapolating the apparent first order constants to zero concentration. The rate constant for unimolecular fission in the range 150–180° in *n*-octane was found to be:

(10) $k_d$(*t*-butyl hydroperoxide in *n*-octane) =

$$1 \times 10^{15} \exp\{-39.0 \text{ kcal.}/RT\}$$

The decomposition of *t*-butyl hydroperoxide in chlorobenzene is especially interesting.[39] This solvent is apparently very resistant to radical attack, and at 140° a rapid chain decomposition of the hydroperoxide occurs to produce an almost quantitative yield of *t*-butyl alcohol and oxygen. The mechanism very probably is:

$$(CH_3)_3COOH \longrightarrow (CH_3)_3CO\cdot + \cdot OH$$
$$\left.\begin{matrix}(CH_3)_3CO\cdot \\ HO\cdot\end{matrix}\right\} + (CH_3)_3COOH \longrightarrow \left.\begin{matrix}(CH_3)_3COH \\ HOH\end{matrix}\right\} + (CH_3)_3COO\cdot$$
$$2(CH_3)_3COO\cdot \longrightarrow 2(CH_3)_3CO\cdot + O_2$$

### (*b*) *Decomposition of Tetralin Hydroperoxide*

Measurements of the kinetics of the decomposition of α-tetralyl hydroperoxide at low concentrations in tetralin solution under a nitrogen atmosphere indicate a first order rate of reaction (as measured by peroxide destroyed). The measurements were performed in the temperature range 88° to 135°C. Deviation from first order kinetics are noted in solutions of higher concentration. This effect is probably due to chain induced decomposition of the hydroperoxide which generally is more important at higher concentrations.[40]

*(c) Decomposition of Cyclohexenyl Hydroperoxide*

The thermal decomposition of 2-cyclohexen-1-yl hydroperoxide in benzene and various olefin solvents has been studied by Bateman and co-workers.[41] In olefin solvents (*e.g.*, cyclohexene) the decomposition proceeds via a chain mechanism in which secondary radicals from the solvent attack the hydroperoxide. On the other hand, the chain process is almost completely suppressed in benzene. In either type of solvent, however, the initiation step of the decomposition is of second order with respect to the hydroperoxide in the concentration range 0.03–1.4 *M*. At hydroperoxide concentrations lower than specified above, the cyclohexenyl hydroperoxide appears to decompose mainly by a first order process. In order to explain this unique change in reaction order of the primary decomposition process with concentration, it is postulated that the hydroperoxide is associated in solution via hydrogen-bonded complexes. Analysis of the infrared spectrum of cyclohexenyl hydroperoxide on successive dilution in benzene shows that in the undiluted hydroperoxide the OH groups appear entirely in hydrogen-bonded complexes (a broad absorption around 3350 cm.$^{-1}$) which dissociate progressively on dilution until at concentrations below about 0.05 *M* only unbonded groups are detectable (absorption at 3500 cm.$^{-1}$). Thus it is deduced that the kinetic form of the primary decomposition at low concentration arises from the unimolecular breakdown of the hydroperoxide *monomer* while at high concentration the primary decomposition is due to the *unimolecular* breakdown of the hydroperoxide *dimer*.

$$(11)\quad 2RO\cdot + 2HO\cdot \xleftarrow[\text{Monomer decomposition}]{} 2ROOH \rightleftharpoons [ROOH\cdots \underset{\displaystyle H}{\underset{|}{O}}OR] \longrightarrow RO_2\cdot + H_2O + \cdot OR$$

Dimer decomposition

[40] A. Robertson and W. A. Waters, *J. Chem. Soc., 1948*, 1574, 1578.

[41] (a) L. Bateman and H. Hughes, *J. Chem. Soc., 1952*, 4594. (b) L. Bateman, H. Hughes and A. L. Morris, *Faraday Soc. Discussion, 14*, 190 (1953).

Various factors such as temperature or solvent media may influence the equilibrium between the monomeric and dimeric hydroperoxide structures and thereby alter the decomposition path. With other hydroperoxides having bulky substituent groups, steric factors may largely determine the degree of association.

Studies by Stannett and Mesrobian[42] on the thermal decomposition of 1-hydroperoxy-1,4-dimethylcyclohexane in 1,4-dimethylcyclohexane showed somewhat similar results to those presented by Bateman *et al.* Thus in hydroperoxide concentrations below 0.03 $M$ first order kinetics were observed while above 1.9 $M$ second order kinetics were obtained. The two rate constants were found at 120°C. to be: $k_1 = 1.4 \times 10^{-5}$sec.$^{-1}$ and $k_2 = 4.4 \times 10^{-5}$ liter mole$^{-1}$ sec.$^{-1}$. Expressing the rate of decomposition by the equation:

$$(12) \qquad -d(\text{ROOH})/dt = k_1[\text{ROOH}] + k_2[\text{ROOH}]^2$$

on substituting the values for $k_1$ and $k_2$ it can readily be seen that in 0.03 $M$ solutions the first order term will predominate while at a concentration of 1.9 $M$ the second order term becomes overwhelmingly operative. The two rate constants have been calculated to be:

$$(13) \qquad k_1 = 1.6 \times 10^{13} \exp\{-32.8 \text{ kcal.}/RT\}\text{sec.}^{-1}$$

$$(14) \quad k_2 = 2.5 \times 10^{11} \exp\{-28.6 \text{ kcal.}/RT) \text{ liter mole}^{-1} \text{ sec.}^{-1}$$

## IV. Decomposition of Peroxides by One-Electron Transfer Reactions

### 1. *The Haber-Weiss Mechanism*

The decomposition of peroxides may be induced by substances A (ions, molecules, or radicals) which transfer one electron to the peroxide. The peroxide containing the additional electron breaks down to form a radical plus a negative ion.

$$\text{A} + \text{ROOR}' \longrightarrow \text{A}^+ + \text{RO}\cdot + \text{R}'\text{O}^-$$

Although the over-all effect of the reaction is the transfer of one electron to the peroxide, the reaction probably does not occur in this simple fasion but rather via the formation of a complex:

$$\text{A} + \text{ROOR}' \longrightarrow \overset{\text{R}'}{\text{ROO}}\text{:A} \longrightarrow \text{RO}\cdot + \text{R}'\text{O}^- + \text{A}^+$$

[42] V. Stannett and R. B. Mesrobian, *Faraday Soc. Discussion*, *14*, 242 (1953).

The classical example of this type of reaction is the ferrous ion induced decomposition of hydrogen peroxide. Haber and Weiss[43a] proposed the following scheme to explain this reaction.

(1) $$H_2O_2 + Fe^{++} \longrightarrow HO\cdot + OH^- + Fe^{+++}$$

(2) $$HO\cdot + Fe^{++} \longrightarrow HO^- + Fe^{+++}$$

(3) $$HO\cdot + H_2O_2 \longrightarrow H_2O + HO_2\cdot$$

(4) $$HO_2\cdot + H_2O_2 \longrightarrow HO\cdot + H_2O + O_2$$

Later research[43b] indicated that probably even more radical reactions are involved, and in addition the effect of pH is very important, indicating the probable concurrence of ionic type reactions, particularly in solutions of high pH. Furthermore it is very doubtful that the reaction between $HO_2\cdot$ and $H_2O_2$ plays an important role in the reactions, so that oxygen must be produced by other mechanisms.[43b,44b] However, we are concerned here chiefly with reaction (1), which is the only reaction that generates radicals (reactions (3) and (4) produce no *increase* in the number of radicals but merely change the radical species).

The fact that radicals are produced in the reaction between hydrogen peroxide and ferrous ion was demonstrated by Evans and co-workers,[44a] who carried out this decomposition in the presence of water-soluble monomers such as methyl methacrylate and acrylonitrile. In the presence of monomer, the evolution of oxygen is largely repressed and a rapid polymerization of the monomer is induced. The important reactions under these conditions are:

(1) $$H_2O_2 + Fe^{++} \longrightarrow HO\cdot + OH^- + Fe^{+++}$$

(2) $$HO\cdot + Fe^{++} \longrightarrow OH^- + Fe^{+++}$$

(5) $$HO\cdot + CH_2{=}CHX \longrightarrow HOCH_2CHX\cdot \longrightarrow \text{polymerization}$$

When the molality of ferrous ions is equal to or in excess of that of the hydrogen peroxide, the reaction in the absence of monomer is mainly expressed by reactions (1) and (2) and the stoichiometry of the reaction corresponds to two moles of ferrous ion oxidized for every mole of peroxide decomposed, *in solutions of low pH*. However, in

[43] (a) F. Haber and P. Weiss, *Proc. Roy. Soc. London, A147*, 233 (1939). (b) N. Uri, *Chem. Reviews, 50*, 375 (1952).

[44] (a) J. H. Baxendale, M. G. Evans, and G. S. Park, *Trans. Faraday Soc., 42*, 155 (1946). (b) W. G. Barb, J. H. Baxendale, P. George, and K. R. Hargrave, *ibid., 47*, 462, 591 (1951).

the presence of a vinyl monomer, reaction (5) competes with reaction (2), and with sufficiently large concentrations of monomer the stoichiometry will tend toward one mole of ferrous ion oxidized for every mole of peroxide destroyed.

By studying the rate of reaction between hydrogen peroxide and ferrous ion in the presence of excess monomer Baxendale, Evans, and Park[44a] were able to determine the rate constant for the elementary reaction (1):

(6) $k(Fe^{++},H_2O_2) = 1.78 \times 10^9 \exp\{-10.1 \text{ kcal.}/RT\}$ liter mole$^{-1}$ sec.$^{-1}$

(Baxendale, Evans, and Park)

The excess monomer serves as an inhibitor for all induced reactions of types (2), (3), and (4) and the over-all reaction between ferrous ion and hydrogen peroxide is thereby restricted to reaction (1).

A very thorough investigation[44b] of the kinetics of the reaction between ferrous ion and hydrogen peroxide gave the following value for $k(Fe^{++}, H_2O_2)$ which must be considered to be the most reliable to date.

(7) $k(Fe^{++}, H_2O_2) = 4.45 \times 10^8 \exp\{-9.4 \text{ kcal.}/RT\}$

(Barb, Baxendale, George, and Hargrave)

It is interesting to compare the two values given above with the original values of Haber and Weiss:[43a]

(8) $k(Fe^{++},H_2O_2) = 4.0 \times 10^7 \exp\{-8.5 \text{ kcal.}/RT\}$

(Haber and Weiss)

### 2. *The Ferrous Ion Induced Decomposition of Cumene Hydroperoxide and Related Peroxides: The Initial Step*

The decomposition of CHP in the aqueous phase induced by ferrous ion is a very important method for generating radicals and is used in emulsion polymerization recipes to prepare "cold rubber" (copolymers of butadiene and styrene prepared in emulsion at 5°C. or below).

When a water solution of ferrous ammonium sulfate is slowly added to a water suspension of CHP, and the reaction mixture is stirred, the reaction products are indicated by the following equation:[38a]

$$(1)\quad Ph(Me)_2COOH\ (1\ mole) \xrightarrow[(0.47\ mole)]{Fe^{++}} PhC(=O)Me\ (71\%) + CH_3OH\ (44\%) + Ph(Me)_2COH\ (12\%) + C_2H_6\ (11\%) + \text{high boiling oil}\ (10\%)$$

The first step in this reaction is:

$$(2)\quad Ph(Me)_2COOH + Fe^{++} \longrightarrow Ph(Me)_2CO\cdot + Fe^{+++} + OH^-$$

(The ferric ion and hydroxyl ion probably complex to form $FeOH^{++}$.)

The proof that RO· radicals are formed is that this reaction can be used to initiate polymerization. Also, in the presence of nonpolymerizable olefins, or with large ratios of peroxide to butadiene, identifiable adducts are formed. For example, Kharasch *et al.*[38c] isolated the dimer structures A and B when various hydroperoxides (cumene hydroperoxide, tetralin hydroperoxide and *t*-butyl hydroperoxide) were decomposed by ferrous salts in water in the presence of butadiene:

$$ROCH_2CH{=}CHCH_2CH_2CH{=}CHCH_2OR \quad (A)$$

$$ROCH_2CH{=}CHCH_2CH(CH{=}CH_2){-}CH_2OR \quad (B)$$

In the absence of polymerizable monomer or olefin, the radicals produced in the initial step (eq. 2) can induce further decomposition of peroxide, oxidize the ferrous ion, engage in transfer reactions, dismutations, combinations, etc. Some aspects of these reactions will be discussed in the ensuing section (3).

Williams and co-workers[45] carried out kinetic studies of the *primary* reaction:

$$(3)\quad Fe^{++} + ROOH \longrightarrow Fe^{+++} + RO\cdot + OH^-$$

for the case of CHP and related hydroperoxides.

The decomposition of these hydroperoxides by ferrous ion was carried out in dilute aqueous solution of low pH in the presence of acrylonitrile monomer. Under these conditions the experimental data indicate that hydroperoxide and ferrous ion disappear only by equation (3). The monomer captures the RO· radical and prevents the radical induced oxidation of $Fe^{++}$ or the induced decomposition

[45] (a) J. W. L. Fordham and H. L. Williams, *J. Am. Chem. Soc.*, *72*, 4465 (1950); *73*, 1634 (1951). (b) R. J. Orr and H. L. Williams, *Can. J. Chem.*, *30*, 985 (1952).

of the hydroperoxide. The hydroperoxides studied in this fashion are listed below:

Cumene hydroperoxide: $C_6H_5-C(CH_3)_2-OOH$

Isopropylcumene hydroperoxide: $(CH_3)_2CH-C_6H_4-C(CH_3)_2-OOH$

*t*-Butylcumene hydroperoxide: $(CH_3)_3C-C_6H_4-C(CH_3)_2-OOH$

The values for the rate constants of the bimolecular reaction (3) in the three cases given above are:

(4) $k(\text{Fe}^{++}, \text{CHP}) = 1.07 \times 10^{10} \exp\{-12.0 \text{ kcal.}/RT\}$

(5) $k(\text{Fe}^{++}, \text{isopropyl CHP}) = 4.0 \times 10^{9} \exp\{-10.8 \text{ kcal.}/RT\}$

(6) $k(\text{Fe}^{++}, t\text{-butyl CHP}) = 1.8 \times 10^{9} \exp\{-9.90 \text{ kcal.}/RT\}$

### *3. The Ferrous Ion Induced Decomposition of Cumene Hydroperoxide and Related Peroxides: The Subsequent Steps*

By considering the nature of the products and the stoichiometry of the reaction between ferrous ion and cumene hydroperoxide (detailed in eq. (1) of the previous section), Kharasch *et al.* concluded that the reaction was a chain reaction of short kinetic chain length.[38a] Of particular importance for this conclusion is the fact that 0.47 mole of $Fe^{++}$ decompose 1 mole of CHP. The apparent chain length of the decomposition may be defined as moles of hydroperoxide destroyed per mole of ferrous ion consumed.

The RO· radicals formed in the primary step undergo an extensive group of reactions which account for the observed products. Among the most important possibilities are:[38a]

(1) $C_6H_5(CH_3)_2CO\cdot + Fe^{++} + H_2O \longrightarrow C_6H_5(CH_3)_2COH + Fe^{+++} + OH^-$

(2) $C_6H_5(CH_3)_2CO\cdot + C_6H_5(CH_3)_2COOH \longrightarrow CH_3OH + C_6H_5COCH_3 + C_6H_5(CH_3)_2CO\cdot$

(3) $C_6H_5(CH_3)_2CO\cdot \longrightarrow C_6H_5COCH_3 + CH_3\cdot$

(4) $2C_6H_5(CH_3)_2CO\cdot \longrightarrow 2C_6H_5COCH_3 + C_2H_6$

Reaction (1) is a one-electron oxidation of the $Fe^{++}$ ion by the RO· radical; it reduces the apparent chain length of the decomposition. Reaction (2) is an induced decomposition of the peroxide by the primary RO· radical; it is responsible for the chain character of the decomposition. Reaction (3) is a dismutation of the RO· radical, possibly less important than (1) or (2). Reaction (4) is a chain terminating step, being the disproportionation of two alkoxy radicals.

In the presence of a potential hydrogen donor, DH (dextrose, 2-propanol, or hydroquinone), the RO· radical may abstract a hydrogen atom according to equations (5) and (6):

$$(5) \quad C_6H_5(CH_3)_2CO\cdot + DH \longrightarrow C_6H_5(CH_3)_2COH + D\cdot$$

$$(6) \quad C_6H_5(CH_3)_2CO\cdot + DH \longrightarrow C_6H_5COCH_3 + CH_4 + D\cdot$$

With good hydrogen donors such as hydroquinone, reaction (5) is strongly favored. Reaction (6) becomes more prominent when relatively poor hydrogen donors such as dextrose are used.

The donor radical D· can itself oxidize the ferrous ion *or* induce decomposition of the hydroperoxide in reactions similar to (1) and (2).

The chain length of the decomposition can be greatly increased in the presence of certain hydrogen donors. For example in the presence of dextrose 0.08 mole of ferrous ion decompose 1 mole of CHP. This may be due to induced decomposition of CHP by the D· radicals formed in equations (5) and (6). It may also occur through a regeneration of ferrous ion by the D· radical:

$$(7) \quad D\cdot + Fe^{+++} \longrightarrow D^{+} + Fe^{++}$$

Cobaltous acetate initiates a chain decomposition of CHP of long apparent chain length because it can act both as oxidant and reductant to CHP.[38b]

$$(8) \quad C_6H_5(CH_3)_2COOH + Co^{++} \longrightarrow C_6H_5(CH_3)_2CO\cdot + OH^{-} + Co^{+++}$$

$$(9) \quad C_6H_5(CH_3)_2COOH + Co^{+++} \longrightarrow C_6H_5(CH_3)_2COO\cdot + H^{+} + Co^{++}$$

### *4. The Ferrous Ion Induced Decomposition of Tetralin Hydroperoxide and t-Butyl Hydroperoxide*

It is interesting to compare the ferrous ion induced decomposition of CHP with the ferrous ion induced decomposition of tetralin hydroperoxide (a secondary hydroperoxide) and *t*-butyl hydroperoxide (a *t*-alkyl hydroperoxide).[38a]

If CHP is decomposed by ferrous ion in the presence of a large amount of hydroquinone (a very active chain transfer agent or hydrogen donor), the main product of decomposition is α-cumyl alcohol. This of course means that the following reaction predominates:

$$RO\cdot + DH \longrightarrow ROH + D\cdot \tag{1}$$

In the case of tetralin hydroperoxide, however, large amounts of α-tetralone are formed even when the hydroperoxide is decomposed by ferrous ion in the presence of very large excess of hydroquinone.

In contrasting the ferrous ion induced decomposition of CHP with that of *t*-butyl hydroperoxide (*t*-BHP) and *t*-amyl hydroperoxide (*t*-AHP), it is particularly noteworthy that the number of moles of ferrous ion required to decompose 1 mole of hydroperoxide is 0.47 for CHP, 1.25 for *t*-BHP, and 1.00 for *t*-AHP. The important reactions which determine the ratio $[Fe^{++}]/[ROOH]$ are:

$$Fe^{++} + ROOH \longrightarrow Fe^{+++} + RO^- + RO\cdot \tag{2}$$

$$Fe^{++} + RO\cdot + H_2O \longrightarrow Fe^{+++} + ROH + OH^- \tag{3}$$

$$RO\cdot + ROOH \longrightarrow \text{(induced decomposition)} \tag{4}$$

If equation (2) occurred exclusively (as in the presence of an inhibitor such as acrylonitrile used by Williams *et al.*[45]) the ratio would be 1.0. If reactions (2) and (3) occurred quantitatively and to the exclusion of (4), $[Fe^{++}]/[ROOH]$ would be 2.0. If (4) occurred rapidly compared to (3), the ratio $[Fe^{++}]/[ROOH]$ (which is the reciprocal of the apparent chain length) would be very small. The experimental results on the three hydroperoxides CHP, *t*-BHP, and *t*-AHP indicate that reaction (4) is apparently less important compared to (3) in the case of the tertiary alkyl hydroperoxides. The products of decomposition of two *t*-alkyl hydroperoxides with ferrous salts are tabulated in Table B-11.

TABLE B-11

Decomposition of *t*-Butyl and *t*-Amyl Hydroperoxides with Ferrous Salts[38a]

| Hydroperoxide | $Fe^{++}$ consumed | $CH_4$ | $C_2H_6$ | $C_4H_{10}$ | Acetone |
|---|---|---|---|---|---|
| *t*-Butyl | 1.25 | 0.16 | 0.16 | None | 0.5 |
| *t*-Amyl | 1.00 | None | 0.37 | 0.16 | 0.7 |

### *5. Rearrangements Occurring during the Ferrous Ion Induced Decomposition of Triarylmethyl Hydroperoxides*

It has already been mentioned in section III-5 that in the radical RR′R″CO· the relative tendency of the group to participate in the cleavage of the R—C bond increases in the order phenyl, methyl, ethyl, hydrogen. This rule is in accord with the products of decomposition observed during the ferrous ion induced decomposition of cumene hydroperoxide, tetralin hydroperoxide, *t*-butyl hydroperoxide, and *t*-amyl hydroperoxide.

If both aryl groups and alkyl groups are present in the radical RR′R″CO·, the alkyl groups are cleaved to the complete exclusion of the aryl groups. For example, methyl alcohol and methane are found among the decomposition products of CHP during *homolytic* cleavage, while phenol and benzene are found, at most, in trace quantities.

When all three of the groups on the radical RR′R″CO· are aryl groups, no R—C cleavage is found at all, but instead a very interesting rearrangement of the alkoxy radical occurs.[38a,46] This is exemplified by the fact that benzopinacol ether is formed during the thermal decomposition[46b] or the ferrous ion induced decomposition[38a] of triphenyl methyl peroxide. Evidently the $(C_6H_5)_3CO\cdot$ radical that is formed in these cases rearranges and dimerizes to form benzopinacol ether according to the following mechanism:

$$(1)\quad (C_6H_5)_3COOH \xrightarrow{Fe^{++}} (C_6H_5)_3CO\cdot \xrightarrow[H_2O]{Fe^{++}} (C_6H_5)_3COH \quad (60\%)$$

$$(C_6H_5)_3CO\cdot \longrightarrow C_6H_5O\dot{C}(C_6H_5)_2 \longrightarrow \begin{array}{c}(C_6H_5)_2COC_6H_5\\ |\\ (C_6H_5)_2COC_6H_5\end{array} \quad (40\%)$$

A study of the reaction products of several triaryl substituted methyl hydroperoxides ArAr′Ar″CO· suggested the conclusion that the *p*-biphenyl and α-naphthyl groups migrate six times faster than a phenyl group, and that a *p*-tolyl group migrates about as fast as a phenyl group.[46a]

[46] (a) M. S. Kharasch, A. C. Poshkus, A. Fono, and W. Nudenberg, *J. Org. Chem.*, *16*, 1458 (1951). (b) H. Wieland, *Ber.*, *44*, 2553 (1911).

## 6. *Oxidation of Hydroperoxides by Strong Oxidants*[38b]

In the preceding sections the one-electron transfer of hydroperoxides with ferrous ions has been treated. This reaction involves the transfer of an electron from the ferrous ion to the hydroperoxide; *i.e.*, the hydroperoxide is acting as an oxidant and the ferrous ion as a reductant. There are, however, certain substances which act as oxidants toward hydroperoxides and decompose the hydroperoxide by one-electron transfer reaction. The primary step in this reaction is:

(1) $ROOH + Oxidant \longrightarrow RO_2\cdot + H^+ + (Oxidant + e)$

These powerful oxidants belong to two classes; (I) those which decompose the hydroperoxide to produce one equivalent of oxygen for every equivalent of oxidant used; (II) those which decompose hydroperoxides in such manner as to produce many moles of oxygen for each mole of oxidant consumed (obviously a chain reaction).

For oxidants of Class I, the probable course of reaction (after eq. 1) is:

(2) $RO_2\cdot + Oxidant \longrightarrow R^+ + O_2 + (Oxidant + e)$

Ceric salts and lead tetraacetate are examples of oxidants of Class I. The reaction with ceric salts can be written as follows:

(3) $ROOH + Ce^{++++} \longrightarrow Ce^{+++} + RO_2\cdot + H^+$

(4) $RO_2\cdot + Ce^{++++} \longrightarrow R^+ + O_2 + Ce^{+++}$

The over-all reaction is:

(5) $ROOH + 2Ce^{++++} \longrightarrow R^+ + H^+ + O_2 + 2Ce^{+++}$

An example of an oxidant of Class II is cobaltous acetate, which can act as both oxidant and reductant, and therefore produces a chain decomposition of the hydroperoxide.

(6) $ROOH + Co^{++} \longrightarrow RO\cdot + OH^- + Co^{+++}$

(7) $ROOH + Co^{+++} \longrightarrow RO_2\cdot + H^+ + Co^{++}$

(8) $RO\cdot + Co^{++} \longrightarrow RO^- + Co^{+++}$

(9) $RO\cdot + ROOH \longrightarrow$ induced decomposition of peroxide $+ RO\cdot$

(10) $RO_2\cdot + Co^{+++} \longrightarrow R^+ + O_2 + Co^{++}$

## *7. Decomposition of Peroxides by Amines: The Horner-Schlenk Mechanism*

The decomposition of peroxides by amines is a reaction that has not been completely studied, so that only a partial and tentative mechanism for this reaction can as yet be offered. Bartlett and Nozaki[22] noted that the reaction of benzoyl peroxide with amines is extremely rapid if not explosive. Gambarjan and co-workers studied the reaction products of benzoyl peroxide and numerous amines.[47]

Bartlett and Nozaki[22] also made a kinetic investigation of the reaction between benzoyl peroxide and triphenylamine at 79.8°C. They found that the reaction was of first order with respect to peroxide and of first order or lower with respect to amine.

There are two mechanisms which readily suggest themselves as explanations for the extremely rapid reaction between peroxides and amines. First, the induced decomposition of peroxide by amino-type radicals may be an extremely rapid chain reaction. Second, there may be a bimolecular reaction between the peroxide molecule and the amine molecule leading to peroxide decomposition. The bimolecular reaction would most probably be a one-electron transfer. Either possibility is cogent although neither is compelling.

Bartlett and Nozaki gave particular attention to the first mechanism. On the other hand, Horner[48] found that the addition of dimethylaniline will strongly accelerate the polymerization of styrene by benzoyl peroxide. This is compelling evidence that a bimolecular reaction between the benzoyl peroxide and the amine occurs which gives an increased rate of production of radicals. As we have previously stated, this cannot result from an induced decomposition of peroxide, but will occur if there is a reaction of the one-electron transfer type. Horner also noted that benzene solutions of dimethylaniline and benzoyl peroxide absorb large quantities of oxygen, another indication of the production of free radicals by this system. Solutions of aniline or methylaniline with benzoyl peroxide in benzene show no oxygen absorption. In addition, aniline and methylaniline do not accelerate the benzoyl peroxide catalyzed polymerization of styrene but rather inhibit the polymerization.

[47] S. Gambarjan *et al.*, *Ber.*, *B58*, 1775 (1925); *ibid.*, *B60*, 390 (1927); *ibid.*, *42*, 4003 (1910); *Bull. inst. sci. R. S. S. d'Armenie*, 265 (1931); *J. Gen. Chem. (U. S. S. R.)*, *3*, 222 (1933).

[48] L. Horner, *Angew. Chem.*, *61*, 458 (1949).

Horner and Schlenk[49] have proposed a set of mechanisms which they believe explains the reaction products of benzoyl peroxide with aniline, methylaniline and dimethylaniline. In each case they postulate that the first step in the process is a one-electron transfer from amine to peroxide. They state that in these three cases the over-all reaction corresponds to the following equations:

(1) $$2C_6H_5NH_2 + POOP \longrightarrow C_6H_5N{=}NC_6H_5 + 2POH$$

(2) $$C_6H_5N(CH_3)H + POOP \longrightarrow C_6H_5N(CH_3)OP + POH$$

(3) $$2C_6H_5N(CH_3)_2 + POOP \longrightarrow (CH_3)_2N{-}C_6H_4{-}C_6H_4{-}N(CH_3)_2 + 2POH$$

where P represents $C_6H_5C(=O){-}$.

The details of the Horner-Schlenk mechanism are given below:

*Aniline:*

$$2\,C_6H_5\dot{N}H_2 + C_6H_5C(=O)OOC(=O)C_6H_5 \longrightarrow 2\,[C_6H_5\dot{N}H_2]^+\ {}^-OC(=O)C_6H_5$$

$$[C_6H_5\dot{N}H_2]^+\ {}^-OC(=O)C_6H_5 \longrightarrow C_6H_5COOH + C_6H_5\dot{N}H$$

$$2\,C_6H_5\dot{N}H \longrightarrow C_6H_5{-}NH{-}NH{-}C_6H_5$$

$$C_6H_5{-}NH{-}NH{-}C_6H_5 + C_6H_5C(=O)OOC(=O)C_6H_5 \longrightarrow 2C_6H_5COOH + C_6H_5{-}N{=}N{-}C_6H_5$$

[49] L. Horner and E. Schlenk, *Angew. Chem.*, *61*, 411 (1949).

*Methylaniline:*

$$C_6H_5NHCH_3 + C_6H_5COOCOC_6H_5 \longrightarrow [C_6H_5\dot{N}HCH_3]^+ \; {}^-OCOC_6H_5 + C_6H_5CO\cdot$$

$$[C_6H_5\dot{N}HCH_3]^+ \; {}^-OCOC_6H_5 \longrightarrow C_6H_5\dot{N}CH_3 + C_6H_5COOH$$

$$C_6H_5\dot{N}CH_3 + C_6H_5CO\cdot \longrightarrow C_6H_5N(CH_3){-}O{-}COC_6H_5$$

*Dimethylaniline:*

$$C_6H_5\ddot{N}(CH_3)_2 + C_6H_5COOCOC_6H_5 \longrightarrow [C_6H_5\dot{N}(CH_3)_2]^+ \; {}^-OCOC_6H_5 + C_6H_5CO\cdot$$

$$[C_6H_5\dot{N}(CH_3)_2]^+ \; {}^-OCOC_6H_5 \longrightarrow \cdot C_6H_4{-}\ddot{N}(CH_3)_2 + C_6H_5COOH$$

$$2\,\cdot C_6H_4\ddot{N}(CH_3)_2 \longrightarrow (CH_3)_2\ddot{N}C_6H_4{-}C_6H_4\ddot{N}(CH_3)_2$$

The postulated primary step in all of these reactions is an electron transfer from the unshared pair of the N atom to one of the peroxidic oxygens, resulting in the breaking of the O—O bond. In all three cases "free" radicals appear among the intermediates of the Horner-Schlenk mechanism. However, only in the case of dimethylaniline do the experimental results indicate that the radicals can initiate vinyl polymerization. This may result from the fact that the primary and secondary amines also act as inhibitors for vinyl polymerization.

# V. Heterolytic Cleavages of Peroxides

## *1. Introduction*

In this section various cases of heterolytic cleavage of peroxides will be discussed. This subject is in the early stages of development, and a comprehensive treatment is not possible at present. Heterolytic reactions in organic solvents present certain inherent difficulties of interpretation compared to free radical reactions. A few of these difficulties are outlined below.

Consider a peroxide ROOR′ undergoing heterolytic cleavage at the O—O linkage in a solvent S. R and R′ may be alkyl, acyl, or hydrogen and R will be considered as more electron-attracting than R′. The solvent S will first be regarded as playing no other role than that of a continuous medium of a given dielectric constant. The higher the dielectric constant of the solvent the greater will be the heterolytic cleavage tendency of ROOR′.

The heterolytic cleavage tendency of ROOR′ may in principle run the entire gamut from complete dissociation into free ions, through partial dissociation into free ions, through formation of ion pairs, down to a slight polarization of the O—O linkage.

$$\text{ROOR}' \longrightarrow \text{RO}^- + \text{R}'\text{O}^+ \tag{1}$$

$$\text{ROOR}' \longrightarrow (\text{RO}^-)(\text{R}'\text{O}^+) \tag{2}$$

$$\text{ROOR}' \longrightarrow \text{RO}^{\delta-}\text{ - - - }^{\delta+}\text{OR}^- \tag{3}$$

In addition, the solvent may play a very important role in solvating the ions or ion pairs, *e.g.*:

$$\text{ROOR}' + (x + y)\text{S} \longrightarrow [\text{RO}^-][\text{S}]_x + [\text{R}'\text{O}^+][\text{S}]_y \tag{4}$$

The role of the solvent may be even more pronounced if the solvent is regarded as a generalized Lewis acid (A) or a generalized base B. In these cases the heterolytic cleavages may be written as:

$$\text{ROOR}' + \text{A} \rightleftharpoons (\text{ROOR}')(\text{A}) \longrightarrow [\text{AOR}]^- + \text{R}'\text{O}^+ \tag{5}$$

$$\text{ROOR}' + \text{B} \rightleftharpoons (\text{ROOR}')(\text{B}) \longrightarrow \text{RO}^- + [\text{R}'\text{OB}]^+ \tag{6}$$

If the solvent can itself ionize, the situation is even more complex, since the ions arising from the solvent may act as generalized Lewis acids or bases toward ROOR′. For example, a solution of perchloric acid in acetic acid has been used to study heterolytic decompositions of hydroperoxides and peroxides. In this "superacid" solution the perchloric acid is highly ionized. One can consider the heterolytic cleavage of ROOR′ in this solution to proceed as follows:

$$\text{(7)} \qquad \text{ROOR}' + \text{H}^+ \rightleftharpoons (\text{ROOR}')(\text{H}^+) \longrightarrow \text{ROH} + \text{R}'\text{O}^+$$

Detailed kinetic studies which would enable distinctions to be drawn as to the exact mechanism of the primary heterolytic cleavage of peroxides have not yet been carried out. In other words, in any given instance there is no certainty as to which of the equations (1) to (7) best describes the primary cleavage process. In the subsequent discussion, the primary heterolytic cleavage step will be written down somewhat arbitrarily but generally on the basis of the mechanism of greatest probability.

In addition to heterolytic cleavage at the O—O linkage, there may also occur heterolytic cleavage at the C—O bonds, *e.g.*:

$$\text{(8)} \qquad \text{ROOR}' \rightleftharpoons \text{ROO}^- + \text{R}'^+$$

$$\text{(9)} \qquad \text{ROOR}' + \text{H}^+ \rightleftharpoons \text{ROOH} + \text{R}'^+$$

In the case of hydroperoxides, the heterolytic cleavage of the O—H linkage is also very important. This is illustrated by the reaction of hydroperoxide with base:

$$\text{(10)} \qquad \text{ROOH} + :\bar{\text{B}} \rightleftharpoons \text{RO}_2^- + \text{BH}$$

$$\text{(11)} \qquad \text{ROOH} + \text{OH}^- \rightleftharpoons \text{RO}_2^- + \text{H}_2\text{O}$$

In some cases other bonds in the peroxide may be more readily subject to heterolytic cleavage than the linkage involving an oxygen atom. For example:

$$\text{(12)} \qquad \text{R—}\overset{\text{R}}{\underset{\text{H}}{\text{C}}}\text{—OO—}\overset{\text{R}}{\underset{\text{R}}{\text{C}}}\text{R} + :\bar{\text{B}} \longrightarrow \text{BH} + \left[\text{R—}\overset{\text{R}}{\underset{\cdot\cdot}{\text{C}}}\text{OO—}\overset{\text{R}}{\underset{\text{R}}{\text{C}}}\text{R}\right]^-$$

## 2. *Relative Tendencies for Heterolytic and Homolytic Cleavage among the Peroxide Classes*

For the purposes of this discussion, the organic peroxides may be conveniently divided into five classes: alkyl hydroperoxides (I), acyl hydroperoxides or peroxy acids (II), dialkyl peroxides (III), diacyl peroxides (IV), and alkyl-acyl peroxides or peroxy esters (V). A representative of each of these classes is listed below:

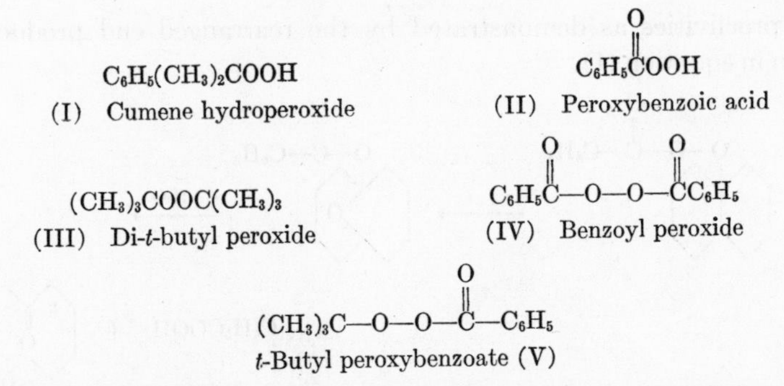


All five classes are subject to both homolytic and heterolytic cleavage, although large differences exist in their relative tendencies toward the two modes of cleavage.[50] Most representatives of classes I, III, and IV have a pronounced tendency to undergo homolytic cleavage, and therefore are capable on decomposition of inducing radial chain reactions such as vinyl polymerization. On the other hand, representatives of classes I, III, and IV also undergo heterolytic cleavage under favorable circumstances as will be discussed later.

Peroxides of class II (peracids or acyl hydroperoxides) react entirely differently with olefins or vinyl monomers than the classes I, III, and IV. Peroxybenzoic acid, for example, reacts with olefins or vinyl monomers to give epoxides and benzoic acid and is not an effective initiator for vinyl polymerization. The reaction of peracids with olefins to form epoxides is undoubtedly an ionic or polar reaction. However, under certain conditions peracids may react to form radicals. For example, the radical chain oxidation of acetaldehyde by molecular oxygen is catalyzed by the addition of cobaltous acetate. This has been explained as due to the formation of initiating radicals from the reactions of cobaltous ion and peroxyacetic acid.[51]

Peroxides of class V (peroxy esters or alkyl-acyl peroxides), include representatives that behave as classes I, III, and IV (pronounced tendency for homolytic cleavage) as well as representatives that behave as Class II (pronounced tendency for heterolytic cleavage). *t*-Butyl perbenzoate, for example, is an effective initiator of vinyl polymerization,[52,53] while 9-decalyl perbenzoate exhibits hetero-

[50] P. D. Bartlett, Winter, 1950, issue of *Record of Chemical Progress*.
[51] C. E. H. Bawn and J. B. Williamson, *Trans. Faraday Soc.*, *47*, 735 (1951).
[52] N. A. Milas and D. M. Surgenor, *J. Am. Chem. Soc.*, *68*, 642 (1946).
[53] R. P. Perry and K. P. Seltzer, *Modern Plastics*, *25*, No. 3, 134 (1947).

lytic proclivities as demonstrated by the rearranged end products shown in equation (1).

(1) 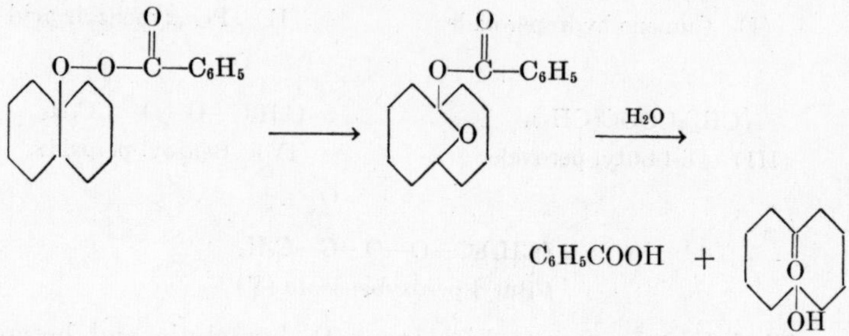 [decalyl perbenzoate, $O—O—\overset{O}{\overset{\|}{C}}—C_6H_5$] ⟶ [rearranged ester, $O—\overset{O}{\overset{\|}{C}}—C_6H_5$] $\xrightarrow{H_2O}$ $C_6H_5COOH$ + [ketone with OH]

Criegee[54] found that this rearrangement occurred most rapidly in solvents of highest ionizing power. He therefore proposed mechanism (2) for the reaction.

(2) 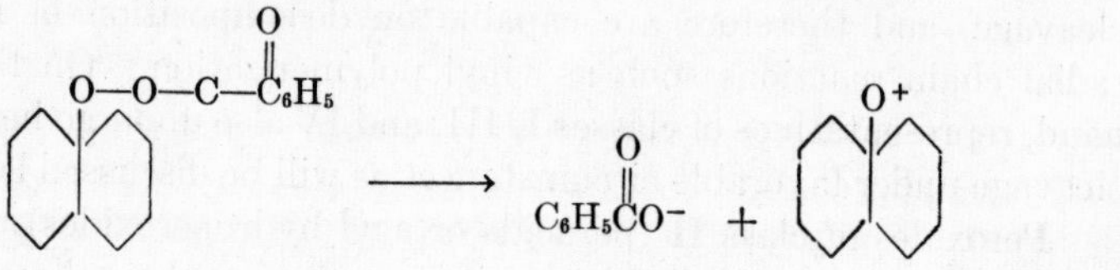 [$O—O—C—C_6H_5$ with C=O] ⟶ $C_6H_5\overset{O}{\overset{\|}{C}}O^-$ + [$O^+$ cation]

(3) [$O^+$ cation] ⟶ [rearranged carbonium ion, +, O]

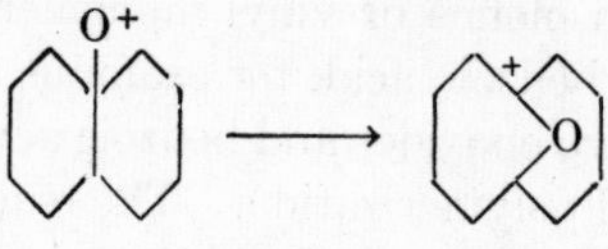

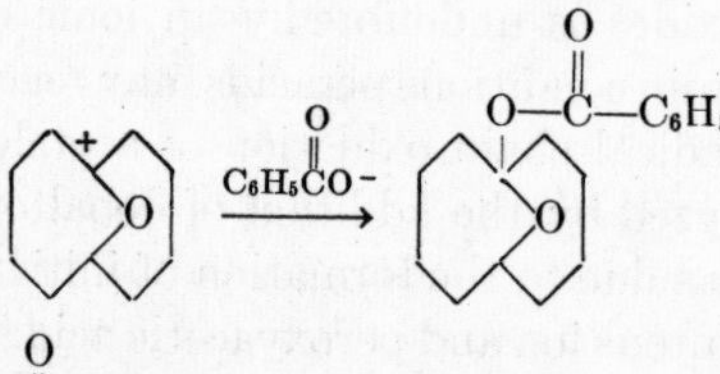

(4) [carbonium ion, +, O] $\xrightarrow{C_6H_5\overset{O}{\overset{\|}{C}}O^-}$ [$O—\overset{O}{\overset{\|}{C}}—C_6H_5$ ester]

(5) [$O—\overset{O}{\overset{\|}{C}}—C_6H_5$ ester] $\xrightarrow{(H_2O)}$ $C_6H_5COOH$ + [ketone with OH]

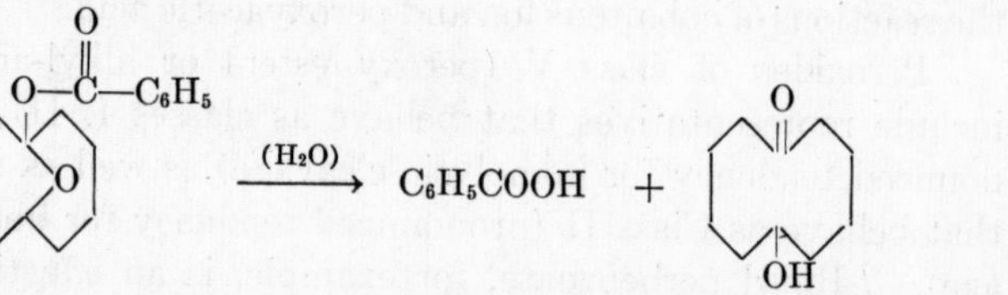

Reaction (2) represents the heterolytic cleavage of the O—O linkage. It is clear that on cleavage the more strongly electron-

[54] R. Criegee and R. Kaspar, *Ann.*, *560*, 127 (1948). See also P. D. Bartlett and J. L. Kice, *J. Am. Chem. Soc.*, *75*, 5591 (1953).

attracting acyl group will be attached to the oxygen atom carrying the negative charge, whereas the electron-donating alkyl group will be attached to the oxygen atom carrying the positive charge (the oxygen cation).

Reaction (3) representing the rearrangement of the oxygen cation into a carbonium ion is the central feature of the mechanism which enables one to understand the formation of the reaction products in question. This rearrangement involves the cleavage of a carbon-carbon bond and the formation of a carbon-oxygen bond. The course of this rearrangement involving other oxygen cations will be discussed subsequently.

The heterolytic cleavage tendency of certain other members of Class V (peresters) may be even more pronounced than that of 9-decalyl perbenzoate. For example, Wieland and Maier found that it was impossible to isolate triphenylmethyl perbenzoate under reaction conditions which were expected to yield this compound.[55]

The situation is best described by equations (6) to (9). Triphenylmethyl perbenzoate (A) is the expected product of reaction

$$(C_6H_5)_3COOH \xrightarrow{C_6H_5\overset{\overset{O}{\|}}{C}-Cl} (C_6H_5)_3C-O-O-\overset{\overset{O}{\|}}{C}-C_6H_5 \quad (A) \tag{6}$$

$$(C_6H_5)_3COO\overset{\overset{O}{\|}}{C}C_6H_5 \longrightarrow (C_6H_5)_3CO^+ + C_6H_5\overset{\overset{O}{\|}}{C}-O^- \tag{7}$$

$$(C_6H_5)_3CO^+ \longrightarrow (C_6H_5)_2\overset{+}{C}OC_6H_5 \tag{8}$$

$$(C_6H_5)_2\overset{+}{C}OC_6H_5 + C_6H_5\overset{\overset{O}{\|}}{C}-O^- \longrightarrow \begin{array}{c} C_6H_5 \quad OC_6H_5 \\ \diagdown \diagup \\ C \\ \diagup \diagdown \\ C_6H_5 \quad O\overset{}{C}-C_6H_5 \\ \quad\quad \| \\ \quad\quad O \end{array} \quad (B) \tag{9}$$

(6). However, the product actually found is (B). This is presumably because (A) undergoes heterolytic cleavage and rearrangement (reactions (7) to (9)) so rapidly that it cannot be isolated.[54]

Oxygen cations have been postulated as intermediates in other chemical reactions. Mosher has advanced the hypothesis that under certain conditions oxidative attack upon an alcohol may involve the removal of a hydride ion from the hydroxy group with the formation of

[55] H. Wieland and J. Maier, *Ber.*, *64*, 1205 (1931).

an oxygen cation.[56] Criegee,[54] Leffler,[57] and Robertson and Waters[40] have given other examples of reactions involving peroxidic substances which seem to be best explained by postulating oxygen cations as intermediates. These reactions include the conversion of aromatic aldehydes into phenols by alkaline hydrogen peroxide, the rearrangement of primary ozonides and the attack of Caro's acid ($H_2SO_5$) on ketones. Friess[58] has applied a polar mechanism to explain the reaction between perbenzoic acid and ketones.

It is profitable at this point to emphasize once again that the exact mechanism of the primary heterolytic cleavage of peroxides is unresolved and that little is known about the lifetime of the postulated oxygen cation and how "free" it actually is. A concerted rearrangement rather than a two-step process is likely for all the heterolytic cleavages discussed here. A good illustration of this point is the epoxidation of olefins by peroxy acids.[50,59] The heterolytic cleavage of peroxybenzoic acid for example has been assumed to yield an unrearrangeable $OH^+$ fragment, since the acyl group is more electron-attracting than hydrogen:

$$C_6H_5\overset{\overset{O}{\|}}{C}{-}OOH \longrightarrow C_6H_5\overset{\overset{O}{\|}}{C}O^- + OH^+ \tag{10}$$

The $OH^+$ fragment may be regarded as donating a positively charged oxygen atom to an olefin:

$$OH^+ + \begin{matrix} CHR' \\ \| \\ CHR \end{matrix} \longrightarrow O\!\!\begin{matrix} \diagup CHR' \\ | \\ \diagdown CHR \end{matrix} + H^+ \tag{11}$$

It has been observed[59] that olefins containing electron-donating groups R and R′ react the most rapidly with peracids to give epoxides. This is in accord with equations (10) and (11). However, the epoxidation reaction proceeds very rapidly even in nonpolar solvents, which casts some doubt upon the complete separation of charge envisaged in the reaction mechanisms (10) and (11). It has been sug-

[56] W. A. Mosher and F. C. J. Whitmore, *J. Am. Chem. Soc., 70,* 2544 (1948). W. A. Mosher *et al., ibid., 71,* 286 (1949). See also F. H. Westheimer and N. Nicolaides, *ibid., 71,* 25 (1949).

[57] J. E. Leffler, *Chem. Reviews, 45,* 385 (1949).

[58] S. L. Friess, *J. Am. Chem. Soc., 71,* 14, 2571 (1949).

[59] D. Swern, *J. Am. Chem. Soc., 69,* 1692 (1947); *Chem. Reviews, 45,* 48 (1949).

gested that a cyclic polar mechanism in which the proton is received by the carbonyl oxygen simultaneously with oxygen addition to the double bond would be a better description of the true mechanism.[60]

$$(12)\quad C_6H_5C(=O)\text{–}O\text{–}O\text{–}H + \begin{matrix}CHR'\\ \| \\ CHR\end{matrix} \longrightarrow C_6H_5C(=O)OH + O\begin{matrix}CHR\\ | \\ CHR\end{matrix}$$

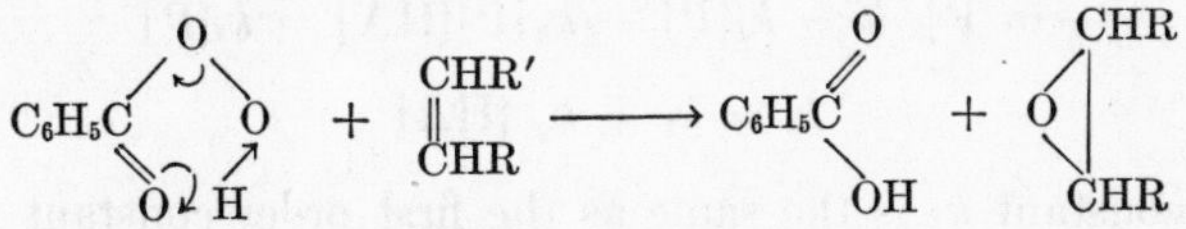

This mechanism, although involving charged particles, has the feature that the charge separation is always small.

Other examples of heterolytic cleavage of peroxides are presented in the succeeding sections.

### 3. *Decomposition of p-Methoxy-p′-nitrobenzoyl Peroxide and Related Peroxides*

In section III it was shown that benzoyl peroxide and a wide variety of substituted benzoyl peroxides decompose by a homolytic cleavage into radicals, followed by a radical induced decomposition. The decomposition of benzoyl peroxide itself is only weakly catalyzed by acids, and then only by very strong acids. The situation is quite different, however, as regards the unsymmetrical analogue *p*-methoxy-*p*′-nitrobenzoyl peroxide (I). Although (I) can decompose via a

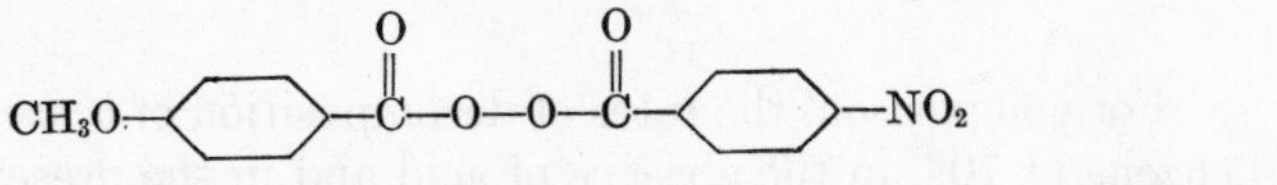

$$CH_3O\text{–}C_6H_4\text{–}C(=O)\text{–}O\text{–}O\text{–}C(=O)\text{–}C_6H_4\text{–}NO_2$$

(I)

radical mechanism in nonpolar solvents such as benzene, a moderate change in the conditions of reaction leads to decomposition by a polar (or ionic) mechanism.[60]

In pure benzene, (I) decomposes to almost equal amounts of *p*-methoxybenzoic acid (anisic acid) and *p*-nitrobenzoic acid, and the unsymmetrical *p*-nitro and *p*-methoxy biphenyls:

$$CH_3O\phi\overset{O}{\overset{\|}{C}}O O\overset{O}{\overset{\|}{C}}\phi NO_2 + C_6H_6 \longrightarrow CH_3O\phi\overset{O}{\overset{\|}{C}}OH + NO_2\phi\overset{O}{\overset{\|}{C}}OH + NO_2\text{—}\phi\text{—}\phi + CH_3O\phi\text{—}\phi$$

[60] J. E. Leffler, *J. Am. Chem. Soc.*, *72*, 67 (1950).

The decomposition of (I) is markedly accelerated by acids. The rate of decomposition of the peroxide, P, in benzene at 70°C. in the presence of acids, HA, is given by:

$$(1) \qquad -d[\mathrm{P}]/dt = k_1[\mathrm{P}] + k_a[\mathrm{P}][\mathrm{HA}] = k_t[\mathrm{P}]$$

$$k_t = k_1 + k_a\,[\mathrm{HA}]$$

The constant $k_1$ is the same as the first order constant in pure benzene. For acetic acid (HOAc) – benzene mixtures at 70°:

$$(2) \qquad k_t\ (\mathrm{hr.}^{-1}) = 0.075 + 0.26[\mathrm{HOAc}]$$

In general $k_a$ follows the Brønsted law of general acid catalysis namely, that there is a linear relation between log $k_a$ and log $K_a$, where $K_a$ is the acid dissociation constant. Values of log $k_a$ and log $K_a$ for a series of acids are shown in Table B-12.

TABLE B-12

Values Cited by J. E. Leffler[60]

| Acid | $-\log K_a$ | $\log k_a$ |
|---|---|---|
| Acetic | 4.73 | −0.605 |
| Monochloroacetic | 2.85 | 0.536 |
| Dichloroacetic | 1.30 | 1.219 |
| Trichloroacetic | 0.70 | 1.656 |

For comparison, the rates of decomposition of *benzoyl peroxide* in benzene at 70°, in the absence of acid and in the presence of acetic, dichloroacetic, and trichloroacetic acids, showed relatively small increases with increasing acidity. For example, on adding 0.3 *M* trichloroacetic acid, the rate of decomposition increases only 50 per cent over the rate in pure benzene. In acetic acid as solvent, 0.179 *M* sulfuric acid increases the rate of decomposition only about 25 per cent.[61] On the other hand, $AlCl_3$ (a strong Lewis acid) has been observed to catalyze the decomposition of benzoyl peroxide at 0° in benzene or chloroform.[62]

The decomposition of *p*-methoxy-*p'*-nitrobenzoyl peroxide summarized by equation (1) appears to be a case of general acid catalysis

[61] P. D. Bartlett and J. E. Leffler, *J. Am. Chem. Soc.*, *72*, 3032 (1950).

[62] H. Gelissen and P. H. Hermans, *Ber.*, *58*, 479 (1925).

superimposed on the radical decomposition. The mechanism of the acid catalyzed reaction was postulated to be the following:

$$(3)\qquad CH_3O\phi\overset{O}{\overset{\|}{C}}O\overset{O}{\overset{\|}{C}}\phi NO_2 \overset{H+}{\rightleftharpoons} CH_3O\phi\overset{O}{\overset{\|}{C}}OO\overset{OH}{\overset{|}{\underset{+}{C}}}\phi NO_2$$

$$CH_3O\phi\overset{O}{\overset{\|}{C}}O{-}\overset{H}{\overset{|}{O}}{-}\underset{+}{C}\phi NO_2 \longrightarrow CH_3O\phi\overset{O}{\overset{\|}{C}}O^+ + HO\overset{O}{\overset{\|}{C}}\phi NO_2$$

Whereas in pure benzene an almost equal amount of anisic and *p*-nitrobenzoic acids are found among the decomposition products of I, in the presence of trichloroacetic acid the decomposition of I gave the theoretical yield of *p*-nitrobenzoic acid with only 1.5 per cent of anisic acids. The exact fate of the $CH_3OPhC({=}O)O^+$ fragment has not been detailed, but a derivative of hydroquinone monomethyl ether was found among the products of decomposition.

Although benzoyl peroxide decomposes at nearly the same rate in benzene and nitrobenzene, the rate of decomposition of (I) is eight times as fast in the more polar solvent at 70°. This is due to the fact that (I) decomposes by a polar mechanism in polar solvents. The course of the polar decomposition in the highly polar solvent thionyl chloride has been studied by isolation of the decomposition products. The postulated mechanism is as follows:

$$(4)\qquad CH_3O\phi\overset{O}{\overset{\|}{C}}OO\overset{O}{\overset{\|}{C}}\phi NO_2 \longrightarrow CH_3O\phi\overset{O}{\overset{\|}{C}}O^+ + {}^-O\overset{O}{\overset{\|}{C}}\phi NO_2$$

$$CH_3O\phi\overset{O}{\overset{\|}{C}}O^+ \longrightarrow CH_3O\phi O\overset{O}{\overset{\|}{C}}{}^+$$

$$CH_3O\phi O\overset{O}{\overset{\|}{C}}{}^+ + {}^-O\overset{O}{\overset{\|}{C}}\phi NO_2 \longrightarrow CH_3O\text{-}C_6H_4\text{-}O\overset{O}{\overset{\|}{C}}O\overset{O}{\overset{\|}{C}}\text{-}C_6H_4\text{-}NO_2 \quad \text{(II)}$$

$$\text{(II)} + H_2O \longrightarrow CH_3O\text{-}C_6H_4\text{-}OH + CO_2 + HOOC\text{-}C_6H_4\text{-}NO_2$$

The product (II) was isolated in 38% yield during the decomposition of I in thionyl chloride. This product can hardly arise from other than an ionic (or polar) mechanism.

One more striking example of the difference between I and benzoyl peroxide is that, although both peroxides can initiate the polymerization of styrene via a radical mechanism, I is unable to initiate the polymerization of acrylonitrile, though benzoyl peroxide does so very effectively. In acrylonitrile, a highly polar solvent, I decomposes by a polar mechanism, and does not produce sufficient radicals to produce perceptible polymerization.

The decomposition of bisphenyl acetyl peroxide (III) has been studied in much the same manner as has *p*-methoxy-*p*′-nitrobenzoyl peroxide.[61] Many of the same conclusions have been drawn for

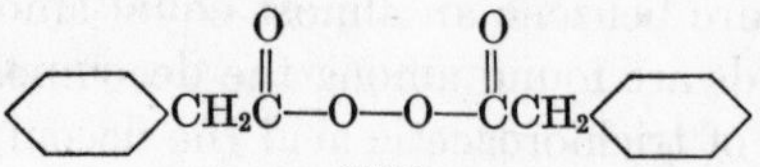

$$C_6H_5CH_2C(=O)—O—O—C(=O)CH_2C_6H_5$$

(III)

both I and III, in particular that they decompose concurrently by radical and polar mechanisms, the relative importance of each mechanism depending on the solvent. On the other hand, it was found necessary to postulate that some primary cleavage in III takes place at the C—C bond, both in the radical and in polar cleavage.[61] Only in this manner could the very rapid decomposition of III be explained.

(5)

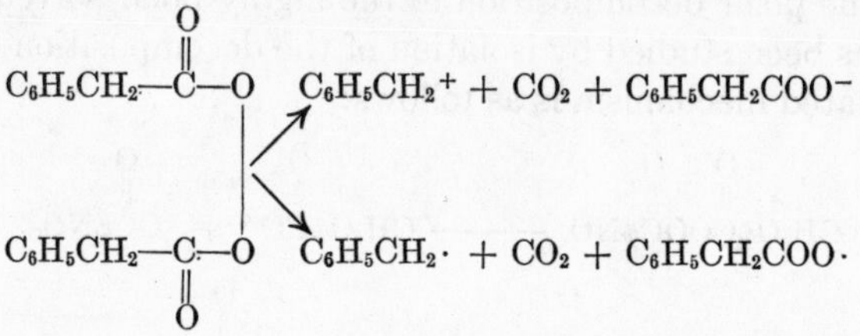

$$C_6H_5CH_2—C(=O)—O—O—C(=O)—CH_2C_6H_5 \nearrow C_6H_5CH_2^+ + CO_2 + C_6H_5CH_2COO^-$$

$$\searrow C_6H_5CH_2\cdot + CO_2 + C_6H_5CH_2COO\cdot$$

A generalization of equation (3) for acid cleavage of all unsymmetrical dialkyl peroxides has been proposed:[63]

$$ROOR' \xrightarrow{H^+} ROH + R'O^+$$

The cleavage products are predictable upon the basis of the relative electron-attracting ability of the radicals R and R′. The carbinol formed is predominantly, if not exclusively, that derived from the radical of greater electron-attracting power.

[63] M. S. Kharasch and J. G. Burt, *J. Org. Chem.*, *16*, 150 (1951).

### 4. *The Acid Catalyzed Decomposition of Cumene Hydroperoxide and Other Hydroperoxides*

The acid catalyzed decomposition of cumene hydroperoxide (CHP) was first reported by Hock and Lang,[10] who employed boiling 10% aqueous sulfuric acid to effect the conversion to phenol and acetone.

$$C_6H_5-\overset{\displaystyle CH_3}{\underset{\displaystyle CH_3}{\overset{|}{\underset{|}{C}}}}-OOH \xrightarrow{H_2SO_4} C_6H_5OH + CH_3COCH_3 \quad (1)$$

The decomposition of CHP and several other hydroperoxides by strong acids was further studied by Kharasch and co-workers.[63-65] These workers carried out the decompositions in glacial acetic acid to which 0.1 mole per cent of perchloric acid had been added. The perchloric acid is the effective catalyst since CHP is stable in acetic acid at room temperature. In general, decomposition of CHP according to equation (1) is effected only by *strong* Lewis acids. HCl in acetic acid is weaker than perchloric acid and is relatively ineffective toward decomposing CHP. $FeCl_3$ in alcohol is a weak acid and causes no decomposition of CHP in that solvent; however, $FeCl_3$ is a strong acid in benzene, and in this solvent it readily converts CHP to phenol and acetone. The decomposition of CHP by strong acids is highly exothermic and proceeds at an appreciable rate even at −80°C.

The over-all reaction for the acid catalyzed cleavage of all the hydroperoxides studied to date can be written as follows:

$$R_1R_2R_3COOH \xrightarrow{H+} R_2R_3CO + R_1OH \quad (2)$$

The following cases studied by Kharasch *et al.* are illustrative:

*α-Phenylethyl Hydroperoxide*

$$C_6H_5-\overset{\displaystyle H}{\underset{\displaystyle CH_3}{\overset{|}{\underset{|}{C}}}}-OOH \xrightarrow{H+} CH_3CHO + C_6H_5OH \quad (3)$$

[64] M. S. Kharasch, A. Fono, and W. Nudenberg, *J. Org. Chem.*, *15*, 748 (1950).

[65] M. S. Kharasch, A. Fono, and W. Nudenberg, *ibid.*, *16*, 128 (1951).

*α-Tetralyl Hydroperoxide*

(4) 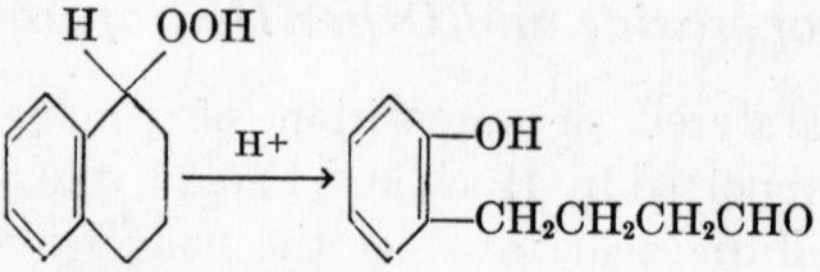 H OOH (tetralin ring) $\xrightarrow{H+}$ (benzene ring) —OH, —$CH_2CH_2CH_2CHO$

*2-Cyclohexen-1-yl Hydroperoxide*

(5) 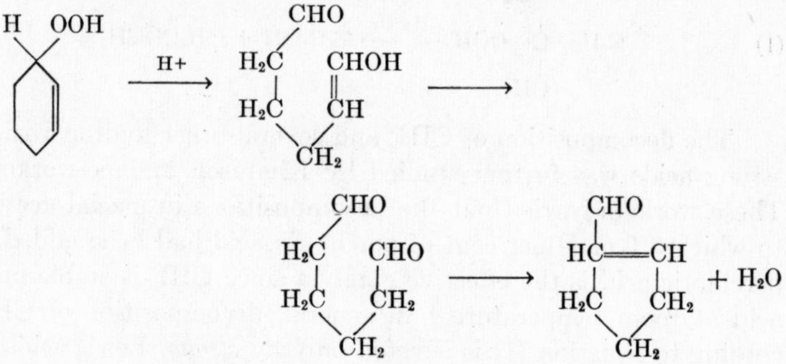 H OOH (cyclohexene ring) $\xrightarrow{H+}$ CHO, $H_2C$, CHOH, $H_2C$, CH, $CH_2$ $\longrightarrow$

CHO, $H_2C$, CHO, $H_2C$, $CH_2$, $CH_2$ $\longrightarrow$ CHO, HC═CH, $H_2C$, $CH_2$, $CH_2$ + $H_2O$

*α-p-Xylyl Hydroperoxide*

(6) 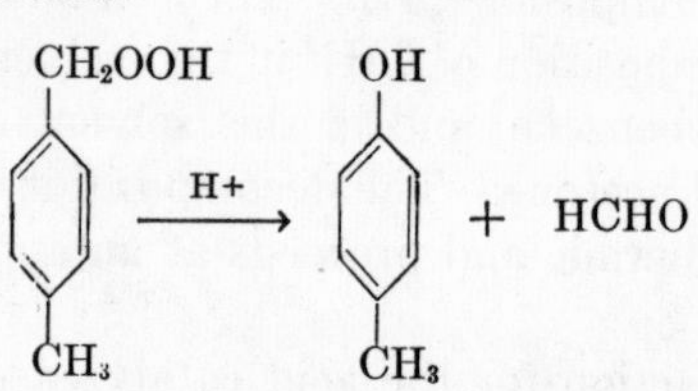 $CH_2OOH$ (benzene ring) $CH_3$ $\xrightarrow{H+}$ OH (benzene ring) $CH_3$ + HCHO

The question of course arises as to which group $R_1$, $R_2$, or $R_3$ in equation (2) will migrate to form ROH. The above examples (eqs. 1 and 3–6) show that aryl groups or allylic groups migrate to the complete exclusion of alkyl groups or hydrogen. Among the substituted aryls, the group of greatest electron donating power migrates. For example, the reaction of mono-*p*-nitrotriphenylmethyl hydroperoxide with sulfuric or perchloric acid proceeds as follows:[66]

$$(7)\quad NO_2C_6H_4\text{—}\underset{C_6H_5}{\overset{C_6H_5}{C}}\text{—}OOH \xrightarrow{H+} C_6H_5OH + NO_2C_6H_4COC_6H_5$$

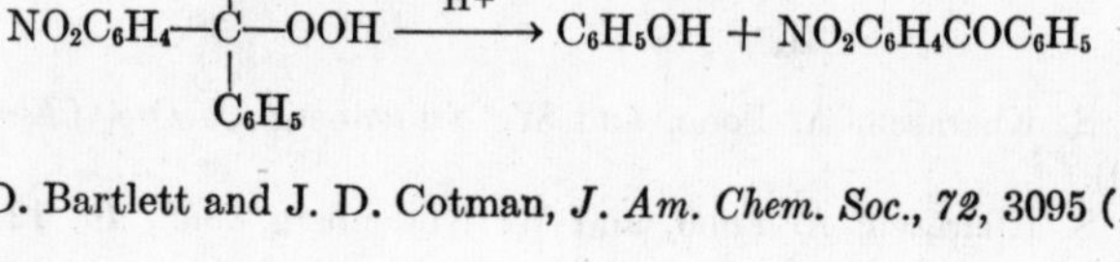

[66] P. D. Bartlett and J. D. Cotman, *J. Am. Chem. Soc.*, *72*, 3095 (1950).

In this case the phenyl group migrates rather than the electron attracting *p*-nitrophenyl group. On the hand, simple heating of the above hydroperoxide yields more *p*-nitrophenol than phenol, suggesting that, under conditions of free radical fission of the O—O bond, the *p*-nitrophenyl group has a greater migration aptitude than the phenyl.

$$NO_2C_6H_4\text{—}\underset{C_6H_5}{\overset{C_6H_5}{\underset{|}{\overset{|}{C}}}}\text{—OOH} \xrightarrow{\text{heat}} NO_2C_6H_4OH + C_6H_5COC_6H_5 \tag{8}$$

The kinetics of the decomposition of cumene hydroperoxide to phenol and acetone in 50 per cent aqueous acetic acid containing various amounts of *p*-toluenesulfonic acid has been investigated by Seubold and Vaughan.[67] The ionic strength of the solution was maintained at unity by addition of lithium chloride where necessary. Although the acetic acid increases the solubility of the cumene hydroperoxide, it was shown that catalysis of the decomposition by molecular acetic acid was negligible. The reaction exhibits specific acid catalysis by the hydronium ion. The rate of decomposition was shown to obey the following rate law very accurately.

$$-\frac{d[\text{ROOH}]}{dt} = k_2\,[H_3O^+][\text{ROOH}] \tag{9}$$

where:

$$k_2 = 1 \times 10^{10} \exp\{-21.3 \text{ kcal.}/RT\} \text{ kg. mole}^{-1} \text{ sec.}^{-1} \tag{10}$$

The probable mechanism for the decomposition postulated by Seubold and Vaughan is:

$$C_6H_5\text{—}\underset{CH_3}{\overset{CH_3}{\underset{|}{\overset{|}{C}}}}\text{—OOH} + H^+ \overset{K}{\rightleftharpoons} C_6H_5\text{—}\underset{CH_3}{\overset{CH_3}{\underset{|}{\overset{|}{C}}}}\text{—}OOH_2^+ \tag{11}$$

$$C_6H_5\text{—}\underset{CH_3}{\overset{CH_3}{\underset{|}{\overset{|}{C}}}}\text{—}OOH_2^+ \xrightarrow[-H_2O]{k} CH_3\text{—}\underset{CH_3}{\overset{+}{\underset{|}{C}}}\text{—}OC_6H_5 \tag{12}$$

[67] F. H. Seubold and W. E. Vaughan, *J. Am. Chem. Soc.*, *75*, 3790 (1953).

or:

$$C_6H_5-\underset{CH_3}{\overset{CH_3}{C}}-OOH_2^+ \xrightarrow[-H_2O]{} C_6H_5-\underset{CH_3}{\overset{CH_3}{C}}-O^+ \longrightarrow CH_3-\underset{CH_3}{\overset{+}{C}}-OC_6H_5$$

$$\text{(13)}\quad CH_3-\underset{CH_3}{\overset{+}{C}}-OC_6H_5 + H_2O \longrightarrow CH_3-\underset{CH_3}{\overset{\overset{+}{OH_2}}{C}}-OC_6H_5 \longrightarrow C_6H_5OH + CH_3COCH_3 + H^+$$

In the above equations the hydronium ion $H_3O^+$ has been written as $H^+$ for simplicity.

The above mechanism (11–13) gives the following expression for the rate of disappearance of hydroperoxide.

$$\text{(14)}\quad -\frac{d[ROOH]}{dt} = kK[H_3O^+][ROOH] = k_2[H_3O^+][ROOH]$$

The measured rate constant $k_2$ is therefore the product of an equilibrium constant $K$ and a simple first order rate constant $k$. The measured "activation energy" of $k_2$, which is 21.3 kcal., is clearly the sum of a heat of reaction (for the equilibrium (11)) plus a true activation energy for the decomposition of the complex by equation (12).

### 5. *The Base Catalyzed Decomposition of Tertiary Hydroperoxides*[38b]

Under the influence of alkali (NaOH) most secondary hydroperoxides decompose at or above room temperature to give alcohols, ketones, and other products. Oxygen is not reported among the decomposition products of the secondary hydroperoxides thus far studied.

On the other hand, oxygen is one of the primary products arising from the base catalyzed decomposition of tertiary hydroperoxides.

An aqueous solution of cumene hydroperoxide decomposes relatively slowly in the presence of NaOH at temperatures below 60°. Under these relatively mild conditions the sodium salt of the hydroperoxide is formed. At temperatures between 60° and 100° the decomposition of CHP by NaOH is fairly rapid. Very significantly, at each temperature there appears to be an optimum concentration of NaOH for which the decomposition rate of CHP is most rapid. For example, an aqueous solution of CHP is relatively stable even at 90° when a large excess of alkali is added to it. Under these conditions the alkali salt of the hydroperoxide is formed. The decomposition is much faster with 20 mole per cent NaOH (based on CHP) than with a full equivalent of alkali.

This suggests that the main reaction responsible for the decomposition is attack of the $RO_2^-$ anion on the undissociated molecule of hydroperoxide.

$$\text{(1)} \qquad ROOH + NaOH \longrightarrow RO_2^- + Na^+ + H_2O$$

$$\text{(2)} \qquad RO_2^- + ROOH \longrightarrow RO^- + ROH + O_2$$

Other reactions also occur, since the decomposition of CHP by alkali between 60° and 100° produces not only oxygen and $\alpha$-cumyl alcohol but acetophenone, benzoic acid, and other products.

Certain additives such as succinonitrile, acrylonitrile, and carbon disulfide activate the basic decomposition of tertiary hydroperoxides in a (thus far) unexplained manner. With the additives present, CHP is decomposed quite rapidly by NaOH even at room temperature. Under these conditions a nearly stoichiometric production of oxygen and $\alpha$-cumyl alcohol is achieved.

If a *secondary* alcohol is present in a basic solution of *tertiary* hydroperoxide, there is a competition between oxygen formation (eq. 2) and oxidation of the alcohol to a ketone:

$$\text{(3)} \qquad RO_2^- + R'R''CHOH \longrightarrow RO^- + R'R''C(OH)_2 \longrightarrow R'R''C{=}O + H_2O + RO^-$$

Alcohols can also sometimes serve as the *base* to hydroperoxides as illustrated in the thermal decomposition of CHP in $\alpha$-phenylethanol at elevated temperatures. Considerable amounts of oxygen are formed during this decomposition. To explain this very interesting fact, one of the primary steps in the decomposition of CHP in $\alpha$-phenylethanol was postulated to be:

$$\text{(4)} \qquad C_6H_5(CH_3)_2COOH + C_6H_5(CH_3)CHOH \rightleftharpoons C_6H_5(CH_3)_2COO^- + [C_6H_5(CH_3)CHOH_2]^+$$

Oxygen is then produced by reaction (2).

### *6. The Base Catalyzed Decompositions of Secondary Hydroperoxides and Certain Dialkyl Peroxides*

Di-*t*-butyl peroxide is inert to bases such as potassium hydroxide or piperidine. On the other hand, potassium hydroxide, sodium ethoxide, and piperidine catalyze the decomposition of 1-phenylethyl-*t*-butyl peroxide:[68]

$$\text{(1)}\quad C_6H_5\text{—}\overset{\overset{CH_3}{|}}{\underset{\underset{H}{|}}{C}}\text{—O—O—}\overset{\overset{CH_3}{|}}{\underset{\underset{CH_3}{|}}{C}}\text{—}CH_3 \longrightarrow C_6H_5\text{—}\overset{\overset{O}{\|}}{C}\text{—}CH_3 + HO\text{—}\overset{\overset{CH_3}{|}}{\underset{\underset{CH_3}{|}}{C}}\text{—}CH_3$$

It is believed that only those dialkyl peroxides and alkyl hydroperoxides having a hydrogen on the carbon attached to the peroxide linkage will undergo base catalyzed decomposition. The mechanism is believed to be the following:

$$\text{(2)}\quad \bar{:}\text{Base} + C_6H_5\text{—}\overset{\overset{CH_3}{|}}{\underset{\underset{H}{|}}{C}}\text{—O—O—}C(CH_3)_3 \longrightarrow \text{H:Base} + [C_6H_5\overset{\overset{CH_3}{|}}{\underset{\cdot\cdot}{C}}\text{—O—O—}C(CH_3)_3]^-$$

$$\text{(3)}\quad [C_6H_5\text{—}\overset{\overset{CH_3}{|}}{\underset{\cdot\cdot}{C}}\text{—O—O—}C(CH_3)_3]^- \longrightarrow C_6H_5\text{—}\overset{\overset{CH_3}{|}}{C}\text{=O} + {}^-OC(CH_3)_3$$

$$\text{(4)}\quad (CH_3)_3C\text{—}O^- + \text{H:Base} \rightleftharpoons (CH_3)_3COH + \bar{:}\text{Base}$$

The decomposition of tetralin hydroperoxide to tetralone and water is catalyzed by bases such as sodium hydroxide. The mechanism described above explains this reaction as follows:

$$RR'CHOOH + \bar{:}\text{Base} \longrightarrow [RR'COOH]^- + \text{H:Base} \longrightarrow$$
$$RR'C\text{=O} + OH^- + \text{H:Base} \longrightarrow RR'C\text{=O} + HOH + \bar{:}\text{Base}$$

The mechanism, however, fails to explain the formation of cyclohexanol in the base catalyzed decomposition of cyclohexene hydroperoxide.

The fact that oxygen is not listed among the reported decomposition products of secondary hydroperoxides thus far studied indicates that the C—H linkage is more readily attacked by base than the O—H linkage.

[68] N. Kornblum and H. E. DeLamare, *J. Am. Chem. Soc.*, *73*, 880 (1951).

# C. INITIATION OF VINYL POLYMERIZATION BY PEROXIDE DECOMPOSITION

## I. General Nature of Vinyl Type Polymerization

### *1. Introduction*

The vinyl monomers may be regarded as monosubstituted derivatives of ethylene, of the structure $CH_2{=}CHX$. One must, however, include in any discussion of vinyl polymerization monomers of the following general structures (where X and Y are substituents other than hydrogen):

| | | |
|---|---|---|
| (1) | $CH_2{=}CHX$ | Vinyl monomers |
| (2) | $CH_2{=}CXY$ | 1,1-Disubstituted ethylenes and vinylidene monomers |
| (3) | $CHX{=}CHY$ | 1,2-Disubstituted ethylenes |
| (4) | $CF_2{=}CXY$ | Tetrafluoroethylene derivatives |
| (5) | $CH_2{=}CH{-}CH{=}CH_2$ | Butadiene and butadiene derivatives |

These substances shall be referred to as vinyl type monomers, or more simply and less accurately, as vinyl monomers and their conversion to high polymers shall be referred to as vinyl polymerization.

Not all compounds which have structures corresponding to those written above have been polymerized, at least to the present date. However, it is quite striking how very high a proportion *have* been converted into high polymers. It is equally notable how high a proportion of these polymers have proved to be of commercial importance.

The phenomenon of copolymerization, in which mixtures of any of the above-mentioned substances are allowed to coreact to produce chain molecules with residues of each monomer incorporated in the chain, enhances enormously the synthetic possibilities. In many cases, monomers such as the 1,2-disubstituted ethylenes which polymerize with difficulty by themselves will enter into copolymerization reactions with great ease.

Vinyl-type polymerization may be propagated by a free radical chain mechanism, a carbonium ion chain mechanism, or a carbanion chain mechanism, depending on the type of catalyst employed. This also enhances the synthetic possibilities since monomers such as isobutylene and propylene, for example, which cannot be polymerized by free radical producing catalysts, will polymerize very readily in the presence of cationic catalysts. However, vinyl polymerization initiated by radical producing catalysts and therefore propagated by growing free radical chains is the most widely used and most important mechanism.

Table C-1 presents a partial list of vinyl type monomers. The monomers discussed most frequently in this chapter are styrene (I) and methyl methacrylate (II).

$$CH_2{=}CH(C_6H_5) \quad \text{(I) Styrene}$$

$$CH_2{=}C(CH_3)\text{—}C({=}O)\text{—}OCH_3 \quad \text{(II) Methyl methacrylate}$$

TABLE C-1

Partial List of Vinyl, Vinylidene, and Diene Monomers

| 1. Monomers Having the Structure $CH_2{=}CHX$ | |
|---|---|
| Ethylene | $H_2C{=}CH_2$ |
| Vinyl chloride | $H_2C{=}CH\text{—}Cl$ |
| Vinyl acetate | $H_2C{=}CH\text{—}OCOCH_3$ |
| Acrylic acid | $H_2C{=}CH\text{—}COOH$ |
| Methyl acrylate | $H_2C{=}CH\text{—}COOCH_3$ |
| Ethyl acrylate | $H_2C{=}CH\text{—}COOC_2H_5$ |
| Allyl chloride | $H_2C{=}CHCH_2Cl$ |
| Acrylonitrile | $H_2C{=}CH\text{—}CN$ |
| Acrylamide | $H_2C{=}CH\text{—}CONH_2$ |

TABLE C-1 (*Continued*)

|  |  |
|---|---|
| Styrene | $H_2C{=}CH-C_6H_5$ |
| 2,5-Dichlorostyrene | $H_2C{=}CH-C_6H_3Cl_2$ (Cl at 2- and 5-positions) |
| 4-Vinylpyridine | $H_2C{=}CH-C_5H_4N$ (4-pyridyl) |
| *n*-Vinylpyrrolidone | $H_2C{=}CH-N$ (ring: $CH_2-CH_2-CH_2-C{=}O$) |
| Vinylnaphthalene | $H_2C{=}CH-C_{10}H_7$ |
| 2. Monomers Having the Structure $CH_2{=}CXY$ | |
| Isobutylene | $H_2C{=}C(CH_3)_2$ |
| Vinylidene chloride | $H_2C{=}C(Cl)_2$ |
| Methyl methacrylate | $H_2C{=}C(CH_3)-COOCH_3$ |
| α-Methylstyrene | $H_2C{=}C(C_6H_5)-CH_3$ |
| Vinylidene chlorocyanide | $H_2C{=}C(CN)-Cl$ |
| 2-Nitropropene | $H_2C{=}C(NO_2)-CH_3$ |

*Table continued*

TABLE C-1 (*Continued*)

| | |
|---|---|
| **3. Monomers Having the Structure CHX=CHY** | |
| Maleic anhydride | 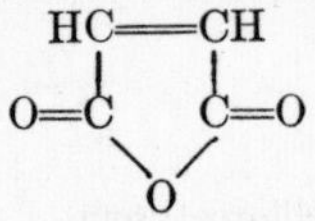 |
| Crotonic acid | $CH_3CH{=}CHCOOH$ |
| Acenaphthalene | 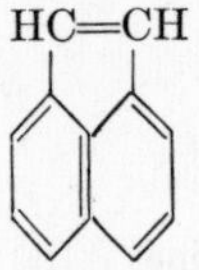 |
| Coumarone | 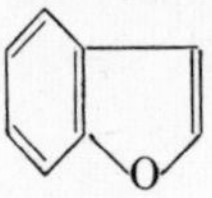 |
| Indene | 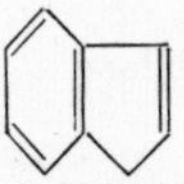 |
| **4. Derivatives of Tetrafluoroethylene Having the Structure $CF_2{=}CXY$** | |
| Tetrafluoroethylene | $F_2C{=}CF_2$ |
| Trifluoromonochloroethylene | $F_2C{=}CFCl$ |
| **5. Butadiene and Derivatives of Butadiene** | |
| Butadiene | $H_2C{=}CH{-}CH{=}CH_2$ |
| Chloroprene | $H_2C{=}C(Cl){-}CH{=}CH_2$ |
| Isoprene | $H_2C{=}C(CH_3){-}CH{=}CH_2$ |
| 2,3-Dimethylbutadiene | $H_2C{=}C(CH_3){-}C(CH_3){=}CH_2$ |

## 2. *Size Distribution and Average Degree of Polymerization*

Vinyl-type monomers containing one double bond are bifunctional compounds in the sense originated by Carothers.[1] These molecules will in general polymerize to linear chain molecules.

$$x CH_2{=}CHX \longrightarrow Y{-}(CH_2CHX)_x{-}Z \qquad (1)$$

[1] *Collected Works of Wallace Hume Carothers on High Polymeric Substances*, Interscience, New York-London, 1940.

where Y and Z are end groups which may be fragments of the initiator or fragments of the solvent in which the polymerization was carried out. Frequently the simple linear structure of the polymer is modified by the existence of several branches, which will be explained in a later section. The polymeric substance that is formed is never monodisperse, but consists of a mixture of molecular species of all sizes. The degree of polymerization of a single molecule may be identified with the quantity $x$ in equation (1). The distribution of sizes is defined by the discrete function $N(x)$, which is the number of moles of $x$-mer in the heterodisperse polymeric system. Two types of average degrees of polymerization are of particular importance: the number-average degree of polymerization, $\bar{P}_n$, and the weight-average degree of polymerization, $\bar{P}_w$. These are defined as follows:

$$\bar{P}_n = \sum xN(x)/\sum N(x) \tag{2}$$

$$\bar{P}_w = \sum x^2N(x)/\sum xN(x) \tag{3}$$

The summations are carried out over molecular species of all sizes except for unreacted monomer. The quantities $\bar{P}_n$ and $\bar{P}_w$ partially specify the size distribution. They are of particular importance because they can be measured experimentally, the former by measuring colligative properties such as the osmotic pressure, the latter by measuring turbidity (light scattering from solutions of the polymer). The complete distribution of sizes $N(x)$ can be obtained only by fractionation.[2]

### 3. *Distinguishing Characteristics of Vinyl Polymerization Proceeding via a Free Radical Mechanism*

Highly purified styrene and methyl methacrylate can be polymerized by heat alone or by ultraviolet radiation. These polymerizations are referred to as thermal polymerization and photopolymerization, respectively. Small amounts of substances which decompose thermally into active free radicals markedly accelerate the polymerization of these and other vinyl monomers. Similarly, substances which are decomposed into active free radicals by ultraviolet light or even visible light will markedly accelerate the photopolymerization.

[2] H. Mark and A. V. Tobolsky, *The Physical Chemistry of High Polymeric Systems*, Interscience, New York-London, 1950, Chapters II and VIII.

All the above-mentioned polymerizations proceed via the same (free radical) mechanism. This is strikingly demonstrated by copolymerization studies, because an equimolar mixture of styrene and methyl methacrylate will produce a copolymer containing 51 per cent styrene when polymerized by any of the above-mentioned methods. On the other hand, such a mixture will give a copolymer containing more than 99 per cent styrene when polymerized by cationic catalysts such as $AlCl_3$; the same mixture will give a copolymer containing more than 99 per cent methyl methacrylate when polymerized by anionic catalysts such as metal alkyls.[3]

Among the substances which catalyze the polymerization of vinyl monomers via a radical mechanism are first and foremost peroxides, also azo compounds, persulfates, and disulfides.

Vinyl polymerization proceeding via a radical mechanism is strikingly different in its kinetic aspects from a stepwise condensation reaction which is characteristic of materials such as hydroxy acids, $HO(CH_2)_xCOOH$. In the latter case, the degree of polymerization increases as the fraction of reacted functional groups increases. High polymers can be obtained only when nearly all the functional groups have reacted. Furthermore, there is no sharp distinction between unreacted monomer and polymer in the size distribution of a condensation polymer. On the other hand, in vinyl-type polymerization, very high molecular weight polymer is produced from the very beginning of reaction. Very often the average degree of polymerization remains relatively independent of the per cent conversion.

Vinyl polymerization is, kinetically speaking, a chain reaction. This is borne out by the fact that very small traces of foreign substances, *e.g.*, peroxides, may exert a very marked catalytic effect. Specifically, a certain very highly purified vinyl monomer such as vinyl acetate may show no appreciable thermal polymerization rate at 40°C. The addition of 0.01 mole per cent of benzoyl peroxide will cause a very rapid polymerization. Many hundreds of molecules of monomer will polymerize for every molecule of benzoyl peroxide that decomposes. Obviously a reaction chain is necessary to explain this fact, just as a reaction chain is necessary to explain why one quantum of absorbed radiation can cause the formation of thousands of HCl molecules in a purified mixture of hydrogen and chlorine.

[3] C. Walling, E. R. Briggs, W. Cummings, and F. R. Mayo, *J. Am. Chem. Soc.*, *72*, 48 (1950).

Similarly, very small quantities of substances such as oxygen, iodine, sulfur, quinones, primary and secondary amines, nitro compounds, and polyhydroxy derivatives of benzene exert a profound inhibitory effect on vinyl polymerizations. In these cases it can be shown that each molecule of inhibitor consumed prevents the polymerization of hundreds of molecules of monomer.

End group analysis confirms the fact that fragments of the initiators used are often found on the ends of the polymer chains.[4] In the case of inhibitors, low molecular adducts of the monomer and inhibitor can often be isolated, indicating that the inhibitor combined with a growing polymer chain before the latter had the chance to add many (or any) monomer units.

One must conclude that the initiation process in this type of polymerization is the following:

$$\text{(1)} \quad R\uparrow + CH_2 \overset{\uparrow\downarrow}{\text{——}} CHX \longrightarrow R\uparrow\downarrow CH_2CHX\uparrow \longrightarrow RCH_2CHX\cdot$$

where $R\uparrow$ represents a free radical arising from the homolytic cleavage of the initiator:

$$\text{(2)} \quad R{:}R \longrightarrow R\cdot + R\cdot$$

The notation $R\cdot$ and $R\uparrow$ are used interchangeably, the arrow merely representing the fact that the odd electron has a spin. The driving force of the reaction between the odd electron on the initiator fragment and the $\pi$ electrons (unsaturation electrons) of the double bond in the monomer is the tendency for two electrons of opposite spin to couple and form a covalent bond. This same driving force is responsible for the continued growth of the polymer chain (the propagation steps):

$$\text{(3)} \quad RCH_2CHX\cdot + CH_2 \overset{\cdot}{\underset{\cdot}{-}} CHX \longrightarrow RCH_2CHXCH_2CHX\cdot \qquad \text{etc.}$$

## 4. *The Elementary Steps in Vinyl Polymerization*

The simplest kinetic situation for vinyl-type polymerization is obtained when a pure vinyl monomer such as styrene or methyl methacrylate is polymerized under constant temperature conditions through the agency of a radical producing catalyst such as benzoyl peroxide. For a homogeneous reaction the polymer and the catalyst should

[4] C. C. Price, *Reactions at Carbon-Carbon Double Bonds,* Interscience, New York-London, 1946.

both be soluble in the monomer. Furthermore one should restrict the discussion to the initial phases of the polymerization (less than 15 per cent of monomer converted to polymer). The discussion can also be extended to the case where the polymerization is carried out in an "ideal" solvent. The definition of an ideal solvent will be clarified in further discussion.

The reaction steps for polymerization under these conditions are:

*Decomposition of Catalyst*

(1) $$\text{Catalyst} \longrightarrow 2\text{R}\cdot$$

The rate of spontaneous homolytic decomposition of the catalyst is $k_d$[Cat]. The rate of formation of primary radicals from the catalyst is $2k_d$[Cat].

*Initiation of Polymer Chains*

(2) $$\text{R}\cdot + \text{M} \longrightarrow \text{RM}_1\cdot$$

The rate of initiation of polymer chains will be denoted by $R_i$.

*Propagation of Polymer Chains*

(3) $$\text{RM}_n\cdot + \text{M} \xrightarrow{k_p} \text{RM}_{n+1}\cdot$$

It is assumed that $k_p$ is the same for the growth of polymeric species of all kinds. The rate of disappearance of monomer by reaction (3) is $k_p[\text{RM}_n\cdot][\text{M}]$.

Let the total concentration of polymeric radicals of all types be denoted by [C*]:

(4) $$[\text{C}^*] = \sum_{n=1}^{\infty} [\text{RM}_n\cdot]$$

Monomer disappears by reactions (2) and (3). The total rate of disappearance of monomer is denoted by $R_p$ (the rate of polymerization) and is given by:

(5) $$\text{R}_p = \text{R}_i + k_p[\text{C}^*][\text{M}]$$

Under almost all circumstances the second term on the right hand side is enormously larger than the first term. The ratio of these two terms is the kinetic chain length of the chain reaction. The material chain length (degree of polymerization) cannot exceed twice the kinetic chain length. Hence in all cases where *high* polymers are formed:

(6) $$R_p = k_p[C^*][M]$$

*Termination of Growing Polymer Chains*

(7) $$RM_n\cdot + RM_p\cdot \xrightarrow{k_{tc}} RM_{n+p}R$$

(8) $$RM_n\cdot + RM_p\cdot \xrightarrow{k_{td}} RM_n + RM_p$$

Two types of termination are possible, although it now appears that one of these predominates under usual conditions. The first is combination (eq. 7); the second is disproportionation (eq. 8). The notation $RM_n$ and $RM_p$ refers to polymeric chains which no longer have their radical activity. The mechanisms of combination and disproportionation are illustrated below in the case of the vinyl monomer $CH_2{=}CHX$:

$$R(CH_2CHX)_{n-1}CH_2CHX\cdot + \cdot CHXCH_2(CHXCH_2)_{p-1}R \xrightarrow{k_{tc}} R(CH_2CHX)_{n+p}R$$

$$R(CH_2CHX)_{n-1}CH_2CHX\cdot + \cdot CHXCH_2(CHXCH_2)_{p-1}R \xrightarrow{k_{td}} R(CH_2CHX)_{n-1}CH_2CH_2X + CHX{=}CH(CHXCH_2)_{p-1}R$$

The rate of disappearance of pairs of radicals by combination and disproportionation respectively is $k_{tc}[C^*]^2$ and $k_{td}[C^*]^2$. The rates of disappearance of *radicals* (moles per liter per second) by these processes are $2k_{tc}[C^*]^2$ and $2k_{td}[C^*]^2$. It is assumed that $k_{tc}$ and $k_{td}$ are independent of the size of the polymeric radicals.

*Transfer Reactions*

The growing polymer radicals can interact with solvent, monomer, initiator, or polymer in the following ways:

(9) $$RM_n\cdot + S \xrightarrow{k_{tr,s}} RM_n + S\cdot$$

(10) $$RM_n\cdot + M \xrightarrow{k_{tr,m}} RM_n + M\cdot$$

(11) $$RM_n\cdot + Cat \xrightarrow{k_{tr,cat}} RM_n + Cat\cdot$$

(12) $$RM_n\cdot + P \xrightarrow{k_{tr,p}} RM_n + P\cdot$$

In the above equations S, M, Cat, and P refer to molecules of solvent, monomer, initiator, and polymer, respectively. These reactions are illustrated for the monomer $CH_2{=}CHX$ for the cases in which toluene and carbon tetrachloride are the solvents and *t*-butyl hydroperoxide is the initiator.

$$RM_n\cdot + C_6H_5CH_3 \longrightarrow RM_nH + C_6H_5CH_2\cdot \tag{13}$$

$$RM_n\cdot + CCl_4 \longrightarrow RM_nCl + CCl_3\cdot \tag{14}$$

$$RM_n\cdot + CH_2{=}CHX \longrightarrow RM_nH + CH_2{=}\dot{C}X \tag{15}$$

$$RM_n\cdot + (CH_3)_3COOH \longrightarrow RM_nH + (CH_3)_3COO\cdot \tag{16}$$

*or*

$$RM_n\cdot + (CH_3)_3COOH \longrightarrow RM_nOH + (CH_3)_3CO\cdot$$

$$RM_n\cdot + RM_pCH_2CHXM_mR \longrightarrow RM_nH + RM_pCH_2\dot{C}XM_mR \tag{17}$$

If the solvent radicals produced by interaction of the solvent with the growing chain (*e.g.*, $C_6H_5CH_2\cdot$ and $CCl_3\cdot$ in the cases illustrated above) react very rapidly with a monomer molecule to start a new growing polymer chain, the solvent may be termed an ideal solvent. When a polymerization is carried out in the presence of such a solvent, the molecular weight of the polymer is markedly affected by the nature of the particular solvent, but the rate of polymerization is affected only by the change of monomer concentration, and is therefore independent of the solvent used at a fixed molar concentration of monomer. If, on the other hand, the radicals produced by the interaction of growing polymer chains with the solvent do not react rapidly with monomer to start new polymer chains, but instead undergo wasteful reactions such as recombination *e.g.*:

$$2C_6H_5CH_2\cdot \longrightarrow C_6H_5CH_2CH_2C_6H_5$$

the solvent is in reality an inhibitor or retarder. In the case of styrene polymerized in toluene, the benzyl radicals formed are fairly reactive toward addition to a monomer molecule and most of them apparently react in this fashion rather than by recombination to form dibenzyl. Toluene is therefore a fairly "ideal" solvent for styrene polymerization, and is not considered as an inhibitor or a retarder. A solvent which exhibits no tendency to enter into transfer reactions may be considered an "inert" solvent.

Substances which are regarded as effective inhibitors or retarders must exert potent effects in very small concentrations. This means that these substances must have a *very* high reactivity toward growing polymer chains (or to the radicals produced by the catalyst), in addition to their property discussed above of forming radicals which do not readily start new polymer chains.

Chain transfer to monomer may occur by the mechanism shown in equation (15) or by transfer of an atom (*e.g.*, a hydrogen atom) from the growing polymer chain to the monomer.

Chain transfer to the initiator, illustrated in equation (16) for the initiator (catalyst) *t*-butyl hydroperoxide, is an example of the multiple role that many reagents have in vinyl-type polymerization.

When growing polymer radicals interact with completed polymer molecules as shown in equation (17), the net effect of the reaction is to transfer radical activity from the end of a polymer chain to some other atom along the chain. This does not affect the rate of polymerization or the number average degree of polymerization of the polymer formed, but causes the production of branched rather than linear polymer molecules.

The rates of all the transfer reactions discussed above (eqs. 9 through 12) are given by:

(18) $$\text{Rate of transfer} = k_{tr,x}[C^*][X]$$

## II. Kinetics of Vinyl Polymerization

### *1. Kinetic Measurements*

The usual type of kinetic study of vinyl polymerization in homogeneous media is exemplified by the researches of G. V. Schulz.[5] In this work a measured amount of benzoyl peroxide was dissolved in pure styrene (or in a solution of styrene in an ideal solvent) and the resulting solution sealed in evacuated tubes and maintained at constant temperature. (It is advisable to keep the solutions in thin tubes in order that the heat of polymerization may be effectively transferred to the surrounding bath.) After suitable time intervals, a tube was opened and the contents rapidly stirred into a large volume of methyl alcohol. This substance is a solvent for styrene monomer, but causes the precipitation of the polymer which appears in the form of a white, amorphous powder. The powder was filtered, dried to constant weight in a vacuum oven, and weighed. The per cent conversion of monomer to polymer was then calculated.

[5] G. V. Schulz and E. Husemann, *Z. physik. Chem.*, *B39*, 246 (1938).

The dried polymer can be redissolved in solvents such as benzene to form dilute polymer solutions. Osmotic pressure measurements made on these polymer solutions give the number-average degree of polymerization of the polymer; light scattering measurements on these same solutions give the weight-average degree of polymerization. Most frequently, however, intrinsic viscosity measurements are made on these polymer solutions because of their simplicity and rapidity. These measurements are converted to number-average degree of polymerization by means of empirically established equations whose constants are calibrated by osmotic pressure measurements.[2,6]

The important measured quantities are the rate of polymerization $R_p$ and the number-average degree of polymerization $\bar{P}_n$, both measured at the initial stages of the polymerization (less than 15 per cent conversion). $R_p$ and $\bar{P}_n$ are determined as functions of monomer concentration, catalyst concentration, and temperature.

Other methods are frequently utilized to measure the rate of polymerization. Since there is generally a measurable volume shrinkage when monomer is converted to polymer, dilatometric techniques have been employed very successfully. Similarly, measurements of refractive index change have been utilized as well as titration for unreacted double bonds in the monomer.

## 2. *Rate of Polymerization*

For a certain set of conditions, *i.e.*, fixed temperature and fixed catalyst and monomer concentrations, there is a definite rate of production of growing polymeric radicals in a polymerizing system which is denoted by $R_i$ (rate of initiation of polymer chains in mole liter$^{-1}$ sec.$^{-1}$). For a catalyzed polymerization $R_i$ is given by the following formula:

$$R_i = 2fk_d[\text{Cat}] + R_{i,th} \qquad (1)$$

In the above equation, $k_d$[Cat] is the rate of spontaneous first order homolytic cleavage of the catalyst. The factor 2 appears because 2 primary radicals are produced by every spontaneous cleavage (at

[6] (a) G. F. D'Alelio, *Experimental Plastics and Synthetic Resins*, Wiley, New York, 1946. (b) E. H. Immergut and K. G. Stern, in *Encyclopedia of Chemical Technology*, edited by R. E. Kirk and D. Othmer, Interscience, New York-London, Volume 9, 1952, page 643.

least for simple catalysts such as benzoyl peroxide). The factor $f$ is the catalyst efficiency, *i.e.*, the fraction of primary radicals which are effective in starting polymer chains. The second term on the right hand side is the rate of purely thermal initiation.

As in other chain reactions, a steady state concentration of active intermediates is rapidly attained. In this case the active intermediates are the growing polymer radicals, whose total concentration can be denoted by [C*]. The steady state condition is characterized by the fact that the rate of initiation of growing polymer radicals is equal to the rate of disappearance of the growing polymer radicals, *i.e.*:

$$R_i = (2k_{tc} + 2k_{td})[\mathrm{C}^*]^2 \qquad (2)$$

The rate of polymerization, $R_p$, is given by the formula:

$$-d[\mathrm{M}]/dt = R_p = k_p[\mathrm{C}^*][\mathrm{M}] \qquad (3)$$

From equations (2) and (3), one obtains:

$$R_p^2 = ([\mathrm{M}]^2/2A'')R_i \qquad (4)$$

where:

$$A'' = (k_{tc} + k_{td})/k_p^2 \qquad (5)$$

Substituting equation (1) in (4), the following is derived:

$$R_p^2 = \frac{R_{i,th}}{2A''}[\mathrm{M}]^2 + \frac{fk_d}{A''}[\mathrm{Cat}]\,[\mathrm{M}]^2 \qquad (6)$$

It has been found empirically that the rate, $R_p$, for catalyzed polymerizations can be expressed as follows:[7]

$$R_p^2 = R_{p,th}^2 + K^2[\mathrm{Cat}][\mathrm{M}]^2 \qquad (7)$$

where $R_{p,th}$ represents the purely thermal rate under the given conditions of temperature and monomer concentration and $K$ is an over-all rate constant. Equations (6) and (7) are in complete accord.* If the initiator is effective and is present in appreciable concentration, the contribution of the thermal polymerization is negligible and equation (7) becomes:

$$R_p = -d[\mathrm{M}]/dt \simeq K[\mathrm{Cat}]^{1/2}[\mathrm{M}] \qquad (8)$$

* See Appendix 4 (p. 183 ff.).

[7] R. N. Haward and W. Simpson, *Trans. Faraday Soc.*, *47*, 212 (1951).

TABLE C-2*

Catalyzed Polymerization of Styrene: $R_p = K[\mathrm{M}][\mathrm{Cat}]^{1/2}$

| Catalyst | $T$, °C. | $K$ | $R_i'/[\mathrm{Cat}]$ | Ref. |
|---|---|---|---|---|
| Benzoyl peroxide | 27 | $1.19 \times 10^{-6}$ | $2.73 \times 10^{-8}$ | a |
| | 34.8 | $4.12 \times 10^{-6}$ | $1.93 \times 10^{-7}$ | b |
| | 40 | $6.30 \times 10^{-6}$ | $3.12 \times 10^{-7}$ | i |
| | 40 | $6.42 \times 10^{-6}$ | $3.25 \times 10^{-7}$ | j |
| | 49.4 | $1.89 \times 10^{-5}$ | $1.54 \times 10^{-6}$ | b |
| | 50 | $1.24 \times 10^{-5}$ | $6.49 \times 10^{-7}$ | a |
| | 50 | $1.83 \times 10^{-5}$ | $1.41 \times 10^{-6}$ | j |
| | 54 | $2.24 \times 10^{-5}$ | $1.69 \times 10^{-6}$ | c |
| | 60 | $4.18 \times 10^{-5}$ | $4.16 \times 10^{-6}$ | d |
| | 60 | $4.85 \times 10^{-5}$ | $5.60 \times 10^{-6}$ | e |
| | 60 | $4.32 \times 10^{-5}$ | $4.45 \times 10^{-6}$ | i |
| | 60 | $4.90 \times 10^{-5}$ | $5.71 \times 10^{-6}$ | j |
| | 61 | $5.18 \times 10^{-5}$ | $5.96 \times 10^{-6}$ | b |
| | 64 | $5.93 \times 10^{-5}$ | $6.96 \times 10^{-6}$ | c |
| | 70 | $1.29 \times 10^{-4}$ | $2.28 \times 10^{-5}$ | j |
| | 74 | $1.57 \times 10^{-4}$ | $2.69 \times 10^{-5}$ | c |
| | 74.8 | $1.89 \times 10^{-4}$ | $3.72 \times 10^{-5}$ | b |
| | 80 | $2.76 \times 10^{-4}$ | $6.15 \times 10^{-5}$ | i |
| | 100 | $1.40 \times 10^{-3}$ | $5.89 \times 10^{-4}$ | j |
| Lauroyl peroxide | 34.8 | $6.46 \times 10^{-6}$ | $4.76 \times 10^{-7}$ | b |
| | 49.4 | $2.78 \times 10^{-5}$ | $3.33 \times 10^{-6}$ | b |
| | 61.0 | $9.24 \times 10^{-5}$ | $1.89 \times 10^{-5}$ | b |
| | 70 | $2.10 \times 10^{-4}$ | $6.05 \times 10^{-5}$ | j |
| | 74.8 | $2.67 \times 10^{-4}$ | $7.41 \times 10^{-5}$ | b |
| | 100 | $2.58 \times 10^{-3}$ | $1.99 \times 10^{-3}$ | j |
| Bi[illegible]lorobenzoyl peroxide | 34.8 | $3.52 \times 10^{-6}$ | $1.41 \times 10^{-7}$ | b |
| | 49.4 | $1.69 \times 10^{-5}$ | $1.23 \times 10^{-6}$ | b |
| | 61.0 | $5.06 \times 10^{-5}$ | $5.69 \times 10^{-6}$ | b |
| | 70 | $1.12 \times 10^{-4}$ | $1.72 \times 10^{-5}$ | j |
| | 74.8 | $1.59 \times 10^{-4}$ | $2.64 \times 10^{-5}$ | b |
| | 100 | $1.22 \times 10^{-3}$ | $4.46 \times 10^{-4}$ | b |
| Bis-2,4-dichlorobenzoyl peroxide | 34.8 | $9.70 \times 10^{-6}$ | $1.07 \times 10^{-6}$ | b |
| | 49.4 | $3.85 \times 10^{-5}$ | $6.40 \times 10^{-6}$ | b |
| | 61.0 | $1.28 \times 10^{-4}$ | $3.64 \times 10^{-5}$ | b |
| | 74.8 | $3.90 \times 10^{-4}$ | $1.58 \times 10^{-4}$ | b |
| | 100 | $3.04 \times 10^{-3}$ | $2.77 \times 10^{-3}$ | b |
| Di-1-naphthoyl peroxide | 40 | $3.47 \times 10^{-5}$ | $9.48 \times 10^{-6}$ | j |
| | 50 | $1.08 \times 10^{-4}$ | $4.93 \times 10^{-5}$ | j |
| | 60 | $2.71 \times 10^{-4}$ | $1.75 \times 10^{-4}$ | j |
| | 70 | $7.35 \times 10^{-4}$ | $7.39 \times 10^{-4}$ | j |
| *t*-Butyl hydroperoxide | 60 | $9.41 \times 10^{-6}$ | $2.11 \times 10^{-7}$ | i |
| | 60 | $7.64 \times 10^{-5}$ | $1.39 \times 10^{-7}$ | d |
| | 80 | $4.51 \times 10^{-5}$ | $1.64 \times 10^{-6}$ | i |
| | 100 | $2.03 \times 10^{-4}$ | $1.24 \times 10^{-5}$ | i |
| *t*-Butyl perbenzoate | 40 | $7.25 \times 10^{-7}$ | $4.13 \times 10^{-9}$ | i |
| | 60 | $7.18 \times 10^{-6}$ | $1.22 \times 10^{-7}$ | i |
| | 80 | $5.31 \times 10^{-5}$ | $2.28 \times 10^{-6}$ | i |

TABLE C-2 (*Continued*)

| Catalyst | $T$, °C. | $K$ | $R_i'/[\text{Cat}]$ | Ref. |
|---|---|---|---|---|
| Cumene hydroperoxide | 60 | $1.90 \times 10^{-5}$ | $8.58 \times 10^{-7}$ | d |
| Di-*t*-butyl peroxide | 80 | $1.69 \times 10^{-5}$ | $2.31 \times 10^{-7}$ | i |
| Cyclohexyl hydroperoxide | 70 | $3.04 \times 10^{-5}$ | $1.26 \times 10^{-6}$ | h |
| Diisopropylperoxy dicarbonate | 54 | $1.22 \times 10^{-4}$ | $4.99 \times 10^{-5}$ | c |
| Acetyl peroxide | 70 | $2.18 \times 10^{-4}$ | $6.50 \times 10^{-5}$ | j |
| 2-Azobisisobutyronitrile | 40 | $1.15 \times 10^{-5}$ | $1.04 \times 10^{-6}$ | i |
| | 47.8 | $1.90 \times 10^{-5}$ | $1.76 \times 10^{-6}$ | f |
| | 60 | $8.61 \times 10^{-5}$ | $1.77 \times 10^{-5}$ | d |
| | 67.8 | $1.28 \times 10^{-4}$ | $2.53 \times 10^{-5}$ | f |
| | 80 | $4.57 \times 10^{-4}$ | $1.70 \times 10^{-4}$ | i |
| Benzene diazotriphenylmethyl | 50 | $4.73 \times 10^{-7}$ | $9.46 \times 10^{-10}$ | g |
| 2-Azobiscyclohexane carbonitrile | 80.3 | $1.17 \times 10^{-5}$ | $1.08 \times 10^{-7}$ | f |
| Tetraphenyl succinonitrile[a] | 100 | $4.18 \times 10^{-4}$ | $5.23 \times 10^{-5}$ | g |
| **Catalyzed Polymerization of Methyl Methacrylate: $R_p = K[\text{M}][\text{Cat}]^{1/2}$** | | | | |
| Benzoyl peroxide | 30 | $9.91 \times 10^{-6}$ | $8.35 \times 10^{-8}$ | k |
| | 50 | $8.54 \times 10^{-5}$ | $1.49 \times 10^{-6}$ | k |
| | 60 | $2.23 \times 10^{-4}$ | $6.86 \times 10^{-6}$ | l |
| | 70 | $5.71 \times 10^{-4}$ | $2.91 \times 10^{-5}$ | k |
| | 80 | $9.17 \times 10^{-4}$ | $4.95 \times 10^{-5}$ | m |
| | 90 | $2.71 \times 10^{-3}$ | $3.00 \times 10^{-4}$ | k |
| | 110 | $1.26 \times 10^{-2}$ | $3.34 \times 10^{-3}$ | k |
| 2,2′-Azobisisobutyronitrile | 50 | $1.27 \times 10^{-4}$ | $3.32 \times 10^{-6}$ | n |
| | 60 | $3.28 \times 10^{-4}$ | $1.48 \times 10^{-5}$ | l |
| | 77 | $1.38 \times 10^{-3}$ | $1.26 \times 10^{-4}$ | n |
| $\alpha,\alpha'$-Azobis-($\alpha,\alpha$-dimethylvaleronitrile) | 77 | $3.29 \times 10^{-3}$ | $7.17 \times 10^{-4}$ | n |
| 1,1′-Azobiscyclohexane carbonitrile | 77 | $2.90 \times 10^{-4}$ | $5.57 \times 10^{-6}$ | n |
| Methyl methacrylate ozonide | 80 | $3.51 \times 10^{-4}$ | $7.26 \times 10^{-6}$ | m |
| | 90 | $8.87 \times 10^{-4}$ | $3.22 \times 10^{-5}$ | m |
| Tetraphenylsuccinonitrile[a] | 113.5 | $9.67 \times 10^{-4}$ | $1.79 \times 10^{-5}$ | g |
| | 132.5 | $2.95 \times 10^{-3}$ | $9.35 \times 10^{-5}$ | g |
| Cumene hydroperoxide | 60 | $5.44 \times 10^{-5}$ | $4.10 \times 10^{-7}$ | l |
| *t*-Butyl hydroperoxide | 60 | $2.35 \times 10^{-5}$ | $7.65 \times 10^{-8}$ | l |

* A. V. Tobolsky and B. Baysal, *J. Polymer Sci.*, *11*, 471 (1953).

[a] This catalyst probably acts in a dual role; as initiator and retarder. See reference (i) for a discussion of this dual role.

(a) G. V. Schulz and E. Husemann, *Z. physik. Chem.*, *B39*, 246 (1938).
(b) L. E. Redington, *J. Polymer Sci.*, *3*, 503 (1948).
(c) S. G. Cohen, *J. Am. Chem. Soc.*, *72*, 612 (1950).
(d) D. H. Johnson and A. V. Tobolsky, *J. Am. Chem. Soc.*, *74*, 938 (1952).
(e) F. R. Mayo, R. A. Gregg, and M. S. Matheson, *J. Am. Chem. Soc.*, *73*, 1691 (1951).
(f) C. G. Overberger, P. Fram, and T. Alfrey, *J. Polymer Sci.*, *6*, 539 (1951).
(g) G. V. Schulz, *Z. Elektrochem.*, *47*, 265 (1941).
(h) A. Farkas and E. Passaglia, *J. Am. Chem. Soc.*, *72*, 3333 (1950).
(i) R. N. Haward and W. Simpson, *Trans. Faraday Soc.*, *47*, 212 (1951).
(j) W. Cooper, *J. Chem. Soc.*, *1951*, 3106.
(k) G. V. Schulz and F. Blaschke, *Z. physik. Chem.*, *51*, 75 (1942).
(l) B. Baysal and A. V. Tobolsky, *J. Polymer Sci.*, *8*, 529 (1952).
(m) R. G. W. Norrish and E. F. Brookman, *Proc. Royal Soc.* (*London*), *A171*, 147 (1939).
(n) L. M. Arnett, *J. Am. Chem. Soc.*, *74*, 2027 (1952).

It is clear from equation (8) that the polymerization rate is first order with respect to monomer concentration. However, for low conversions it can be assumed that one is dealing with a pseudo zero order reaction so that:

$$-d[\mathrm{M}]/dt = -\Delta[\mathrm{M}]/\Delta t$$

and [M] and [Cat] are taken equal to the initial concentrations $[\mathrm{M}]_0$ and $[\mathrm{Cat}]_0$.

$$K = -\frac{\Delta \mathrm{M}/\Delta t}{[\mathrm{Cat}]_0^{1/2}[\mathrm{M}]_0} \quad (9)$$

For a stricter interpretation of runs made at a fixed initial catalyst concentration but carried out to higher conversions, one first must note that the catalyst concentration remains relatively unchanged compared to the monomer concentration. The conversion–time data should then be plotted as ln[M] versus time, as befits a first order reaction. A straight line should be obtained whose intercept is $\ln[\mathrm{M}]_0$ and whose slope is $K[\mathrm{Cat}]_0^{1/2}$.

Equation (8) has, in fact, been used to express the results for catalyzed, homogeneous polymerizations initiated by a wide variety of catalysts in numerous monomers. Table C-2 gives a list of $K$ values obtained with styrene and methyl methacrylate using various initiators at several temperatures. The item given in the fourth column, $R_i'/[\mathrm{Cat}]$, will be discussed later (section III-3).

### (3) *Number-Average Degree of Polymerization*

The number-average degree of polymerization, $\bar{P}_n$, of the polymer produced at any given moment during homogeneous, monoradical catalyzed vinyl polymerization can be calculated from formula (1).[8]

$$\bar{P}_n = \frac{\text{Rate of Polymerization}}{1/2 \times \text{rate of formation of chain ends}} \quad (1)$$

Equation (1) follows inasmuch as $\bar{P}_n$ is equal to the total number of monomer segments incorporated in the polymer divided by the number of polymer molecules.

[8] F. R. Mayo, R. A. Gregg, and M. S. Matheson, *J. Am. Chem. Soc.*, *73*, 1691 (1951).

The rate of polymerization is given by $R_p = k_p[C^*][M]$. The number of chain ends produced in each transfer step and in each disproportionation step is two, whereas each initiation step produces one chain end, and combination produces no chain ends. Using the definitions for the specific rate constants given in section I-4 and inverting equation (1), one obtains (2).[9]

$$\text{(2)} \quad \frac{1}{\bar{P}_n} = \frac{{}^1/_2 R_i + k_{td}[C^*]^2 + k_{tr,m}[C^*][M] + k_{tr,cat}[C^*][Cat] + k_{tr,s}[C^*][S]}{k_p[C^*][M]}$$

Using the relations $R_i = (2k_{tc} + 2k_{td})[C^*]^2$ and $R_p = k_p[C^*][M]$, equation (2) may be converted to equation (3).

$$\text{(3)} \quad \frac{1}{\bar{P}_n} = C_{tr,m} + C_{tr,cat}\frac{[Cat]}{[M]} + C_{tr,s}\frac{[S]}{[M]} + \frac{A'R_p}{[M]^2}$$

$$A' = (2k_{td} + k_{tc})/k_p^2$$
$$C_{tr,m} = k_{tr,m}/k_p$$
$$C_{tr,cat} = k_{tr,cat}/k_p$$
$$C_{tr,s} = k_{tr,s}/k_p$$

The quantities $C_{tr,m}$, $C_{tr,cat}$, and $C_{tr,s}$ are called chain transfer constants and refer to the transfer reaction of growing radicals with monomer, catalyst, and solvent, respectively.

If in equation (3) the catalyst concentration is eliminated by means of $R_p = K[M][Cat]^{1/2}$ one obtains equation (4).[9]

$$\text{(4)} \quad \frac{1}{\bar{P}_n} = C_{tr,m} + \frac{C_{tr,cat}R_p^2}{K^2[M]^3} + C_{tr,s}\frac{[S]}{[M]} + \frac{A'R_p}{[M]^2}$$

For bulk polymerization (absence of solvent) equation (4) reduces to (5).

$$\text{(5)} \quad \frac{1}{\bar{P}_n} = C_{tr,m} + \frac{C_{tr,cat}R_p^2}{K^2[M]^3} + \frac{A'R_p}{[M]^2}$$

In Figure 1 are shown plots of $1/\bar{P}_n$ versus $R_p$ for styrene and methyl methacrylate at 60° initiated by 2-azobisisobutyronitrile (AZO-I), benzoyl peroxide ($Bz_2O_2$), cumene hydroperoxide (CHP), and tertiary butyl hydroperoxide (BHP). For both monomers these plots are straight lines for the catalyst AZO-I, indicating (from eq. 5)

[9] D. H. Johnson and A. V. Tobolsky, *J. Am. Chem. Soc.*, *74*, 938 (1952).

that $C_{tr,cat}$ is zero for this catalyst. The chain transfer constant for benzoyl peroxide in methyl methacrylate is also zero. The values of $C_{tr,cat}$ for the other catalysts can be determined from the curvatures of the plots in Figure 1.[9,10a]

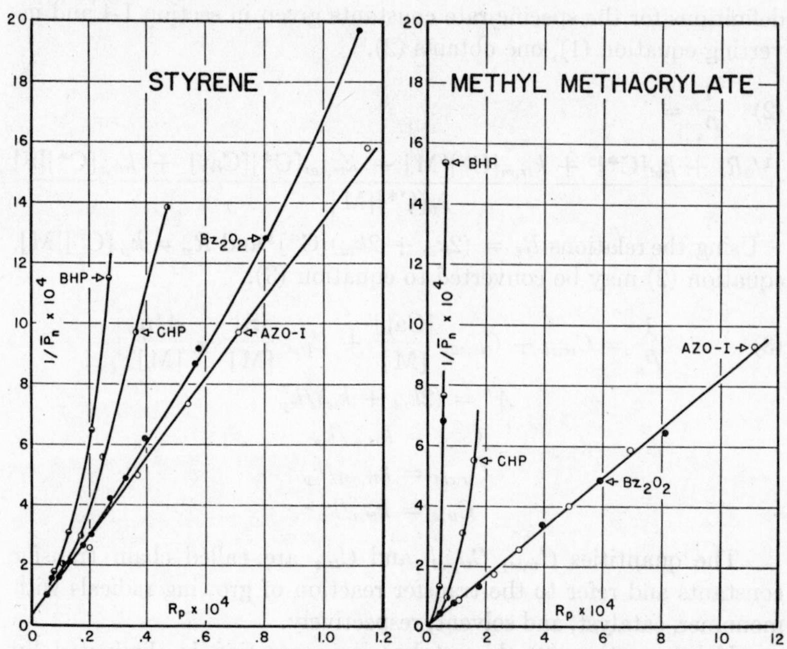


Fig. 1. $1/\bar{P}_n$ versus $R_p$ for styrene and methyl methacrylate. Polymerization at 60°C. Initiated by AZO-I, $Bz_2O_2$, CHP, and BHP.

## III. Rates of Initiation in Vinyl Polymerization: Styrene and Methyl Methacrylate*

### *1. Review of Fundamental Kinetic Equations*

The fundamental equations for vinyl polymerization are:

$$R_i = 2(k_{tc} + k_{td})[C^*]^2 \quad (1)$$

* Section III is essentially reprinted from the article by A. V. Tobolsky and B. Baysal, *J. Polymer Sci., 11*, 471(1953). For convenience, the equations in section III are numbered consecutively throughout all the subsections.

[10] (a) B. Baysal and A. V. Tobolsky, *J. Polymer Sci., 8*, 529 (1952). (b) A. V. Tobolsky and B. Baysal, *ibid., 11*, 471 (1953).

$$R_p = k_p[\mathrm{C}^*][\mathrm{M}] \tag{2}$$

$$R_i = (2A''/[\mathrm{M}]^2)R_p^2 \tag{3}$$

$$A'' = (k_{tc} + k_{td})/k_p^2 \tag{4}$$

In the above equations $R_i$ is the rate of initiation, $R_p$ is the rate of polymerization, and $k_{td}$, $k_{tc}$, and $k_p$ are the specific rate constants for combination, disproportionation, and propagation, respectively (the notation of Mayo *et al.*[8] has been adopted). The concentration of monomer [M] is assumed to be essentially constant since the experiments are confined to less than 15 per cent conversion.

The quantity $A''$ is a characteristic property of each monomer and is a function of temperature only. An absolute method exists for the determination of $A'$, a quantity closely related to $A''$ and defined as follows:

$$A' = \frac{2k_{td} + k_{tc}}{k_p^2} = A''(1 + x) \tag{5}$$

$$x = k_{td}/(k_{tc} + k_{td}) \tag{6}$$

The quantity $x$ can vary only between zero and unity.

The units moles per liter for concentration and seconds for time will be used throughout this section.

### 2. Absolute Method for Determination of A'

The general relation between number-average degree of polymerization, $\bar{P}_n$, and rate of polymerization $R_p$, in the *initial* phase of bulk polymerization in the presence of varying amounts of a given catalyst is:

$$\frac{1}{\bar{P}_n} = C_{tr,m} + \frac{A'R_p}{[\mathrm{M}]^2} + \frac{C_{tr,cat}R_p^2}{K^2[\mathrm{M}]^3} \tag{7}$$

In the above equation $C_{tr,cat}$ is the chain transfer constant to monomer, $C_{tr,cat}$ is the chain transfer constant to catalyst, [M] is the (initial) monomer concentration, and $K$ is defined by the relation (see section II-2):

$$R_p = K[\mathrm{M}][\mathrm{Cat}]^{1/2} \tag{8}$$

The $1/\bar{P}_n$ versus $R_p$ relation for certain catalysts is a straight line. As shown in Figure 1 this is true for styrene initiated by azobisisobutyronitrile and is also true for methyl methacrylate initiated by 2-azobisisobutyronitrile or benzoyl peroxide.[9,10] This is clearly from equation (7) a necessary and sufficient condition for the absence of chain transfer to catalyst. In these cases the value of $A'$ can be directly and unequivocally obtained from the slope of the $1/\bar{P}_n$ versus $R_p$ line.

For many catalysts the $1/\bar{P}_n$ versus $R_p$ plot is definitely not a straight line, *e.g.*, styrene or methyl methacrylate initiated by cumene hydroperoxide or *t*-butyl hydroperoxide. In these cases the curvature of the $1/\bar{P}_n$ versus $R_n$ plot is very pronounced, so that the determination of $A'$ from these curves is difficult and uncertain. For styrene initiated by benzoyl peroxide, however, even though the $1/\bar{P}_n$ versus $R_p$ plot shows curvature at high values of $R_p$ from which $C_{tr,cat}$ can be computed, the value of $K$ is so large that the third term on the right hand side of equation (7) is relatively unimportant at small values of $R_p$. A fairly good determination of the $A'$ value for styrene can therefore be obtained by measuring the limiting slope of the $1/\bar{P}_n$ versus $R_p$ curve produced by benzoyl peroxide in styrene at small values of $R_p$.

Values of $A'$ for styrene and methyl methacrylate have been computed from the slopes of the $1/\bar{P}_n$ versus $R_p$ plots in those cases where the curvature was absent or very small. The data for these plots were obtained from the literature references given in Table C-3, although in some cases the molecular weights given in the original papers were recomputed from the measured intrinsic viscosity values, using the viscosity molecular weight relations established in references (10) and (8). Table C-3 presents values of $A'$ for styrene and methyl methacrylate at several temperatures.

Inasmuch as the values of $A'$ were computed from a number of literature references, it is difficult to give an estimate of the precision of these values. In many cases the slopes could not be specified more precisely than within 10 per cent. In those cases where degrees of polymerization were computed from intrinsic viscosity, the accuracy of the $A'$ values depends very much on the accuracy of the $\bar{P}_n$ versus $[\eta]$ relations established in references (10) and (8). In the cases in which $\bar{P}_n$ was determined osmometrically, the accuracy of the osmometric values in use at the laboratory in question is always a matter of some dispute. In Table C-3 it will be noted that three values of $A'$ for styrene at 60° are given. The two values which were based on intrinsic viscosity measurements agree quite well.

TABLE C-3[10b]

$A'$ Values for Styrene and Methyl Methacrylate

| $T$, °C. | Catalyst | $A'$ | Ref. |
|---|---|---|---|
| | STYRENE | | |
| 27 | Benzoyl peroxide | 9550 | a,g |
| 30 | 2-Azobisisobutyronitrile | 5150 | f |
| 47.8 | 2-Azobisisobutyronitrile | 3180 | b |
| 50 | Benzoyl peroxide | 2560 | a,g |
| 60 | Benzoyl peroxide and 2,2′-azobisisobutyronitrile | 900 | h,i |
| 60 | Benzoyl peroxide | 905 | j |
| 60 | Benzoyl peroxide | 612 | d |
| 67.8 | 2-Azobisisobutyronitrile | 985 | b |
| 80.3 | 1-Azobiscyclohexane carbonitrile | 399 | b |
| | METHYL METHACRYLATE | | |
| 50 | Benzoyl peroxide | 103 | c,k |
| 60 | Benzoyl peroxide and 2-azobisisobutyronitrile | 67.3 | i |
| 60 | 2-Azobisisobutyronitrile | 65.3 | e |
| 70 | Benzoyl peroxide | 44 | c,k |

(a) G. V. Schulz and E. Husemann, *Z. physik. Chem.*, *B39*, 246 (1938).
(b) C. G. Overberger, P. Fram, and T. Alfrey, *J. Polymer Sci.*, *6*, 539 (1951).
(c) G. V. Schulz and G. Haborth, *Makromol. Chemie*, *1*, 106 (1947).
(d) E. P. Bonsall, L. Valentine, and H. W. Melville, *J. Polymer Sci.*, *7*, 39 (1951).
(e) J. L. O'Brien and F. Gornick, presented at the Philadelphia meeting of the American Chemical Society, January 29, 1953.
(f) W. Seitzer, R. Goeckermann, and A. V. Tobolsky, *J. Am. Chem. Soc.*, *75*, 755 (1953).
(g) M. S. Matheson, E. E. Auer, E. B. Bevilacqua, and E. J. Hart, *J. Am. Chem. Soc.*, *73*, 1700 (1951).
(h) D. H. Johnson and A. V. Tobolsky, *J. Am. Chem. Soc.*, *74*, 938 (1952).
(i) B. Baysal and A. V. Tobolsky, *J. Polymer Sci.*, *8*, 529 (1952).
(j) F. R. Mayo, R. A. Gregg, and M. S. Matheson, *J. Am. Chem. Soc.*, *73*, 1691 (1951).
(k) M. S. Matheson, E. E. Auer, E. B. Bevilacqua, and E. J. Hart, *J. Am. Chem. Soc.*, *71*, 497 (1949).

The third value based on osmometry differs by a factor of 1.5. The data for the $1/\bar{P}_n$ versus $R_p$ lines for methyl methacrylate show much less scatter than for styrene, and the precision of the slope determinations is much better.

A plot of $A'$ versus $1/T$ for methyl methacrylate gives a good straight line for the four points in question. A plot of log $A'$ versus $1/T$ for styrene also gives a straight line, but with considerable scatter.

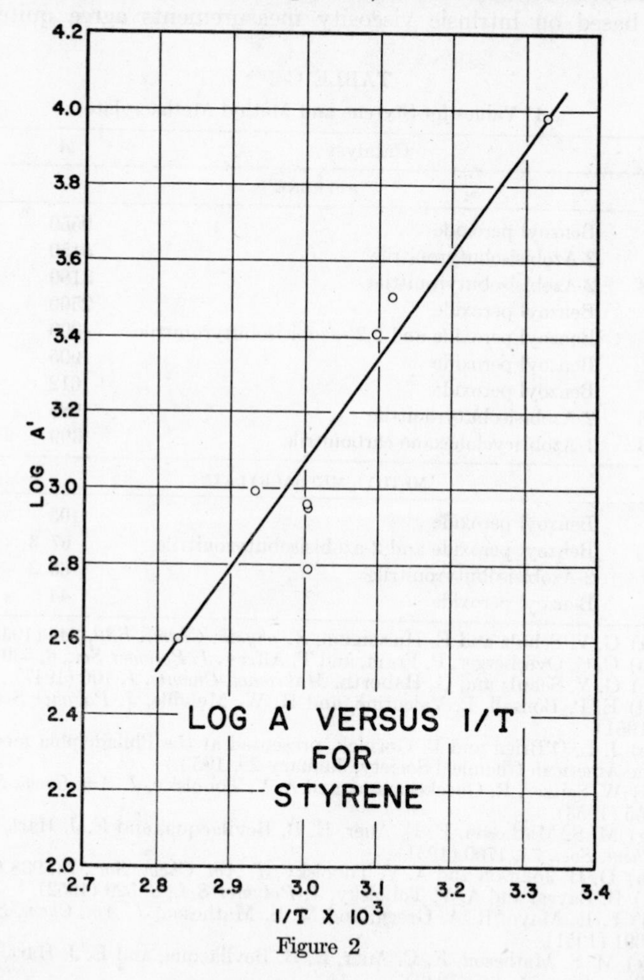


Figure 2

The data plotted in this form are presented in Figures 2 and 3. The equations which best fit the data are:

(9) $$A' = 6.10 \times 10^{-6} \exp\{12.61 \text{ kcal.}/RT\} \text{ for styrene}$$

(10) $$A' = 5.02 \times 10^{-5} \exp\{9.35 \text{ kcal.}/RT\}$$
for methyl methacrylate

There is considerable doubt as to whether the values of $A'$ that are determined from equations (9) and (10) or from Table C-3 are valid to three significant figures, particularly in the case of styrene. However,

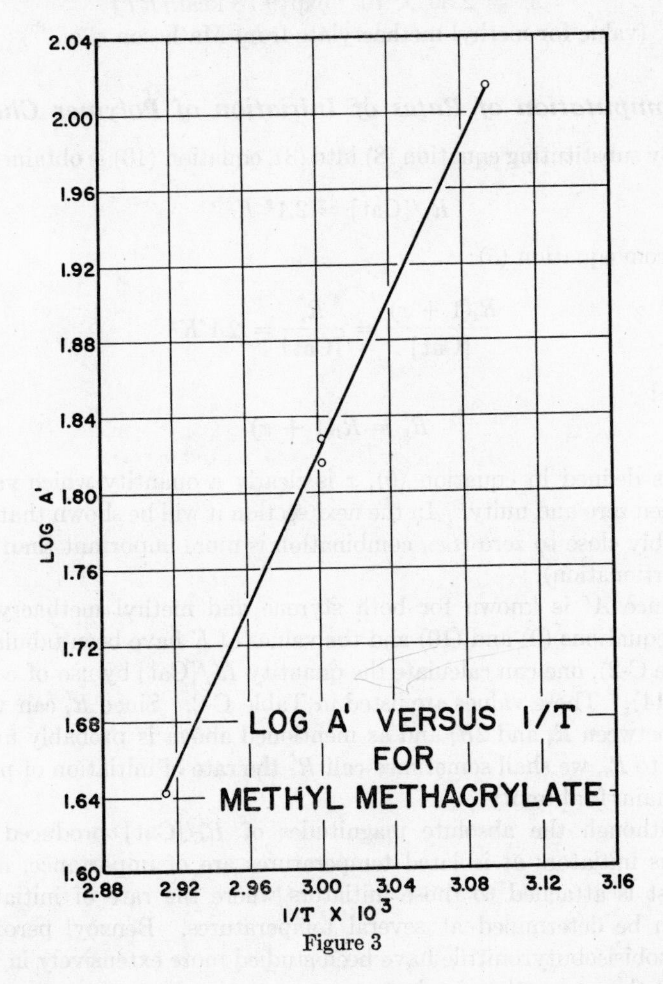

Figure 3

the three figures have been used in calculations, and in some cases may be justified.

The values of $A'$ given in equations (9) and (10) agree quite closely with those that can be computed from the absolute rate constants of Matheson *et al.*[11] The latter values are:

(11) $$A' = 2.77 \times 10^{-6} \exp\{13.15 \text{ kcal.}/RT\}$$
(value for styrene from Matheson *et al.*[11a])

(12) $$A' = 2.59 \times 10^{-5} \exp\{9.78 \text{ kcal.}/RT\}$$
(value for methyl methacrylate from Matheson *et al.*[11b])

### *3. Computation of Rates of Initiation of Polymer Chains*

By substituting equation (8) into (3), equation (13) is obtained:

(13) $$R_i/[\text{Cat}] = 2A'' K^2$$

and from equation (5):

(14) $$\frac{R_i(1 + x)}{[\text{Cat}]} = \frac{R'_i}{[\text{Cat}]} = 2A'K^2$$

where:

$$R'_i = R_i(1 + x)$$

As defined in equation (6), $x$ is clearly a quantity which varies between zero and unity. In the next section it will be shown that $x$ is probably close to zero (*i.e.*, combination is more important than disproportionation).

Since $A'$ is known for both styrene and methyl methacrylate from equations (9) and (10) and the values of $K$ have been tabulated (Table C-2), one can calculate the quantity $R'_i/[\text{Cat}]$ by use of equation (14). These values are listed in Table C-2. Since $R'_i$ can vary only between $R_i$ and $2R'_i$ and as mentioned above is probably much closer to $R_i$, we shall sometimes call $R'_i$ the rate of initiation of polymer chains for brevity.

Although the absolute magnitudes of $R'_i/[\text{Cat}]$ produced by various initiators at isolated temperatures are of importance, chief interest is attached to those initiators where the rate of initiation $R'_i$ can be determined at several temperatures. Benzoyl peroxide and azobisisobutyronitrile have been studied more extensively in this respect than any other catalysts.

Figure 4 (p. 148) plots log $R'_i/[\text{Cat}]$ versus the reciprocal of absolute temperature for all the significant published data involving ben-

[11] (a) M. S. Matheson, E. E. Auer, E. B. Bevilacqua, and E. J. Hart, *J. Am. Chem. Soc.*, *73*, 1700 (1951). (b) *Ibid.*, *71*, 497 (1949).

zoyl peroxide in styrene and methyl methacrylate. Figure 5 (p. 149) presents the same information for azobisisobutyronitrile.

Although there is a little scatter in the data shown in Figure 4, which is taken from a large number of literature sources extending over a period of twenty years, most of the data seem to be concordant, with the possible exception of the very early work of Schulz. The rate of initiation produced by benzoyl peroxide in methyl methacrylate appears to be somewhat higher than that produced by the same catalyst at the same concentration in styrene. Also log $R_i'/[\text{Cat}]$ versus $1/T$ gives good straight lines in both cases which correspond to:

$$R_i'/[\text{Cat}] = 3.39 \times 10^{14} \exp\{-30.0 \text{ kcal.}/RT\} \tag{15}$$
(benzoyl peroxide in methyl methacrylate)

$$R_i'/[\text{Cat}] = 1.00 \times 10^{14} \exp\{-29.4 \text{ kcal.}/RT\} \tag{16}$$
(benzoyl peroxide in styrene)

In Figure 5 log $R_i'/[\text{Cat}]$ is plotted versus $1/T$ for all the published data for the case of azobisisobutyronitrile in styrene and methyl methacrylate.

To a first approximation, the data for both monomers are fitted by the same straight line which corresponds to:

$$R_i'/[\text{Cat}] = 1.88 \times 10^{15} \exp\{-30.7 \text{ kcal.}/RT\} \tag{17}$$
(azobisisobutyronitrile in styrene and methyl methacrylate)

In Figure 6 data for log $R_i'/[\text{Cat}]$ versus $1/T$ are plotted for six peroxides in styrene. These data are again well fitted by straight lines which correspond to the following equations:

$$R_i'/[\text{Cat}] = 8.31 \times 10^{13} \exp\{-28.1 \text{ kcal.}/RT\} \tag{18}$$
(bis-2,4-dichlorobenzoyl peroxide in styrene)

$$R_i'/[\text{Cat}] = 1.45 \times 10^{14} \exp\{-28.9 \text{ kcal.}/RT\} \tag{19}$$
(lauroyl peroxide in styrene)

$$R_i'/[\text{Cat}] = 1.74 \times 10^{13} \exp\{-28.3 \text{ kcal.}/RT\} \tag{20}$$
(bis-*p*-chlorobenzoyl peroxide in styrene)

$$R_i'/[\text{Cat}] = 1.15 \times 10^{11} \exp\{-25.5 \text{ kcal.}/RT\} \tag{21}$$
(*t*-butyl hydroperoxide in styrene)

(22) $$R_i'/[\text{Cat}] = 8.15 \times 10^{15} \exp\{-34.8 \text{ kcal.}/RT\}$$
(*t*-butyl perbenzoate in styrene)

(23) $$R_i'/[\text{Cat}] = 7.95 \times 10^{16} \exp\{-31.5 \text{ kcal.}/RT\}$$
(di-1-naphthoyl peroxide in styrene)

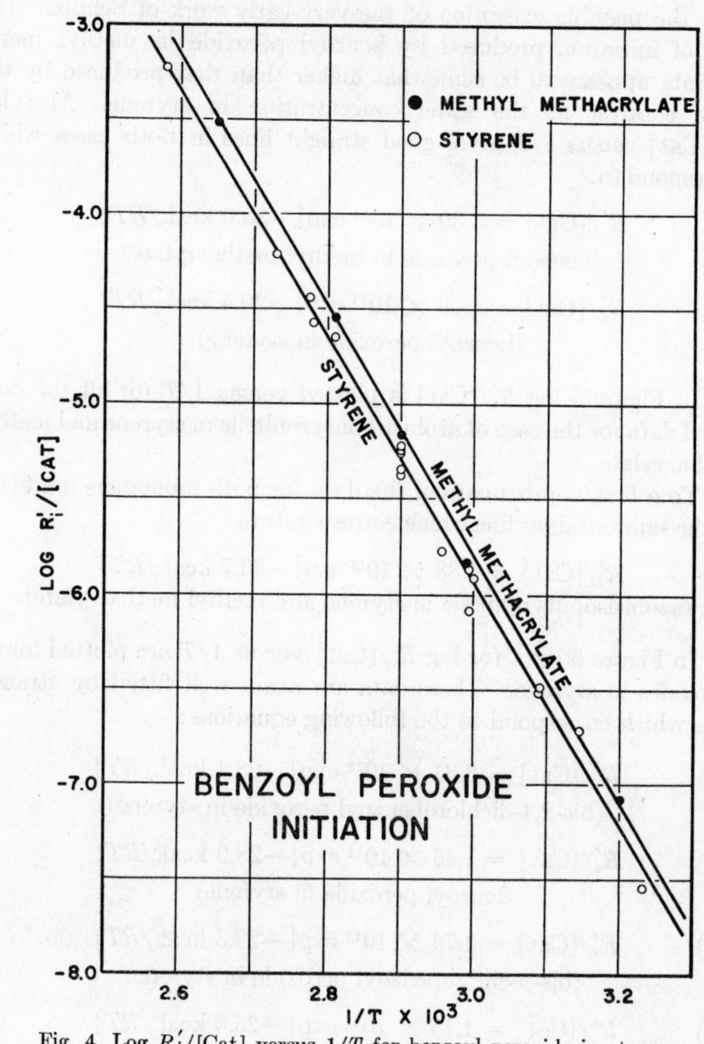


Fig. 4. Log $R_i'/[\text{Cat}]$ versus $1/T$ for benzoyl peroxide in styrene and methyl methacrylate.

The fact that the frequency factors in equations (15) to (23) lie between $1.15 \times 10^{11}$ and $7.95 \times 10^{16}$ and seem to be generally larger for larger activation energies is worthy of note.

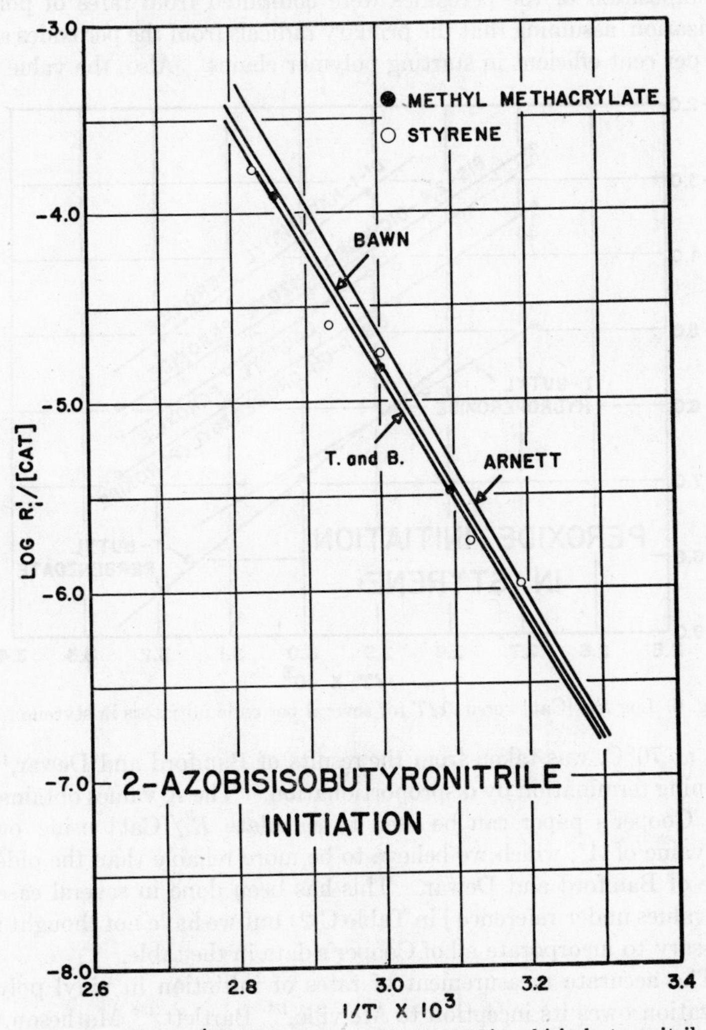


Fig. 5. Log $R'_i$/[Cat] versus $1/T$ for 2,2′-azobisisobutyronitrile in styrene and methyl methacrylate. Lower line marked T. and B. represents best fit to these data. Upper lines represent plots of log $2k_d$ versus $1/T$ according to equations (26) and (27).

The value of $K$ at 70°C. for a very large number of substituted benzoyl peroxides and other acyl peroxides can be computed from the data of Cooper.[12] In this study the specific rates of spontaneous decomposition of the peroxides were computed from rates of polymerization, assuming that the primary radicals from the peroxides are 100 per cent efficient in starting polymer chains. Also, the value of

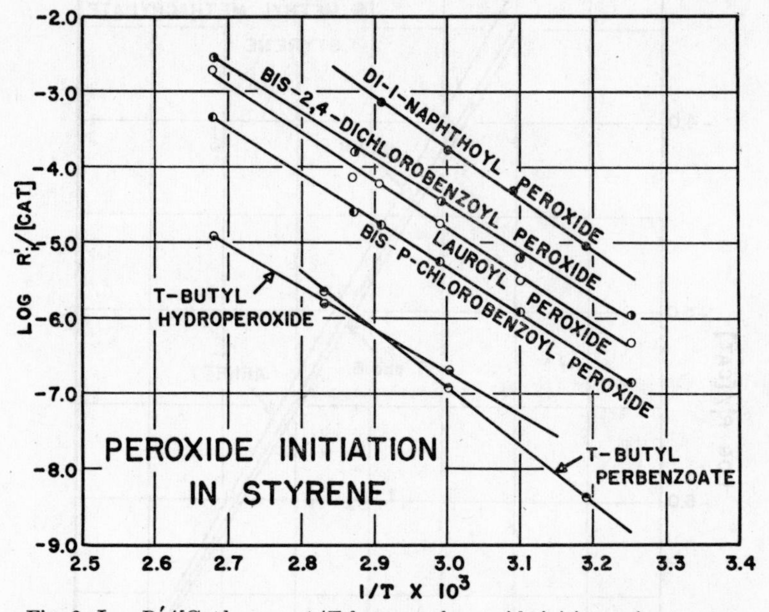


Fig. 6. Log $R_i'$/[Cat] versus $1/T$ for several peroxide initiators in styrene.

$k_p^2/k_t$ at 70°C. was taken from the results of Bamford and Dewar,[13a] assuming termination by disproportionation. The $K$ values obtained from Cooper's paper can be used to calculate $R_i'$/[Cat] using our own value of $A'$, which we believe to be more reliable than the older value of Bamford and Dewar. This has been done in several cases (see values under reference j in Table C-2) but we have not thought it necessary to incorporate all of Cooper's data in the table.

The accurate measurement of rates of initiation in vinyl polymerization owes its inception to Melville,[13b] Bartlett,[13c] Matheson,[11]

[12] W. Cooper, *J. Chem. Soc., 1951*, 3106.

[13a] C. H. Bamford and M. J. S. Dewar, *Faraday Soc. Discussions, 2*, 313 (1947).

Bamford,[13a] and their co-workers as part of the general program of calculating the absolute values of the specific rate constants for propagation and termination. Three methods were used to calculate the rate of initiation:

(1) The inhibitor method was first developed by Melville.[13b] Here the rate of consumption of an inhibitor during the induction period is taken to be equal to the rate of chain initiation in the absence of inhibitor. Melville used benzoquinone as the chain counter whereas Bartlett used 2,2-diphenylpicrylhydrazyl. The inhibitor technique is convenient and accurate in certain cases. However, it assumes that one inhibitor molecule stops exactly one potential polymer chain. Also, it has been shown that in the purely thermal polymerization of styrene the rate of consumption of these inhibitors is much more rapid than the rate of chain initiation in their absence.[13d]

(2) The rate of *spontaneous* cleavage of benzoyl peroxide in the monomer as distinct from the overall decomposition rate was taken by Bartlett to be equal to twice the rate of initiation of polymer chains. Later Matheson[11] used the rate of first order decomposition of 2-azobisisobutyronitrile as a measure of the rate of initiation. This method assumes that the catalyst fragments are 100 per cent efficient in starting polymer chains.

(3) The computation of rate of initiation from overall rate of polymerization and number-average degree of polymerization is inherent in the very mechanism of vinyl polymerization which has been widely accepted since the 1930's. In various forms this method has been used by all workers in the field.[9–13] If termination occurs exclusively by disproportionation, and if chain transfer is absent, the rate of initiation is equal to the rate of polymerization divided by the number average degree of polymerization. In this chapter a systematic and accurate method for correcting for transfer and simultaneous combination-disproportionation has been presented.[9,10]

This method is the only *absolute* method for calculating rates of initiation and therefore permits an independent comparison with the rate of spontaneous cleavage of catalyst and the computation of catalyst efficiencies as will be shown subsequently.

[13b] G. M. Burnett and H. W. Melville, *Proc. Roy. Soc., A189*, 456, 481, 494 (1947).

[13c] C. G. Swain and P. D. Bartlett, *J. Am. Chem. Soc., 68*, 2381 (1946). P. D. Bartlett and H. Kwart, *ibid., 72*, 1051 (1950).

[13d] K. E. Russell and A. V. Tobolsky, *J. Am. Chem. Soc.*, *75*, 5052 (1953).

### 4. *Combination versus Disproportionation*

By the use of radioactive 2,2′-azobisisobutyronitrile as an initiator for methyl methacrylate polymerization, Arnett[14,15] was able to show by direct experiment that $x$ (eq. 5) is close to zero. It is known that this initiator does not transfer with growing polymer chains, and the only way that it can appear in the polymer is as an initiating fragment. Arnett showed that the number-average molecular weight determined by osmometry was very nearly the same as the number-average molecular weight determined from the radioactive end group measurement assuming that *two* initiator fragments are to be found on each chain. This proves that the chains must terminate by combination, neglecting the minor effect of chain transfer to monomer.

In order to take chain transfer of any kind into account, and still use the radioactive initiator method to compute $x$, one may proceed as follows: By use of the radioactive initiator azobisisobutyronitrile it is possible to measure $R_i$ directly by measuring the rate at which radioactive fragments appear in the polymer. Since $R_i$ and $R_p$ can both be measured, $A''$ can be computed from equation (3). The value of $A'$ under the same conditions can be determined from equation (7) as discussed in a previous section. The value of $x$ can therefore be obtained from equation (5). This procedure is completely independent of any assumption concerning catalyst efficiency.

Arnett also computed the efficiency of azobisisobutyronitrile in starting chains in numerous monomers by comparing the rate $R_i$ at which catalyst fragments were appearing in the polymer with the rate of decomposition of catalyst. This measurement is wholly independent of any knowledge of the value of $x$. In section 5 below the conclusion of Arnett that the efficiency of initiation of methyl methacrylate by azobisisobutyronitrile is only 50 per cent will be questioned.

The conclusion that combination of radicals occurs more rapidly than disproportionation is also reached by studies of the reaction products formed by simple analogues of styrene and methyl methacrylate radicals.[16] The products arising from disproportionation were not negligible, being about 14% in the case of the $(CH_3)_2\dot{C}CO_2CH_3$ radical at 80° and about 35% in the case of the benzyl radical at 185°.

[14] L. M. Arnett, *J. Am. Chem. Soc., 74*, 2027 (1952).

[15] L. M. Arnett and J. H. Peterson, *J. Am. Chem. Soc., 74*, 2031 (1952).

[16] A. F. Bickel and W. A. Waters, *Rec. trav. chim., 69*, 312 (1950).

Bickel and Waters found no fragments of the solvents combined with these radicals and so concluded that transfer reactions with solvent, which would disrupt their calculations, do not occur. The percentage of disproportionation by the benzyl radical (which is the analogue of the polystyryl radical) is probably smaller in the temperature range 30–100° than the figure of 35 per cent quoted at 185°. This work would appear to indicate that $x$ is small but not zero for both styrene and methyl methacrylate. More recent studies by Bywater and Talat-Erben indicate that these values may be even smaller.[16a]

Other contributory evidence for the fact that $x$ is small arises from the studies of the molecular weight distribution in methyl methacrylate as measured by comparing the number-average, weight-average, and viscosity-average molecular weights.[17,18]

### 5. *Catalyst Efficiencies*

The initiator azobisisobutyronitrile (AZO-I) decomposes by a first order reaction at nearly the same rate in all solvents. The rate of decomposition is therefore believed to be a measure of the rate of production of monoradical pairs. The catalyst efficiency, $f$, of this initiator is defined as the rate of initiation divided by twice the rate of initiator decomposition.

$$f_{\text{AZO-I}} = \frac{R_i}{2k_d[\text{Cat}]} = \frac{R_i/[\text{Cat}]}{2k_d} \tag{24}$$

Inasmuch as values of $R_i'/[\text{Cat}]$ have been computed rather than $R_i/[\text{Cat}]$, it is convenient to define a quantity $f'$ which can be directly calculated as follows:

$$f' = f(1 + x) = \frac{R_i'/[\text{Cat}]}{2k_d} \tag{25}$$

There exist two sets of data for $k_d$ of AZO-I. The first equation is by Arnett,[14] who found that $k_d$ is very nearly independent of the solvent, and the second is by Bawn and Mellish,[19] who found that $k_d$ varies slightly with the solvent. These equations for $k_d$ are:

[16a] M. Talat-Erben and S. Bywater, Fifth Canadian High-Polymer Forum, London, Ontario, Nov. 19–20, 1953.
[17] J. Harris and R. G. J. Miller, *J. Polymer Sci.*, *7*, 377 (1951).
[18] B. Baysal and A. V. Tobolsky, *J. Polymer Sci.*, *9*, 171 (1952).
[19] C. E. H. Bawn and S. F. Mellish, *Trans. Faraday Soc.*, *47*, 1216 (1951).

$$k_d = 1.07 \times 10^{16} \exp\{-32.1 \text{ kcal.}/RT\} \qquad (26)$$

(Arnett (all solvents))

$$k_d = 1.0 \times 10^{15} \exp\{-30.7 \text{ kcal.}/RT\} \qquad (27)$$

Bawn and Mellish (benzene)

In Figure 5 we have plotted log $2k_d$ versus $1/T$ according to Arnett and Bawn in order to show a direct comparison with our calculated values of $R_i'/[\text{Cat}]$ for AZO-I in both styrene and methyl methacrylate.

It is clear from this figure that $f'_{\text{AZO-I}}$ defined by equation (25) is fairly temperature-independent no matter which equation for $k_d$ one selects. If Bawn's equation is taken as correct, one obtains from equations (17), (25), and (27):

$$f_{\text{AZO-I}} = 0.94/(1 + x) \qquad (28)$$

(for all temperatures in styrene and methyl methacrylate)

Our results as expressed in equation (28) are contradictory to those of Arnett,[14,15] who found that for methyl methacrylate $x = 0$ and $f = 0.50$. This difference is not attributable to the slight difference between the $k_d$ of Bawn and Arnett. For styrene and other monomers, Arnett found the efficiency to be nearly unity.

There is no immediate way by which this difference can be resolved short of careful repetition of the experiments with radioactive initiators. Arnett's conclusion for methyl methacrylate has the advantage that it is based on direct experimental measurement of $f$ and $x$. Our conclusion, on the other hand, as expressed in Figure 4, has the advantage that the results are consistent over a wide temperature range, collate the results of several independent workers (including Arnett), and show no major difference between styrene and methyl methacrylate. The very small if not negligible temperature dependence of the efficiency is related to the fact that the efficiency is nearly unity.

Arnett also concludes that since $f_{\text{AZO-I}}$ in methyl methacrylate is 0.50 (by his measurements), only the radical $(CH_3)_2C(CN){-}N{=}N\cdot$ is capable of initiating polymer chains in methyl methacrylate and this with 100 per cent efficiency. If this were true, the rate of decomposition of AZO-I in methyl methacrylate as measured by nitrogen evolution would be equal to zero.

In the case of benzoyl peroxide, the decomposition in various solvents can be represented as the sum of a spontaneous cleavage into radicals plus a radical induced decomposition. The spontaneous cleavage is nearly the same in all solvents but the induced decomposition depends very much on the nature of the solvent. The catalyst efficiency $f'_{Bz_2O_2}$ is defined by:

$$f'_{Bz_2O_2} = \frac{R'_i/[Bz_2O_2]}{2k_d} \tag{29}$$

where $k_d$ is the specific rate of *spontaneous* decomposition of benzoyl peroxide. The rate of spontaneous cleavage of benzoyl peroxide can be measured either by kinetic analysis[20–22] or by the use of an inhibitor[19,23] which suppresses the induced decomposition.

The various workers agree that the specific rate of spontaneous decomposition varies slightly among various solvents. We have collected some of the values below:

$$k_d = 6.0 \times 10^{14} \exp\{-30.7 \text{ kcal.}/RT\} \tag{30}$$

(Nozaki and Bartlett (benzene))

$$k_d = 1.0 \times 10^{14} \exp\{-29.9 \text{ kcal.}/RT\} \tag{31}$$

(Hartman *et al.* (benzene))

$$k_d = 1.7 \times 10^{14} \exp\{-30.0 \text{ kcal.}/RT\} \tag{32}$$

(Swain *et al.* (dioxane))

$$k_d = 3.0 \times 10^{13} \exp\{-29.6 \text{ kcal.}/RT\} \tag{33}$$

(Bawn and Mellish (benzene))

The value of $2k_d$ given by Swain *et al.*[23] (from eq. 32) is identical with the equation we have already selected as giving the best fit to the $R'_i/[\text{Cat}]$ data for methyl methacrylate initiated by benzoyl peroxide.

If the spontaneous decomposition in dioxane and methyl meth-

[20] K. Nozaki and P. D. Bartlett, *J. Am. Chem. Soc., 68,* 1686 (1946); *69,* 2299 (1947).

[21] P. F. Hartman, H. G. Sellers, and D. Turnbull, *J. Am. Chem. Soc., 69,* 2416 (1947).

[22] D. J. Brown, *J. Am. Chem. Soc., 70,* 1208 (1948).

[23] C. G. Swain, W. H. Stockmayer, and J. T. Clarke, *J. Am. Chem. Soc., 72,* 5426 (1950).

acrylate were identical, this would indicate from equations (15) and (32) an efficiency of 1.0 at all temperatures. At 60°, Mayo *et al.*[8] give a value of $k_d$ in styrene, namely, $k_d = 2.83 \times 10^{-6}$. Taken in conjunction with equation (16), this gives the value of $f'_{Bz_2O_2}$ in styrene at 60° as 0.85. Although the values for $k_d$ in styrene and methyl methacrylate have not yet been determined as functions of temperature, it is clear that the efficiencies $f'_{Bz_2O_2}$ in both cases must be quite close to unity and nearly if not exactly temperature independent.

The catalyst efficiency $f'$ at 80° in styrene for bis-*p*-chlorobenzoyl peroxide can be obtained from equation (20) and reference (23). The numerical value of $f'$ at this temperature is 0.77. The catalyst efficiency $f'$ for 1-azobiscyclohexanecarbonitrile at 80.3° in styrene is 0.64.[9]

It therefore appears that among the initiators for which data are available the catalyst efficiencies are all high and nearly temperature independent. The catalyst efficiency must also be independent of catalyst concentration if equation (11) or (12) has been shown to accurately represent the experimental data. If the catalyst efficiency did depend on catalyst concentration, the rate $R_p$ would be proportional to a power of catalyst concentration other than 0.50. The dependence of catalyst efficiency on monomer concentration is discussed in Appendix 4 (p. 183).

The use of styrene and methyl methacrylate as chemical clocks to measure quantitatively the rate of initiation of polymer chains produced by various peroxide radicals has been shown to be in complete accord with the established concepts of spontaneous homolytic cleavage developed in Chapter B.

## Appendix 1

# PHYSICAL CONSTANTS OF SELECTED ORGANIC PEROXIDES

The organic peroxides listed in the table on the following pages are presented in the following order:

I. Peroxides of structure ROOH (hydroperoxides)
   A. Saturated aliphatic hydroperoxides
   B. Olefin hydroperoxides
   C. Aralkyl hydroperoxides
   D. Hydroperoxides of heterocyclic compounds

II. Peroxides of structure ROOR (dialkyl and diaralkyl peroxides)
   A. Dialkyl peroxides
   B. Diaralkyl (hexaarylethane) peroxides
   C. Transannular peroxides

III. Peroxides of Structure RC(=O)OOH (peroxy acids)
   A. Aliphatic peroxy acids
   B. Aromatic peroxy acids

IV. Peroxides of structure RC(=O)OOR (peroxy esters)

V. Peroxides of Structure RC(=O)OO(O=)CR (diacyl and diaroyl peroxides)
   A. Diacyl peroxides
   B. Diaroyl peroxides
   C. Dialkyl peroxydicarbonates

VI. Peroxy derivatives of aldehydes and ketones
   A. 1-Hydroxyalkyl hydroperoxides
   B. Bis(1-hydroxyalkyl) peroxides
   C. Polyalkylidene peroxides
   D. Alkyl 1-hydroxyalkyl peroxides
   E. Peroxy acetals

The literature references concerning these peroxides are given at the conclusion of the data. The intention has been to include representatives of each class, rather than to incorporate all the known peroxides.

## I. PEROXIDES OF STRUCTURE ROOH (HYDROPEROXIDES)

### A. Saturated Aliphatic Hydroperoxides

| Name | Formula | $n_D^{20}$ | M.p., °C. | B.p., °C./mm. Hg | Ref.[a] |
|---|---|---|---|---|---|
| Methyl hydroperoxide | $CH_3OOH$ | 1.3608 | −72 to −78 | log $p$ = 8.38 − 1972/$T$. (°K.) | 1,*2* |
| Ethyl hydroperoxide | $C_2H_5OOH$ | 1.3801 | glass @ −100 | log $p$ = 8.834 −2228/$T$ (°K.) | 1,*2*,3,4,5 |
| Propyl hydroperoxide | $C_3H_7OOH$ | 1.3890 (25°) | glass @ −90 | 35/20 | *4*,6 |
| Isopropyl hydroperoxide | $(CH_3)_2CHOOH$ (CH₃ and CH₃ on CHOOH) | 1.8861 (23°) | — | 107 to 109/760 | 5,*6* |
| *n*-Butyl hydroperoxide | $CH_3CH_2CH_2CH_2OOH$ | 1.4032 | — | — | *114* |
| *sec*-Butyl hydroperoxide | $C_2H_5(CH_3)CHOOH$ | 1.4052 | — | — | *114* |
| *t*-Butyl hydroperoxide[b] | $(CH_3)_3COOH$ | 1.4007 | −8 to −10 | log $p$ = 8.891 − 2342/$T$ (°K.) | *2*,5,7,8,9, 10,11 |
| *t*-Amyl hydroperoxide | $C_2H_5(CH_3)_2COOH$ | 1.4161 | — | 26/3 | 5,*12* |
| 1,1-Diethylpropyl hydroperoxide | $(C_2H_5)_3COOH$ | 1.4379 | 2 to 3 | 27.5 to 28/2 | 9,10,*13* |
| 1,1,2-Trimethylpropyl hydroperoxide | $(CH_3)_2CH{-}C(CH_3)_2{-}OOH$ (CH—COOH with CH₃ above and below each) | — | — | 51 to 58/12 | *10* |
| 1-Methylhexyl hydroperoxide | $C_5H_{11}C(H)(CH_3)OOH$ | 1.4305 | — | 38/0.08 | *14* |
| 1,1,2,2-Tetramethylpropyl hydroperoxide | $CH_3{-}C(CH_3)_2{-}C(CH_3)_2{-}OOH$ | — | 113 to 114 | — | *10*,13 |

| Name | Formula | $n_D^{20}$ | M.p., °C. | B.p., °C./mm. Hg | Ref.[a] |
|---|---|---|---|---|---|
| Cyclohexyl[b] hydroperoxide | cyclohexane ring–OOH | 1.4638 (25°) | −20 | — | *15* |
| 1-Methylcyclohexyl hydroperoxide[b] | cyclohexane ring bearing $CH_3$ and OOH on C-1 | 1.4642 | — | 53/0.1 | 10,16,*17* |
| *trans*-Decalin hydroperoxide[b] (*trans*-Decahydro-4*a*-naphthyl hydroperoxide) | decalin ring with OOH at ring junction | — | 94 to 95 | — | *10* |
| Hexahydro-3*a*-indanyl hydroperoxide[b] | hydrindane ring with OOH at ring junction | — | — | 73 to 75/0.2 | *18* |
| 2,5-Dihydroperoxy-2,5-dimethylhexane[b] (2,5-Dimethylhexylidene 2,5-hydroperoxide) | $CH_3-C(OOH)(CH_3)-CH_2CH_2-C(OOH)(CH_3)-CH_3$ | — | 106.5 | — | 10,*19* |
| 2,7-Dihydroperoxy-2,7-dimethyloctane (2,7-Dimethyloctylidene 2,7-hydroperoxide) | $CH_3-C(OOH)(CH_3)-CH_2CH_2CH_2CH_2-C(OOH)(CH_3)-CH_3$ | — | 66 | — | *10* |

*Table continued*

[a] The physical constants are taken from the italicized reference.
[b] These peroxides have been prepared by oxidation of the corresponding hydrocarbon with molecular oxygen.

| Name | Formula | $n_D^{20}$ | M.p., °C. | B.p., °C./mm. Hg | Ref.[a] |
|---|---|---|---|---|---|
| A. Saturated Aliphatic Hydroxides (*continued*) | | | | | |
| 2-Hydroperoxy-2,4-dimethyl-3-pentanone[b] | $(CH_3)_2C(OOH)—C(=O)—CH(CH_3)_2$ | 1.4321 | — | 62 to 69/0.8 | *107* |
| 1,1,6,6-Tetrahydroperoxycyclodecane | HOO OOH / HOO OOH (cyclodecane ring) | — | 116 to 118 | — | *10* |
| B. Olefin Hydroperoxides | | | | | |
| 2-Cyclopenten-1-yl hydroperoxide[b] | —OOH[c] (cyclopentene ring) | — | — | 35/0.01 | *20* |
| 2-Cyclohexen-1-yl hydroperoxide[b] | —OOH (cyclohexene ring) | 1.4892 | — | 40 to 41/0.2 | 20,21,*108* |
| 2-Methyl-2-cyclohexen-1-yl hydroperoxide[b] | $CH_3$—, HOO— (cyclohexene ring)[c] | — | — | 64 to 67/0.2 | 20,*21*,22 |
| 2,3-Dimethyl-2-cyclohexen-1-yl hydroperoxide[b] | $CH_3$, $CH_3$—, —OOH (cyclohexene ring) | — | — | 67 to 70/0.5 | *19*,20 |

| Name | Formula | $n_D^{20}$ | M.p., °C. | B.p., °C./mm. Hg | Ref.[a] |
|---|---|---|---|---|---|
| *d,l*-3-*p*-Menthenyl-8-hydroperoxide[b] | 4-methylcyclohexenyl–$C(CH_3)_2$–OOH | 1.47812 | — | 57.5/0.05 | *23* |
| 3-Methyl-3-hydroperoxy-1-butyne (1,1-Dimethyl-2-propynyl hydroperoxide) | $HC{\equiv}C{-}C(OOH)(CH_3){-}CH_3$ | 1.4295 (25°) | — | 42 to 42.2/17 | *24* |
| 2,5-Dimethyl-2,5-dihydroperoxy-3-hexyne (1,1,4,4-Tetramethyl-2-butynylene dihydroperoxide) | $CH_3C(OOH)(CH_3){-}C{\equiv}C{-}C(OOH)(CH_3){-}CH_3$ | — | 107 to 109 (dec.) | — | *24* |
| C. Aralkyl Hydroperoxides | | | | | |
| α-Methylbenzyl hydroperoxide[b] | $H_3C{-}CH(OOH){-}C_6H_5$ | 1.52695 | — | 45/0.05 | *25* |

*Table continued*

[a] The physical constants are taken from the italicized reference.
[b] These peroxides have been prepared by oxidation of the corresponding hydrocarbon with molecular oxygen.
[c] Not isolated in pure form.

| Name | Formula | $n_D^{20}$ | M.p., °C. | B.p., °C./mm. Hg | Ref.[a] |
|---|---|---|---|---|---|
| C. Aralkyl Hydroperoxides (*continued*) | | | | | |
| Cumene hydroperoxide[b] α,α-Dimethylbenzyl (hydroperoxide) | $C_6H_5C(CH_3)_2OOH$ | 1.5237 | — | 65/0.18 | 26,27,28, *106* |
| α-Methyl-α-ethylbenzyl hydroperoxide[b] | $C_6H_5C(CH_3)(C_2H_5)OOH$ | 1.5208 | — | 48 to 49/0.002 | *29*,30 |
| α-p-Xylyl hydroperoxide[b] | $p-CH_3C_6H_4CH_2OOH$ | 1.5322 | 2 | 51/0.05 | *25* |
| Diphenylmethyl hydroperoxide[b] | $(C_6H_5)_2CHOOH$ | — | 51 | — | *27* |
| Triphenylmethyl hydroperoxide[b] | $(C_6H_5)_3COOH$ | — | 82 | — | 31,*32*,33 |
| Tetralin hydroperoxide[b] (1,2,3,4-Tetrahydro-1-naphthyl hydroperoxide) | $C_{10}H_{11}OOH$ (1-OOH-tetralin) | 1.54471 (78.7°, He) | 56 | — | *34*,35 |

| Name | Formula | $n_D^{20}$ | M.p., °C. | B.p., °C./mm. Hg | Ref.[a] |
|---|---|---|---|---|---|
| 1,2,3,4-Tetrahydro-1-methyl-1-naphthyl hydroperoxide[b] | $CH_3$, —OOH | — | — | 99 to 100/0.01 | *31* |
| 9-Fluorenyl hydroperoxide[b] | H OOH | — | 93 | — | *36* |
| 1-Indanyl hydroperoxide[b] | OOH | 1.56214 | — | 64 to 65/0.01 | *37* |
| D. Hydroperoxides of Heterocyclic Compounds | | | | | |
| Tetrahydro-2-furyl hydroperoxide[b] | —OOH, O | 1.6933 | — | — | *38b* |
| Tetrahydrocarbazole hydroperoxide[b] (1,2,3,4-Tetrahydro-4a*H*-isocarbazol-4*a*-yl hydroperoxide) | OOH, N | — | 123 to 124 | — | *39b* |

The hydroperoxides of several indole derivatives are discussed in reference 39c. In addition, hydroperoxides having the structure, $R_1N{=}N{-}C(OOH)(R_3){-}R_2$, where $R_1$, $R_2$, $R_3$ are hydrogen, alkyl, or aryl groups, have been prepared by autoxidation of the hydrazones of ketones and aldehydes (see reference 40).

[a] The physical constants are taken from the italicized reference.

[b] These peroxides have been prepared by oxidation of the corresponding hydrocarbon with molecular oxygen.

*Table continued*

## II. PEROXIDES OF STRUCTURE ROOR (DIALKYL AND DIARALKYL PEROXIDES)

### A. Dialkyl Peroxides

| Name | Formula | $n_D^{20}$ | M.p., °C. | B.p., °C./mm. Hg | Ref.[a] |
|---|---|---|---|---|---|
| Dimethyl peroxide | $CH_3OOCH_3$ | 1.35029 | −100 to −105 | 13.5/740 | 41,42,*43* |
| Methyl ethyl peroxide | $CH_3OOC_2H_5$ | 1.3698 | −68 to −69.5 | log $p$ = 7.356 − 1517/T (°K.) | *2*,43 |
| Diethyl peroxide | $C_2H_5OOC_2H_5$ | 1.37156 | — | 64/740 | 41,43,*44* |
| Dipropyl peroxide | $C_3H_7OOC_3H_7$ | 1.3911 (20.5°) | — | — | 3,*4*,41,43 |
| Diisopropyl peroxide | $(H_3C)_2CHOOCH(CH_3)_2$ | — | — | 53 to 54/760 | *45* |
| Methyl *t*-butyl peroxide | $CH_3OOC(CH_3)_3$ | 1.3761 | −102.1 | 23/119 | *46* |
| Ethyl *t*-butyl peroxide | $C_2H_5OOC(CH_3)_3$ | 1.3840 | −83.1 | 35/84 | *46* |
| Isopropyl *t*-butyl peroxide | $(H_3C)_2CHOOC(CH_3)_3$ | 1.3860 | glass | 52/125 | *46* |
| *n*-Butyl *t*-butyl peroxide | *n*-$C_4H_9OOC(CH_3)_3$ | 1.4001 | glass | 53/30 | *46* |
| *sec*-Butyl *t*-butyl peroxide | *sec*-$C_4H_9OOC(CH_3)_3$ | 1.3959 | −67.7 | 53/50 | *46* |
| Di-*t*-butyl peroxide[b] | $(CH_3)_3COOC(CH_3)_3$ | 1.3890 | −40.0 | 111/760 | *46* |
| *t*-Butyl *t*-amyl peroxide[b] | $(CH_3)_3COOC(CH_3)_2C_2H_5$ | 1.4000 | — | 91 to 92/760 | *47* |
| Di-*t*-amyl peroxide[b] | $C_2H_5(CH_3)_2COOC(CH_3)_2C_2H_5$ | 1.4091 | — | 58.5/14 | *11*,47 |
| *t*-Butyl 1-methylcyclohexyl peroxide | 1-$CH_3$-1-$OOC(CH_3)_3$-cyclohexane (ring structure) | 1.4350 | — | 28 to 29/2.5 | *13* |

| Name | Formula | $n_D^{20}$ | M.p., °C. | B.p., °C./mm. Hg | Ref.[a] |
| --- | --- | --- | --- | --- | --- |
| Di-(3-methyl-pentynyl)-3-peroxide (Bis(1-methyl-1-ethyl-2-propynyl) peroxide) | $C_2H_5-C(CH_3)(C\equiv CH)-OO-C(CH_3)(C\equiv CH)-C_2H_5$ | 1.4390 (25°) | — | 53 to 55/2 | *24* |
| 1-Methyl-1-*t*-butyl-peroxy-3,5-di-*t*-butyl-2,5-cyclo-hexadiene-4-one | $(CH_3)_3C$ O $C(CH_3)_3$ $H_3C$ $OOC(CH_3)_3$ | — | 74 | — | *109* |
| Methyl 1,2,3,4-tetrahydro-1-naphthyl peroxide | $-OOCH_3$ | 1.53406 | — | 72.5/0.03 | *23* |
| Methyl 2-cyclohexen-1-yl peroxide | $-OOCH_3$ | 1.4625 | — | 19.5/0.1 | *23* |
| Di-$\alpha$-cumyl peroxide | $C_6H_5(CH_3)_2COOC(CH_3)_2C_6H_5$ | 1.5360 (21°) (supercooled liquid) | 39 | — | *110* |
| B. Diaralkyl (Hexaarylethane) Peroxides | | | | | |
| Ditriphenylmethyl peroxide[b] | $(C_6H_5)_3COOC(C_6H_5)_3$ | — | 185 to 186 | — | *48* |
| A wide variety of hexaarylethane peroxides have been prepared by the oxidation of symmetrical or unsymmetrical hexaarylethanes; consult, for example, reference 49. | | | | | |

*Table continued*

[a] The physical constants are taken from the italicized reference.
[b] These peroxides have been prepared by oxidation of the corresponding hydrocarbon with molecular oxygen.

| Name | Formula | $n_D^{20}$ | M.p., °C. | B.p., °C./mm. Hg | Ref.[a] |
|---|---|---|---|---|---|
| | | C. Transannular Peroxides | | | |
| Ascaridole[b] (1,4-Epidioxy-2-*p*-menthene) | 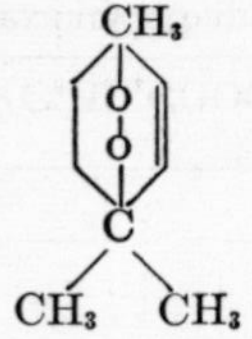 $CH_3$, O, O, C, $CH_3$ $CH_3$ | 1.4769 (25°) | — | 96 to 97/8 | 50,*51*,52, 113 |
| Ergosterol peroxide[b] | 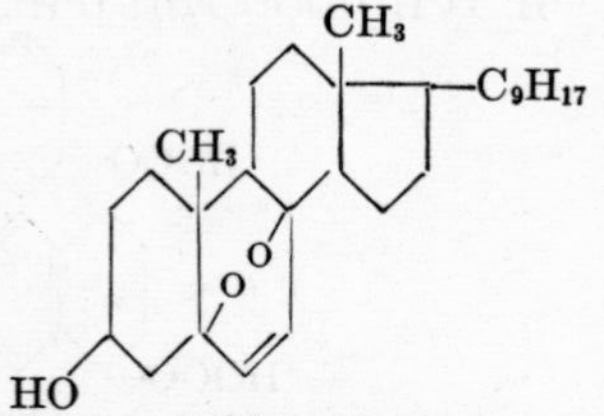 $CH_3$, $C_9H_{17}$, $CH_3$, O, O, HO (Most probable structure) | — | 178 | — | *53*,54 |
| Anthracene peroxide[b] (9,10-Dihydro-9,10-epidioxy anthracene) | 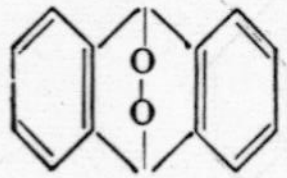 O, O | — | 120 (dec.) | — | 54,*55* |
| Rubrene peroxide[b] (5,6,11,12-Tetra-phenyl-5,12-epidi-oxynaphthacene) | 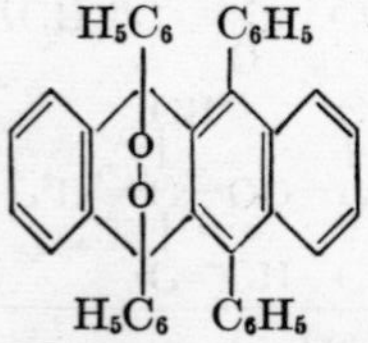 $H_5C_6$ $C_6H_5$, O, O, $H_5C_6$ $C_6H_5$ | — | Starts to lose oxygen at 100°C. | — | 54,*56* |

| Name | Formula | $n_D^{20}$ | M.p., °C. | B.p., °C./mm. Hg | Ref.[a] |
|---|---|---|---|---|---|
| Cyclohexadiene peroxide[b] (1,4-Epidioxy-2-cyclohexene) | | 1.453 (85°) | 82 to 83 | 40 to 55/0.3 | *50* |
| 2,8-*endo*-Peroxyisoindene[b] (2,3*a*-Epidioxyisoindene) | | 1.566 (22°) | 16 to 18 | 80/0.1 | 36,*50* |
| **III. PEROXIDES OF STRUCTURE RC(=O)OOH (PEROXY ACIDS)** | | | | | |
| **A. Aliphatic Peroxy Acids** | | | | | |
| Peroxyformic acid[b] | $HC(=O)—OOH$[c] | — | — | — | 57,58 |
| Peroxyacetic acid[b] | $CH_3C(=O)—OOH$ | — | 0.1 | 20 to 30/10 to 20 | *59*,61,60,62 |
| Peroxypropionic acid[b] | $C_2H_5C(=O)—OOH$ | — | −13.5 | — | *59*,61,62,63 |
| Peroxycaproic acid | $C_4H_9C(=O)—OOH$ | — | 15 | 61 to 62/13 | *64* |
| Peroxymonochloroacetic acid | $CH_2ClC(=O)—OOH$ | — | — | 33 to 34 (dec.) | *65*,66 |

*Table continued*

[a] The physical constants are taken from the italicized reference.
[b] These peroxides have been prepared by oxidation of the corresponding hydrocarbon with molecular oxygen.
[c] Not isolated in pure form.

| Name | Formula | $n_D^{20}$ | M.p., °C. | B.p., °C./mm. Hg | Ref.[a] |
|---|---|---|---|---|---|
| B. Aromatic Peroxy Acids | | | | | |
| Peroxybenzoic acid[b] | $C_6H_5C(=O)—OOH$ | — | 41 | 97 to 110/13 to 15 | 62,*67* |
| Monoperoxyphthalic acid | $C_6H_4(C(=O)—OH)(C(=O)—OOH)$ (ortho) | — | 110 (dec.) | — | 62,*67* |
| The preparation of a number of para substituted peroxybenzoic acids is given in reference 111. | | | | | |
| IV. PEROXIDES OF STRUCTURE RC(=O)OOR (PEROXY ESTERS) | | | | | |
| Ethyl peroxyacetate | $CH_3C(=O)—OOC_2H_5$[d] | — | — | — | *68* |
| Diethyl peroxyterephthalate | $C_2H_5OO—C(=O)—C_6H_4—C(=O)—OOC_2H_5$ (para) | — | 37 | — | *68* |
| *trans*-9-Decalyl peroxybenzoate | $C_{10}H_{17}—OOC(=O)—C_6H_5$ (9-decalyl) | — | 67 to 68 | — | *69* |
| *t*-Butyl peroxybenzoate | $C_6H_5C(=O)—OOC(CH_3)_3$ | 1.5007 | — | 75 to 77/2 | *70* |

## V. PEROXIDES OF STRUCTURE RC(=O)OO(O=)CR (DIACYL AND DIAROYL PEROXIDES)

### A. Diacyl Peroxides

| Name | Formula | M.p., °C. | B.p., °C./mm. Hg. | Ref. |
|---|---|---|---|---|
| Diacetyl peroxide | $(CH_3C(=O)-O-)_2$ | 30 | 63/21 | *71*,72,73 |
| Dichloroacetyl peroxide | $(CH_2ClC(=O)-O-)_2$ | 36 | 85 (dec.) | *74* |
| Di-*n*-butyryl peroxide[d] | $(CH_3CH_2CH_2C(=O)-O-)_2$ | — | — | 75 |
| Dilauroyl peroxide | $(C_{11}H_{23}C(=O)-O-)_2$ | 48–50 | — | *112* |
| Di-α-thionyl peroxide | (2-thienyl–C(=O)–O–)$_2$ | 92 to 93 (dec.) | — | *76* |
| Di-2-furoyl peroxide | (2-furyl–C(=O)–O–)$_2$ | 86 to 87 (dec.) | — | *77* |

### B. Diaroyl Peroxides

| Name | Formula | M.p., °C. | Solvent for recrystn. | Ref.[a] |
|---|---|---|---|---|
| Dibenzoyl peroxide | $(C_6H_5C(=O)-O-)_2$ | 106 to 107 | 2:1 MeOH—$CHCl_3$ | 78,*79* |
| Bis(*p*-methoxybenzoyl) peroxide | $(p\text{-}CH_3OC_6H_4C(=O)-O-)_2$ | 129 (dec.) | Benzene | *79*,80 |

[a] The physical constants are taken from the italicized reference.
[b] These peroxides have been prepared by oxidation of the corresponding hydrocarbon with molecular oxygen.
[d] Properties not given.

*Table continued*

### B. Diaroyl Peroxides (*continued*)

| Name | Formula | M.p., °C. | Solvent for recrystn. | Ref.[a] |
|---|---|---|---|---|
| *p*-Monomethoxybenzoyl peroxide | $p\text{-}CH_3OC_6H_4C(=O)\text{—}O\text{—}O\text{—}C(=O)C_6H_5$ | 68 to 74 | 3:1 Cyclohexane–benzene | *79*,81 |
| Bis(*p*-nitrobenzoyl) peroxide | $(p\text{-}NO_2C_6H_4C(=O)\text{—}O\text{—})_2$ | 158 (dec.) | Benzene | *79*,82 |

A number of other substituted diaroyl peroxides are described in reference 79.

### C. Dialkyl Peroxydicarbonates

| Name | Formula | $n_D^{20}$ | M.p., °C. | B.p., °C./mm. Hg | Ref.[a] |
|---|---|---|---|---|---|
| Diethyl peroxydicarbonate | $C_2H_5OC(=O)\text{—}OO\text{—}C(=O)OC_2H_5$ | 1.4017 | 28 to 35 (dec.) | — | *83* |

A number of other dialkyl peroxydicarbonates are described in reference 83b.

## VI. PEROXY DERIVATIVES OF ALDEHYDES AND KETONES

### A. 1-Hydroxyalkyl Hydroperoxides

| Name | Formula | $n_D^{20}$ | M.p., °C. | B.p., °C./mm. Hg | Ref.[a] |
|---|---|---|---|---|---|
| Hydroxymethyl hydroperoxide | $HOCH_2OOH$ | 1.4205 (16°) | — | — | *84* |
| 1-Hydroxyethyl hydroperoxide | $CH_3CH(OH)OOH$ | 1.4150 (24°) | — | — | *85*,86 |
| 1-Hydroxyheptyl hydroperoxide | $C_6H_{13}CH(OH)OOH$ | — | 40 | — | *85* |
| 1-Hydroxydodecyl hydroperoxide | $C_{11}H_{23}CH(OH)OOH$ | — | 65 to 67 | — | *85*,87 |

| Name | Formula | $n_D^{20}$ | M.p., °C. | B.p., °C./mm. Hg | Ref.[a] |
|---|---|---|---|---|---|
| 1-Hydroxycyclohexyl hydroperoxide | 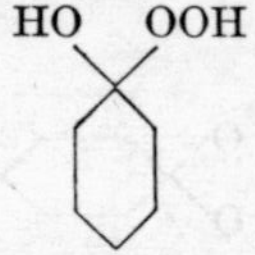 1-hydroxy-1-hydroperoxycyclohexane (HO and OOH on the same ring carbon) | — | 76 to 78 | — | *88* |
| **B. Bis(1-hydroxyalkyl) Peroxides** | | | | | |
| Bishydroxymethyl peroxide | $CH_2(OH)OOCH_2(OH)$ | — | 62 to 64 | — | *89*,90 |
| Bis(1-hydroxyethyl) peroxide | $CH_3CH(OH)OOCH(OH)CH_3$ | 1.4265 (16°) | — | — | *89* |
| Bis(α-hydroxybenzyl) peroxide | $C_6H_5CH(OH)OOCH(OH)C_6H_5$ | — | — | — | *91*,92 |
| Bis(α-hydroxy-β,β,β-trichloroethyl) peroxide | $CCl_3CH(OH)OOCH(OH)CCl_3$ | — | 122 | — | *92* |
| Bis(1-hydroxycyclohexyl) peroxide | 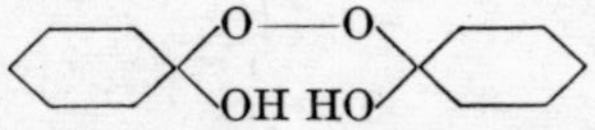 two cyclohexane rings, each carbon bearing OH, joined through O—O | — | 68 to 70 | — | 88,*93* |
| **C. Polyalkylidene Peroxides** | | | | | |
| Dimeric acetone peroxide | 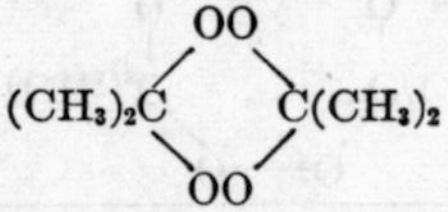 six-membered ring: $(CH_3)_2C$ and $C(CH_3)_2$ joined by two OO bridges | — | 132 | — | 93,*94*,95, 96,97 |

*Table continued*

[a] The physical constants are taken from the italicized reference.

C. Polyalkylidene Peroxides (*continued*)

| Name | Formula | $n_D^{20}$ | M.p., °C. | B.p., °C./mm. Hg | Ref.[a] |
|---|---|---|---|---|---|
| Trimeric acetone peroxide | 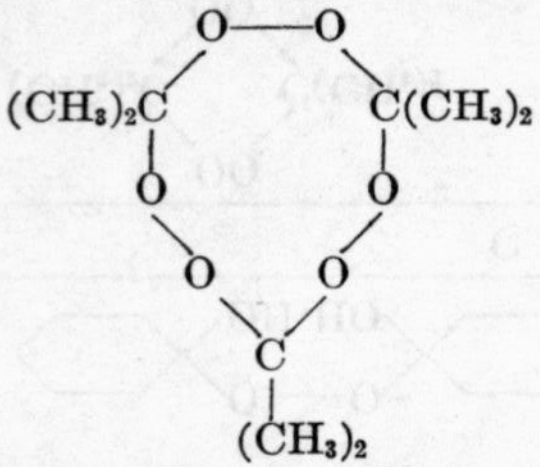 O—O<br>$(CH_3)_2C$ $C(CH_3)_2$<br>O O<br>O O<br>C<br>$(CH_3)_2$ | — | 98.5 | — | 94,95,96, 97,*98* |
| Dimeric benzaldehyde peroxide | 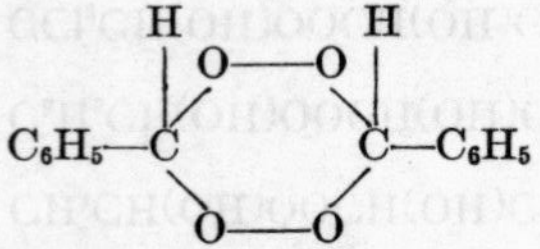 H H<br>O—O<br>$C_6H_5$—C C—$C_6H_5$<br>O—O | — | 202 | — | *99* |
| Dimeric benzophenone peroxide | 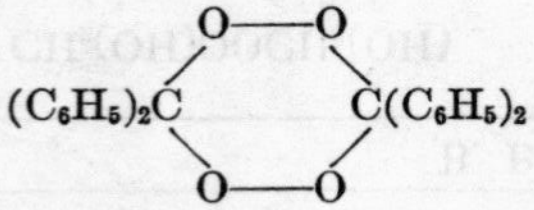 O—O<br>$(C_6H_5)_2C$ $C(C_6H_5)_2$<br>O—O | — | 212.5 | — | *100* |
| Trimeric cyclohexanone peroxide | 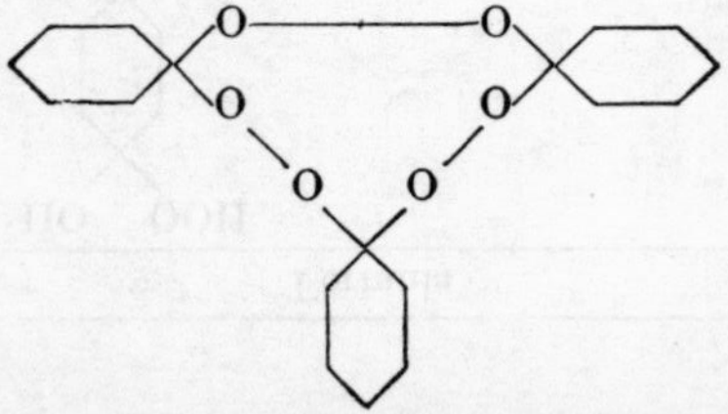 O——O<br>O O<br>O O | — | 93 | — | *93* |

| Name | Formula | $n_D^{20}$ | M.p., °C. | B.p., °C./mm. Hg | Ref.[a] |
|---|---|---|---|---|---|
| **D. Alkyl 1-Hydroxyalkyl Peroxides** | | | | | |
| Methyl hydroxymethyl peroxide | $CH_3OOCH_2OH$ | 1.3983 (15°) | — | 45/17 | *101* |
| Ethyl hydroxymethyl peroxide | $C_2H_5OOCH_2OH$ | 1.4043 (16°) | — | 46 to 48/13 | *101* |
| 1-Tetralyl hydroxymethyl peroxide | 1-Tetralyl–$OOCH_2OH$ | — | 46.5 | — | *102* |
| *t*-Butyl hydroxymethyl peroxide | $(CH_3)_3COOCH_2OH$ | 1.4128 | — | — | 103,104, *105* |
| Methyl 1-hydroxyethyl peroxide | $CH_3CH(OH)OOCH_3$ | 1.3930 (15°) | — | 29 to 31/22 | *101* |
| Ethyl 1-hydroxyethyl peroxide | $CH_3CH(OH)OOC_2H_5$ | 1.4021 (21.4°) | — | 50 to 52/50 | *101* |
| *t*-Butyl α-hydroxy-β,β,β-trichloroethyl peroxide | $(CH_3)_3COOCH(OH)CCl_3$ | — | 50 to 51 | — | 103,104, *105* |
| **E. Peroxy Acetals** | | | | | |
| 2,2-Bis(*t*-butylperoxy) propane | $(CH_3)_3COOC(CH_3)_2OOC(CH_3)_3$ | 1.4098 | — | — | 103,104, *105* |
| Bis(*t*-butylperoxy) phenylmethane | $(CH_3)_3COOCH(C_6H_5)OOC(CH_3)_3$ | 1.5770 | — | — | 103,104, *105* |

A number of other peroxyacetals are reported in reference 105.

[a] The physical constants are taken from the italicized reference.

## References to Appendix I

1. Rieche, A., and Hitz, F., *Ber.*, *62*, 2458 (1929).
2. Egerton, A. C., Emte, W., and Minkoff, G. J., *Faraday Society, Discussion on Hydrocarbons*, *10*, 278 (1951).
3. Baeyer, A., and Villiger, V., *Ber.*, *34*, 738 (1901).
4. Harris, E. J., *Proc. Roy. Soc.* (*London*), *A173*, 126 (1939).
5. Milas, N. A., U. S. Pat. 2,176,407 (Oct. 17, 1939).
6. Medvedev, S. S., and Alekseeva, E. N., *Ber.*, *65*, 133 (1932); *J. Gen. Chem.* (*U. S. S. R.*), *1*, 1193, 2000 (1931).
7. Milas, N. A., U. S. Pat. 2,223,807 (Dec. 3, 1940).
8. Milas, N. A., and Harris, S. A., *J. Am. Chem. Soc.*, *60*, 2434 (1938).
9. Milas, N. A., and Surgenor, D. M., *J. Am. Chem. Soc.*, *68*, 205 (1946).
10. Criegee, R., and Dietrich, H., *Ann.*, *560*, 135 (1948).
11. Vaughan, W. E., and Rust, F. F., U. S. Pats. 2,403,771 and 2,403,772 (July 9, 1946).
12. Milas, N. A., and Surgenor, D. M., *J. Am. Chem. Soc.*, *68*, 643 (1946).
13. Milas, N. A., and Perry, L. H., *J. Am. Chem. Soc.*, *68*, 1938 (1946).
14. Ivanov, K. I., Savinova, V. K., and Zhakhovskaya, V. P., *Doklady Akad. Nauk. S. S. S. R.*, *72*, 903 (1950).
15. Farkas, A., and Passaglia, E., *J. Am. Chem. Soc.*, *72*, 3333 (1950).
16. Gasson, E. J., Hawkins, E. G. E., Millidge, A. F., and Quin, D. C., *cf.* Hawkins, E. G. E., *Quarterly Reviews*, *4*, 251 (1950).
17. Ivanov, K. I., and Savinova, V. K., *Doklady Akad. Nauk S. S. S. R.*, *59*, 493 (1948).
18. Criegee, R., and Zogel, H., *Ber.*, *84*, 215 (1951).
19. Wibaut, J. P., *Faraday Society, Discussion on Hydrocarbons*, *10*, 332 (1951).
20. Criegee, R., Pilz, H., and Flygare, H., *Ber.*, *B72*, 1799 (1939).
21. Farmer, E. H., and Sundralingham, A., *J. Chem. Soc.*, *1942*, 121.
22. Farmer, E. H., and Sutton, D. A., *J. Chem. Soc.*, *1946*, 10.
23. Hock, H., and Lang, S., *Ber.*, *75*, 300, 313 (1942).
24. Milas, N. A., and Mageli, O. L., *J. Am. Chem. Soc.*, *74*, 1471 (1952).
25. Hock, H., and Lang, S., *Ber.*, *76*, 169 (1943).
26. British Pats. 610,293 (Oct. 13, 1948) and 629,637 (Sept. 23, 1949). Armstrong, G. P., Hall, R. H., and Quin, D. C., *J. Chem. Soc.*, *1950*, 666.
27. Hock, H., and Lang, S., *Ber.*, *77–79*, 257 (1944–46).
28. U. S. Pats. 2,484,841 (Oct. 18, 1949) and 2,491,926 (Dec. 20, 1949), to Hercules Powder Co. See *C. A.*, *44*, 2558, 5908 (1950).
29. Ivanov, K. I., Savinova, V. K., and Zhakhovskaya, V. P., *Doklady Akad. Nauk S. S. S. R.*, *59*, 905 (1948).
30. Hawkins, E. G. E., *J. Chem. Soc.*, *1949*, 2076.
31. Hock, H., Depke, F., and Knauel, G., *Ber.*, *83*, 238 (1950).
32. Wieland, H., and Maier, J., *Ber.*, *64*, 1205 (1931).
33. Ziegler, K., Ewald, L., and Seib, A., *Ann.*, *504*, 182 (1933).
34. Hock, H., and Susemihl, W., *Ber.*, *66*, 61 (1933).
35. Hartmann, M., and Seiberth, M., *Helv. Chim. Acta*, *15*, 1390 (1932).
36. Hock, H., Lang, S., and Knauel, G., *Ber.*, *83*, 227 (1950).
37. Hock, H., and Lang, S., *Ber.*, *75*, 1051 (1942).
38. (a) Robertson, A., *Nature*, *162*, 153 (1948). (b) Rein, H., and Criegee, R., *Angew. Chem.*, *62*, 120 (1950).

39. (a) Beer, R. S., McGrath, G., Robertson, A., and Woodier, A. B., *Nature*, *164*, 362 (1949). (b) Beer, R. S., McGrath, G., and Robertson, A., *J. Chem. Soc.*, *1950*, 2118. (c) Witkop, B., *J. Am. Chem. Soc.*, *72*, 1428 (1950); *73*, 2196 (1951).
40. (a) Criegee, R., and Lohaus, G., *Ber.*, *84*, 219 (1951). (b) Pausacker, K. H., *J. Chem. Soc.*, *1950*, 3478.
41. Wiley, R. H., U. S. Pat. 2,357,298 (Sept. 5, 1944).
42. Rieche, A., and Brumshager, W., *Ber.*, *61*, 951 (1928).
43. Rieche, A., and Hitz, F., *Ber.*, *62*, 218 (1929).
44. Baeyer, A., and Villiger, V., *Ber.*, *33*, 3387 (1900).
45. Bockemuller, W., and Pfeuffer, L., *Ann.*, *537*, 178 (1939).
46. Rust, F. F., Seubold, F. H., and Vaughan, W. E., *J. Am. Chem. Soc.*, *72*, 338 (1950).
47. Dutch Pat. 65,254 (Feb. 15, 1950); *cf. C. A.*, *44*, 4489 (1950).
48. Gomberg, M., *J. Am. Chem. Soc.*, *22*, 757 (1900).
49. G. W. Wheland, *Advanced Organic Chemistry*, 2nd ed., Wiley, New York, 1949, p. 687.
50. Hock, H., and Depke, F., *Ber.*, *84*, 122 and 349 (1951).
51. Nelson, E. K., *J. Am. Chem. Soc.*, *33*, 1404 (1911); *35*, 84 (1913).
52. *Schimmel & Co.*, *Reports*, April (1908).
53. Windaus, A., and Brunken, J., *Ann.*, *460*, 225 (1928).
54. Bergmann, W., and McLean, M. J., *Chemical Reviews*, *28*, 367 (1941).
55. Dufraisse, C., and Gerard, M., *Compt. rend.*, *201*, 428 (1935).
56. Moureu, C., Dufraisse, C., and Dean, P. M., *Compt. rend.*, *182*, 101, 1584 (1926).
57. D'Ans, J., and Frey, W., *Ber.*, *45*, 1845 (1912); *Z. anorg. Chem.*, *84*, 145 (1914). D'Ans, J., and Kneip, A., *Ber.*, *48*, 1136 (1915).
58. Cantieni, R., *Helv. Chim. Acta*, *19*, 1153 (1936).
59. D'Ans, J., and Frey, W., *Ber.*, *45*, 1845 (1912).
60. Arbuzow, B. A., *J. prakt. Chem.*, *131*, 357 (1931).
61. German Pat. 272,738 (1913). U. S. Pat. 1,179,421 (1916).
62. Swern, D., *Chemical Reviews*, *45*, 1 (1949).
63. Wieland, H., and Richter, D., *Ann.*, *486*, 226 (1931).
64. Fichter, F., and Zumbrunn, R., *Helv. Chim. Acta*, *10*, 869 (1927).
65. D'Ans, J., German Pat. 251,802 (1911).
66. Panizzon, L., *Helv. Chim. Acta*, *15*, 1187 (1932).
67. Baeyer, A., and Villiger, V., *Ber.*, *33*, 1569 (1900).
68. Baeyer, A., and Villiger, V., *Ber.*, *34*, 738 (1901).
69. Criegee, R., *Ber.*, *77*, 22 (1944).
70. Milas, N. A., and Surgenor, D. M., *J. Am. Chem. Soc.*, *68*, 642 (1946).
71. Brodie, B. C., *Ann.*, *3* (suppl.), 200 (1864).
72. Nef, V., *Ann.*, *298*, 297 (1897).
73. Gambarjan, S., *Ber.*, *42*, 4003 (1909).
74. Vanino, L., and Uhlfelder, E., *Ber.*, *33*, 1043 (1900).
75. Kharasch, M. S., Kane, S. S., and Brown, H. C., *J. Am. Chem. Soc.*, *63*, 526 (1941).
76. Breitenbach, J. W., and Karlinger, H., *Monats.*, *80*, 739 (1949).
77. Milas, N. A., and McAlevy, A., *J. Am. Chem. Soc.*, *56*, 1219 (1934).
78. Baeyer, A., and Villiger, V., *33*, 1574 (1900). Pechman, H. v., and Vanino, L., *Ber.*, *27*, 1511 (1894). Sonnenschein, R., *Monats.*, *7*, 522 (1876).

79. Swain, C. G., Stockmayer, W. H., and Clarke, J. T., *J. Am. Chem. Soc.*, *72*, 5426 (1950).
80. Vanino, L., and Uhlfelder, E., *Ber.*, *37*, 3624 (1904).
81. Wieland, H., *Ann.*, *480*, 157 (1930).
82. Price, C. C., and Krebs, E., *Org. Syntheses*, *23*, 65 (1943).
83. (a) Cohen, S. G., and Sparrow, D. P., *J. Am. Chem. Soc.*, *72*, 611 (1950). (b) Strain, F., Bissinger, W. E., Dial, W. R., Rudoff, H., DeWitt, B. J., Stevens, H. C., and Langston, J. H., *ibid.*, *72*, 1254 (1950).
84. Reiche, A., and Meister, R., *Ber.*, *68*, 1465 (1935).
85. Rieche, A., *Ber.*, *64*, 2328 (1931).
86. Leadbeater, M. R., *Compt. rend.*, *230*, 829 (1950). See also Magat, M., *Faraday Society, Discussion on Hydrocarbons*, *10*, 330 (1950).
87. Späth, E., Pailer, M., and Schmid, M., *Ber.*, *74*, 1552 (1941).
88. Milas, N. A., Harris, S. A., and Panagiotakos, P. C., *J. Am. Chem. Soc.*, *61*, 2430 (1939).
89. Wieland, H., and Wingler, A., *Ann.*, 431, 301 (1923).
90. Fischer, F. G., *Ann.*, 233 (1929). Briner, E., and Schnorf, P., *Helv. Chim. Acta*, *12*, 154 (1929).
91. Nef, V., *Ann.*, *298*, 292 (1897).
92. Baeyer, A., and Villiger, V., *Ber.*, *33*, 2479 (1900).
93. Criegee, R., Schnorrenberg, W., and Becke, J., *Ann.*, *565*, 7 (1949).
94. Rieche, A., and Koch, K., *Ber.*, *75*, 1016 (1942).
95. Ivanov, K. I., Savinova, V. K., and Mikhailova, G., *J. Gen. Chem.* (*U. S. S. R.*), *16*, 1003 (1946).
96. Baeyer, A., and Villiger, V., *Ber.*, *32*, 3625 (1899); *33*, 124, 854 (1900).
97. Dilthey, W., Inckel, M., and Stephan, H., *J. prakt. Chem.*, *154*, 219 (1940).
98. Wolffenstein, K., *Ber.*, *28*, 2265 (1895).
99. Baeyer, A., and Villiger, V., *Ber*,. *33*, 2484 (1900).
100. Marvel, C. S., and Nichols, V., *J. Org. Chem.*, *6*, 296 (1941).
101. Rieche, A., *Ber.*, *63*, 2642 (1930).
102. Ivanov, K. I., Savinova, V. K., and Mikhailova, E. G., *J. Gen. Chem.* (*U. S. S. R.*), *8*, 51 (1938).
103. U. S. Pats. 2,400,041 and 2,455,569 (to Shell Development Co.).
104. Dickey, F. H., Raley, J. H., Rust, F. F., Tresede, K. S., and Vaughan, W. E., *Ind. Eng. Chem.*, *41*, 1673 (1949).
105. Dickey, F. H., Rust, F. F., and Vaughan, W. E., *J. Am. Chem. Soc.*, *71*, 1432 (1949).
106. Barnard, D., and Hargrave, K. R., *Anal. Chim. Acta*, *5*, 476 (1951).
107. Sharp, D. B., Patton, L. W., and Whitcomb, S. E., *J. Am. Chem. Soc.*, *73*, 5600 (1951).
108. Shreve, O. D., Heether, M. R., Knight, M. R., and Swern, D., *Anal. Chem.*, *23*, 282 (1951).
109. Campbell, T. W., and Coppinger, G. M., *J. Am. Chem. Soc.*, *74*, 1496 (1952).
110. Kharasch, M. S., Fono, A., and Nudenberg, W., *J. Org. Chem.*, *15*, 753 (1950).
111. Overberger, C. G., and Cummins, R. W., *J. Am. Chem. Soc.*, *75*, 4250 (1953)
112. Long, L., *Chemical Reviews*, *27*, 437 (1940).
113. Schenck, G. O., and H. Ziegler, *Naturwiss.*, *32*, 157 (1944); *38*, 356 (1951).
114. Lindstrom, E. G., *J. Am. Chem. Soc.*, *75*, 5123 (1953).

# Appendix 2

# EXPLOSIVE NATURE OF PEROXIDES[a]

| Peroxide | Remarks concerning explosiveness | Reference |
|---|---|---|
| | ALKYL HYDROPEROXIDES | |
| Methyl hydroperoxide | Explodes violently; sensitive to jarring especially at warm temps.; greatest caution in making, Ba salt in dry state extremely explosive | A. Rieche and F. Hitz, *Ber.*, *62*, 2458 (1929) |
| Ethyl hydroperoxide | Explodes on superheating quite violently, Ba salt, heat and percussion sensitive | A. Baeyer and V. Villiger, *Ber.*, *34*, 738 (1901) |
| Isopropyl hydroperoxide | Explodes just above b.p. | S. Medvedev and E. N. Alexejeva, *Ber.*, *65*, 133 (1932) |
| *t*-Butyl hydroperoxide | By distn. under normal pressures explosions can result; otherwise relatively harmless | N. A. Milas and D. Surgenor, *J. Am. Chem. Soc.*, *68*, 205 (1946) |
| Tetralin hydroperoxide | Detonated by superheating | H. Hock and W. Susemiehl, *Ber.*, *66*, 61 (1933) |
| Decalin hydroperoxide | Very stable; can be sublimed in small quantities at atm. pressure | R. Criegee, *Ber.*, *77*, 22 (1944) |
| Triphenylmethyl hydroperoxide | Not explosive | H. Wieland and J. Maier, *Ber.*, *64*, 1205 (1931) |
| Phenylhydrazone hydroperoxide | Detonates in dry state after a short time with no evident cause | W. Busch and W. Dietz, *Ber.* *47*, 3277 (1914) |
| | DIALKYL PEROXIDES | |
| Dimethyl peroxide | Extremely explosive on heating and jarring; vapors also sensitive to shock | A. Rieche and W. Brumshagen, *Ber.*, *61*, 951 (1928) |
| Methyl ethyl peroxide | Liquid and vapor forms shock-sensitive; explodes violently on superheating | A. Rieche, *Ber.*, *62*, 218 (1929) |

[a] R. Criegee, "Herstellung und Umwanglung von Peroxyden," in Houben-Weyl, *Methoden der organischen Chemie*, 4th ed., Thieme, Stuttgart, Vol. VIII, pp. 6–9, 1952. Reproduced courtesy of Dr. R. Criegee.

| Peroxide | Remarks concerning explosiveness | Reference |
|---|---|---|
| Diethyl peroxide | Likewise still highly explosive, but not sensitive to shock at room temp. | A. Baeyer and V. Villiger, *Ber.*, *33*, 3387 (1900). A. Rieche, *Alkyl Peroxide und Ozonide*, p. 33 (1931) |
| Di-*t*-butyl peroxide | Very stable; can be distd. at atm. pressure without decompn. | N. A. Milas and D. Surgenor, *J. Am. Chem. Soc.*, *68*, 205 (1946) |
| Polymeric butadiene peroxide | Highly explosive | D. A. Scott, *Chem. Zbl.*, *1941*, *I*, 2428 |
| Polymeric isoprene and dimethyl butadiene peroxide | Highly explosive liquids | K. Bodendorf, *Arch. Pharm.*, *271*, *I* (1933) |
| Ascaridole | Dec. explosively on heating from 130 to 150°C. | Schimmel & Co., *Chem. Zbl.*, *1908*, *I*, 1839 |
| Polymeric peroxides of phellandrene and of 1,3-cyclohexadiene | Explode at 110°C. | K. Bodendorf, *Arch. Pharm.*, *271*, *I* (1933) |
| Polymeric peroxides of methacrylic acid esters and styrene | Explode over 40°C. | C. E. Barnes, R. M. Elofson, and G. D. Jones, *J. Am. Chem. Soc.*, *72*, 210 (1950) |
| Polymeric peroxide of asym. diphenylethylene | Detonate on heating | H. Staudinger, *Ber.*, *58*, 1075 (1925) |
| Peroxide of dimethyl ketene | Explodes in dry state by rubbing at −80°C. | H. Staudinger *et al.*, *Ber.*, *58*, 1079 (1925) |
| Photo-oxide of anthracene | Dec. explosively at 120° | C. Dufraisse and M. Gérard, *Compt. rend.*, *201*, 428 (1935) |
| PEROXY ACIDS | | |
| Peroxyformic acid | Extremely explosive [in high concn.] | J. D'Ans and A. Kneip, *Ber.*, *48*, 1137 (1915) |
| Peroxyacetic acid | Extremely explosive [in high concn.] | J. D'Ans and W. Frey, *Ber.*, *45*, 1846 (1912) |
| Peroxybenzoic acid | Detonates weakly on heating | A. Baeyer and V. Villiger, *Ber.*, *33*, 1577 (1900) |
| Peroxycaproic acid | Detonates on heating with appearance of fire | F. Fichter and R. Zumbrunn, *Helv. Chim. Acta*, *10*, 869 (1927) |
| PEROXY ESTERS | | |
| *p*-Nitrobenzoic acid esters of tert. hydroperoxides | Detonate in a flame | R. Criegee and H. Dietrich, *Ann.*, *560*, 135 (1948) |
| 1,1-Bisbenzoperoxycyclohexane | Detonates actively in a flame | " " |
| 1,1-Bis-*p*-nitrobenzoperoxycyclohexane | Explodes at 120°C. | " " |
| Tetraacetate of 1,1,4,4-tetrahydroperoxycyclohexane | Weak rubbing easily causes strong explosion | " " |
| Oxalic acid ester of *t*-butyl hydroperoxide | Detonates on removal from a freezing mixture | W. E. Vaughan, private communication |

| Peroxide | Remarks concerning explosiveness | Reference |
|---|---|---|
| | DIACYL PEROXIDES | |
| Diacetyl peroxide | Highly explosive; to be handled only with extraordinary caution | L. P. Kuhn, *Chem. Eng. News*, *26*, 3197 (1948) |
| Dicapronyl peroxide | Detonates at 85°C. | F. Fichter and R. Zumbrunn, *Helv. Chim. Acta*, *10*, 869 (1927) |
| Bishexahydrobenzoyl peroxide | Large quantities can explode without apparent reason | F. Fichter and W. Siegrist, *Helv. Chim. Acta*, *15*, 1304 (1932) |
| Difuroyl peroxide | Explodes violently by rubbing and heating | N. A. Miles and A. McAlevy, *J. Am. Chem. Soc.*, *56*, 1219 (1934) |
| Dibenzoyl peroxide | Exploded by heat; carry out recrystns. of large quantities without heating | K. Nozaki and P. D. Bartlett, *J. Am. Chem. Soc.*, *68*, 1686 (1946) |
| 1-Naphthoyl peroxide | Explodes by rubbing | S. Medededco and O. Bloch, *Chem. Zbl.*, *1935 I*, 2670 |
| | PEROXY DERIVATIVES OF ALDEHYDES AND KETONES | |
| Hydroxymethyl hydroperoxide | Explodes on heating; not sensitive to friction; higher homologs not explosive | A. Rieche and R. Meister, *Ber.*, *68*, 1465 (1935). A. Rieche, *Ber.*, *64*, 2328 (1931) |
| Hydroxymethyl methyl peroxide | Violently explosive, on heating becomes percussion-sensitive | A. Rieche and F. Hitz, *Ber.*, *62*, 2458 (1929) |
| 1-Hydroxyethyl ethyl peroxide | Detonates on heating | A. Rieche, *Ber.*, *63*, 2642 (1930) |
| Bishydroxymethyl peroxide | Highly explosive; strongly friction-sensitive | H. Wieland, and H. Sutter, *Ber.*, *63*, 66 (1930) |
| Bis(1-hydroxycyclohexyl) peroxide | Harmless by itself; but explodes on attempted vacuum distn. | M. Stoll and W. Scherrer, *Helv. Chim. Acta*, *13*, 142 (1930) |
| Bishydroperoxydicyclohexyl peroxide | Detonates very actively in a flame | R. Criegee, W. Schnorrenberg, and J. Becke, *Ann.*, *565*, 7 (1949) |
| 1-Hydroperoxy-1-acetoxycyclodecan-6-one | Detonates on removal from a freezing mixture | R. Criegee and G. Wenner, *Ann.*, *564*, 9 (1949) |
| Dimeric ethylidene peroxide | Explodes with extreme violence just by touching; *greatest caution!* | A. Rieche and R. Meister, *Ber.*, *72*, 1933 (1939) |
| Polymeric ethylidene peroxide (ether peroxide) | Extremely explosive, even below 100°C. | *E.g.*, A. Rieche and R. Meister, *Angew. Chem.*, *49*, 101 (1936) |
| Trimeric propylidene peroxide | Extremely explosive; very friction-sensitive | A. Rieche and R. Meister, *Ber*, *72*, 1938 (1939) |
| Dimeric acetone peroxide | Explodes violently by percussion and rubbing | A. Baeyer and V. Villiger, *Ber.*, *32*, 3632 (1899) |
| Trimeric acetone peroxide | Very explosive; can penetrate a plate of iron when heated on it | " " |

| Peroxide | Remarks concerning explosiveness | Reference |
| --- | --- | --- |
| Dimeric cyclohexanone peroxide | Detonates by percussion | W. Dilthey, M. Inckel, and H. Stephan, *J. prakt. Chem.*, *154*, 219 (1940) |
| 2,2-Bis(*t*-butylperoxy)-butane | Explosive above 86°C. | F. H. Dickey *et al.*, *Ind. Eng. Chem.*, *41*, 1673 (1949) |
| | OZONIDES | |
| Ethylene ozonide | Explodes extremely violently upon heating, rubbing, or jarring | C. Harries and R. Kötschal, *Ber.*, *42*, 3305 (1909) |
| Butylene ozonide | Explosive; but not sensitive to shock at room temp. | A. Rieche, R. Meister, and H. Sauthoff, *Ann.*, *553*, 187 (1942) |
| Ozonide of 1,2-dimethylcyclopentene | Not explosive | Dissertation, G. Lohaus, Karlsruhe, 1952 |
| Ozonide of maleic anhydride | Explosion temp. −40°C. | E. Briner and D. Frank, *Helv. Chim. Acta*, *20*, 1211 (1937) |
| Diozonide of phorone | Ignites at room temp. | C. Harries and H. O. Turk, *Ann.*, *374*, 338 (1910) |
| Triozonide of benzene | Extremely explosive at slightest touch | C. Harries and V. Weiss *Ber.*, *31*, 3431 (1904) |

## Appendix 3

# SOME COMMERCIALLY AVAILABLE ORGANIC PEROXIDES[a]

| Peroxide (trade name) | Physical form | Typical peroxide assay (%) | Active oxygen (%) | Manufacturer[b] |
|---|---|---|---|---|
| ALKYL HYDROPEROXIDES | | | | |
| *t*-Butyl | Liquid | 60 | 10.60 | Lucidol |
| Cumene | Liquid | 73 | — | Hercules |
| Diisopropylbenzene | Liquid | 53 | — | Hercules |
| Menthane | Liquid | 52 | — | Hercules |
| *p*-*t*-Butylcumene | Liquid | — | — | Phillips |
| DITERTIARY ALKYL PEROXIDES | | | | |
| Di-*t*-butyl | Liquid | 97–98 | — | Shell, Lucidol |
| 1-HYDROXYALKYL PEROXIDES FROM ALDEHYDES AND KETONES | | | | |
| Hydroxyheptaldehyde | Fine powder | 95 | 5.80 | Lucidol |
| Dibenzal diperoxide compounded with tricresyl phosphate (Luperco ETC) | Thick paste | 50 | 6.60 | Lucidol |
| Methyl ethyl ketone in dimethyl phthalate (Lupersol DDM) | Liquid | 60 | 11.00 | Lucidol |
| Methyl isobutyl ketone in dimethyl phthalate (Lupersol FDM) | Liquid | 80 | 11.00 | Lucidol |
| Methyl amyl ketone | Liquid | 95 | 15.50 | Lucidol |
| Cyclohexanone | Granular | 90 | 11.00 | Lucidol |
| DIACYL PEROXIDES | | | | |
| Acetyl in dimethyl phthalate | Liquid | 30 | — | Buffalo |
| Lauroyl (Alperox C) | Soft granular | 95 | 3.76 | Lucidol |
| Benzoyl (Lucidol) | Powder or fine granular | 96 | 6.30 | Lucidol |
| Benzoyl in tricresyl phosphate (Luperco ATC) | Thick paste | 50 | 3.30 | Lucidol |
| *p*-Chlorobenzoyl | Fine granular | 95 | 4.90 | Lucidol |

| Peroxide (trade name) | Physical form | Typical peroxide assay (%) | Active oxygen (%) | Manu- facturer[b] |
|---|---|---|---|---|
| DIACYL PEROXIDES (*continued*) | | | | |
| *p*-Chlorobenzoyl in dibutyl phthalate (Luperco BTC) | Thick paste | 50 | 2.50 | Lucidol |
| 2,4-Dichlorobenzoyl in dibutyl phthalate (Luperco CDB) | Thick paste | 50 | 2.10 | Lucidol |
| PEROXY ACIDS | | | | |
| Peracetic in acetic acid stabilized with $\alpha,\alpha'$-dipicolinic acid | Liquid | 40 | — | Buffalo |
| PEROXY ESTERS | | | | |
| *t*-Butyl peracetate | Liquid | 95 | — | Lucidol |
| *t*-Butyl perbenzoate | Liquid | 95 | 7.80 | Lucidol |
| Di-*t*-butyl diperphthalate | Granular | 95 | 9.80 | Lucidol |
| *t*-Butyl permaleic acid | Fine cryst. | 95 | 8.10 | Lucidol |
| *t*-Butyl perphthalic acid | Fine granular | 95 | 6.40 | Lucidol |
| Diisopropyl peroxydicarbonate | Liquid | — | — | Columbia |

[a] Based on information given in reference 4, Chapter A, and the article by C. H. Rybolt and T. C. Swigert, *Modern Plastics*, 26, No. 8, 101 (1949). The latter also includes information on peroxide type and percentage and usual range of cure temperature employed in curing of polyester resins.
[b] Buffalo, Buffalo Electrochemical Co. Columbia, Columbia Southern Chemicals Division, Pittsburgh Plate Glass Co. Hercules, Hercules Powder Co. Lucidol, Lucidol Division, Novadel-Agene Corp. Phillips, Phillips Petroleum Co. Shell, Shell Chemical Corp.

## Appendix 4

# CATALYST EFFICIENCY

For high monomer concentrations in an ideal solvent (3 moles per liter or higher), the rate of catalyzed polymerization is experimentally *first* order with respect to monomer concentration, as shown in equation (8), page 135. At very low monomer concentrations in an ideal solvent, the rate of catalyzed polymerization may in theory become three-halves order with respect to monomer concentration. This has been explained formally in terms of a catalyst efficiency $f$, which depends on monomer concentration.[1]

If in equation (6), page 135, we neglect the rate of thermal polymerization, we obtain for the rate of catalyzed polymerization:

$$R_p = \left(\frac{fk_d}{A''}\right)^{1/2} [\mathrm{Cat}]^{1/2}[\mathrm{M}] \tag{1}$$

In terms of a "cage model," in which it is considered that the two radical fragments from the dissociating catalyst may *either* react with each other to form inactive products *or* add to monomer to start polymer chains, Matheson[1] deduced the following formula for catalyst efficiency:

$$f = \frac{K[\mathrm{M}]}{1 + K[\mathrm{M}]} \tag{2}$$

In equation (2), $K$ represents the relative rate at which the members of the radical pair will add to monomer compared to the rate at which they will recombine. It is clear that for large values of $K[\mathrm{M}]$ the efficiency will become equal to unity leading to a first order dependence of $R_p$ on [M] in equation (1) above. For very small values of $K[\mathrm{M}]$, $f$ is clearly equal to $K[\mathrm{M}]$, and so the dependence of $R_p$ on [M] in equation (1) above is three-halves order.

[1] M. S. Matheson, *J. Chem. Phys.*, *13*, 584 (1945).

The vast majority of the data compiled in Table C-II (pages 136 and 137) have been taken from experiments performed in pure monomer (concentration range 8–10 moles per liter); a few of the experiments were performed in solvents with the monomer concentrations ranging between 3 moles per liter and pure monomer. In this concentration range the observed dependence of $R_p$ upon [M] is first order, as shown in equation (8), page 135.

The computation of $R_i'/[\mathrm{Cat}] = R_i(1 + x)/[\mathrm{Cat}]$ can be made directly through equation (3):

$$\frac{R_i'}{[\mathrm{Cat}]} = \frac{2A'}{[\mathrm{M}]^2} \frac{R_p^2}{[\mathrm{Cat}]} \tag{3}$$

without the necessity of assuming that $R_p = K[\mathrm{Cat}]^{1/2}[\mathrm{M}]$. These computations when carried out on the rate data tabulated in Table C-II show no effect of the monomer concentration on $R_i'/[\mathrm{Cat}]$ for $[\mathrm{M}] \geq 3$ moles per liter. The catalyst efficiencies as defined on page 135 and as computed later on pages 153–156 are independent of monomer concentration in this interval. Since the catalyst efficiencies will be shown to be close to unity in all cases studied thus far, the results are not in disagreement with equation (2) of this appendix.

# AUTHOR INDEX

# SUBJECT INDEX